The Hymn Book

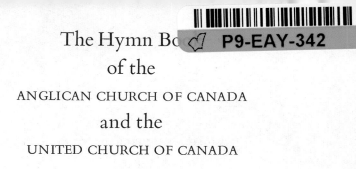

of the

ANGLICAN CHURCH OF CANADA

and the

UNITED CHURCH OF CANADA

1971

A NEW CREED

We are not alone, we live in God's world. *

We believe in God:
  who has created and is creating,
  who has come in Jesus, the Word
    made flesh, to reconcile
    and make new,
  who works in us and others
    by the Spirit.

We trust in God.

We are called to be the Church:
  to celebrate God's presence,
  to love and serve others,
  to seek justice and resist evil,
  to proclaim Jesus, crucified and risen,
    our judge and our hope.

In life, in death, in life beyond death,
  God is with us

We are not alone.

Thanks be to God.

*This line may be used as a versicle, with the rest as a response.

Approved by 23rd General Council of The United Church of Canada—1968

Revision with inclusive language approved by Executive of General Council, November 1980.

The Hymn Book

The Joint Committee

The Preface

Praise is an integral and inspirational part of Christian worship. The psalter was the hymn book in Jewish worship and became the first hymn book of the Christian church.

'I will sing unto the Lord as long as I live; I will praise my God while I have my being' exclaimed the psalmist. St Paul reminded the members of the Colossian church to encourage one another in their faith by 'psalms and hymns and spiritual songs.' Through the centuries the church has become increasingly 'The Singing Church.' Congregations wish to continue to sing great hymns of the past which have an undiminished vitality and relevance, but they also desire to sing hymns expressive of the Christian faith and life in their own day, and of the church's mission to the world in their own times.

It is generally agreed as stated in the preface to a hymn book published over thirty years ago:

The average life of a hymnal appears to be twenty-five years. Each generation, with its problems and outlook, must ever seek new ways of expressing its ideals and aspirations. Taste in literature and music changes. Your committee has kept this fact continually in mind, and hopes that it has provided for the needs of those who value the new, without unduly depriving others of old hymns hallowed by association with their experiences of their religious life.

The General Council of the United Church of Canada in 1962 instructed the Committee on Church Worship to revise the Hymnary. Subsequently, the United Church invited the Anglican Church to participate in the compilation of a joint hymnal. Meeting at Ancaster on November 4, 1962, the two Committees of Ten of the two Churches appointed to study the problems of church union and prepare a document on the Principles of Union, resolved that 'the two Committees of Ten meeting jointly ... urge upon their respective governing bodies the possibility of producing a common hymn book.' The resolution was passed unanimously.

The General Synod meeting in Vancouver in 1965 acted on this recommendation –'that this General Synod gives authority to the Hymnal Committee to proceed in co-operation with the corresponding committee of the United Church of Canada with the preparation of a common hymn book to be used jointly by the Anglican Church of Canada and the United Church of Canada.'

For five years, the officially appointed members of the Joint Committee have met for a day every month, with the exception of the summer months. Consultants from across Canada have met with the Joint Committee each year for a period of three days. In addition to these meetings, much work has been done by sub-committees, such as the Committee on Texts, the Committee on Tunes, and the Committee on Printing and Publishing. Individual members examined many hymn books (one hundred and fifty in all), and made special studies of such hymns as those of Isaac Watts and Charles Wesley, of the metrical psalms, and of the Ancient Office hymns. All this work was carried on by the members of the Committee with the mutual concern for the traditions and needs of both Churches and with complete frankness of discussion. It has been the earnest intention of the Committee to provide a comprehensive selection of hymns from the best of inherited hymnody. At the same time, it has been their aim to produce a book of contemporary hymns expressive of the church's mission in, and to, the world of our times.

When the Joint Committee commenced its work in 1965, it made certain basic assumptions which have provided the criteria by which the hymns and tunes for a new book were to be selected. To be true to the character of both churches, a hymnal must be comprehensive. It must meet the needs of people of different religious traditions and cultural backgrounds, of widely separated areas and of every age group. It must be useful to churches large and small, rural and urban, old and new. It must reflect the ecumenical dialogue and aspirations of our times. A hymnal that is to be serviceable today must be not only ecumenical but contemporary.

Young people especially wish to sing hymns cast in the style of the twentieth century. Despite the difficulties involved, the church must be hospitable to all creative energies if it is to live as Christ's body in these times, and seek to adapt contemporary modes of poetic and musical expression for use in public worship.

In addition to the foregoing, there are certain standards which must apply to any hymnal if it is to serve the church well. It must be Christian, an expression of faith in God as revealed in Christ, rather than an effusion of generalized religious sentiment. It must provide hymns, the quality of which must be such that they are worthy of being offered to God in praise and reverence with integrity. It must be a vital vehicle of worship, not an anthology of Christian classics, but a well-balanced selection of hymns that will enable a congregation to offer praise appropriate to every service of worship and every season of the Christian Year.

The Committee decided upon the publication of one edition with music. It was felt that many members of congregations would welcome the adventure of a music edition, and that, with the greatly improved musical education that young people receive in our schools today, they would also welcome a book with the tunes printed with the words of the hymns. Practically all the recently published hymn books of the churches on the North American continent are published in one music edition.

Children's hymns have not been placed in a special section, but are distributed throughout the Hymn Book, in order to emphasize the fact that children are a part of the whole worshipping communion.

The greatest care has been exercised in ascertaining the original text of each hymn.

The Committee wishes to pay an enthusiastic tribute to the Rev Stanley L Osborne, BA, MUS D, TH D, the secretary of the Committee. Without his extensive knowledge of hymnology, his skill as a musician, and his indefatigable labours, this book could not have been produced. Dr Osborne has rendered invaluable service with regard to the printing of the music, the clearing of copyrights, and the general publication of the book.

The new Hymn Book, presented in draft form, was adopted by the General Council of the United Church of Canada and by the General Synod of the Anglican Church of Canada on 1 February 1971.

No hymn book prepared today will be of permanent usefulness to the church. There will have to be further revision in another generation, and in each generation thereafter as the world continues to change, and the everlasting Gospel is proclaimed. Our task, however, has been to enable the whole people of God to set forth his praise in an idiom appropriate to our time, that he may be glorified continually throughout his Church.

*It is to be understood that nothing in this Hymn Book is of
any authority on matters relating to faith or doctrine
in the Anglican Church of Canada or the United Church of Canada.*

The Music

In the Christian era hymns were at first an expression of great joy at the good news of God's gift of himself in Christ. Very soon they became a vehicle for teaching the new faith. Synagogue and home could not contain them: streets and fields echoed to the hymns sung by believers in procession or at work. Down through the ages and across every boundary the Christian gospel was carried by music as well as by word and deed.

The compilers of a hymn book are thus able to range over many centuries in the search for tunes. Your Committee has sought to preserve the best of the past and to select from the present what appears to have lasting value for the future. Accordingly, the Hymn Book contains plainsong, chorales of the Reformation period, Genevan psalm tunes. Tudor and Elizabethan music, English and Scottish psalm tunes, French church melodies, folk tunes, Victorian tunes, and evangelistic songs.

But what from this century? The serious composer of church music today has to wrestle with the difficulty of finding a way to write a hymn tune in an idiom that is not only legitimate and contemporary, but also valid. In a word, his tune must be suitable for congregational use. To retrace the well-worn paths of earlier styles is much easier, no doubt, but he who does this loses his own identity.

Many contemporary composers are finding ways to meet this challenge. The Committee invited several, including a number in Canada, to compose tunes to particular hymns. They have provided a noteworthy contribution. Indeed, this hymn book contains the work of more Canadian composers than any hymn book that has preceded it.

In every hymn the function of melody is to reinforce the character, feeling and rhythm of the words and to become a vehicle for congregational response. How well it achieves this objective determines its suitability and value. Consequently, every new tune was tested in one way or another before it was adopted. The emphasis was always upon a singable tune that fitted the words and presupposed a firm harmonic structure.

For each hymn the Committee selected one, and occasionally two tunes. Most hymns have associations with several tunes. In such cases the Committee endeavoured to choose the most suitable tune. Preference was always given to the tune customarily sung, but the Committee did not hesitate to suggest a new tune, if a new association was clearly preferable. A cross reference to a familiar tune is frequently provided.

In accordance with current practice, the quarter note has been selected as the basic rhythmic unit. The words of the first stanza are placed between the staves. The aim has been to maintain a correspondence of 1:1 or 1:2 between the lines of music and the lines of words. A four-line stanza, for example, may have four lines of music, one for each line in the stanza; or it may have two lines of music, one for each two lines in the stanza. A comma immediately above a double stave subdivides the music at the point a new line of words begins. This pattern will greatly facilitate the process of learning a new tune.

Generally, each tune is set for four voices. Some reharmonization has been done where the part-writing was in much need of improvement. In a number of instances, however, voices are to sing in unison. A few descants have been composed specially for this book. As an alternative to the accompaniment of some hymns, chord symbols for the guitar have been provided.

The pitch of the tunes has been selected to provide a medium range for the melody. Rarely does a melody ascend above D in the octave above middle C, and then only because other considerations prevent a lower setting. Organists are encouraged to learn the art of transposing, so that they may freely choose the key that suits the occasion.

In the Liturgical Appendix it will be observed that the aim has been to select only as many chants as may appear conveniently upon the page along with the canticle. The whole note or the half note has been chosen as the reciting note.

The third setting for Holy Communion (509) follows the text approved by the International Consultation on English Texts.

Directions for performance have been kept to a minimum, in order to give freedom to the choirmaster. Whether a stanza should be sung loudly or softly, quickly or rather deliberately, is dependent upon such things as the need and emotion of the moment, the character of the words and the music, and also the size of the building. At times the fermate (⌒) has been retained over those notes at the end of phrases where there may be an occasion to pause, but the Committee recognizes the wide divergence of opinion that exists on its employment, and prefers to leaves its use largely to the discretion of the choirmaster.

The time signature has been omitted. The rhythm of the words in many hymns tends toward a flexibility that might be curbed by the presence of a time signature. In any event, the accentual pattern of any measure is determined not by the time signature, but by the interaction of melody, harmony and word.

In a few hymns the number of syllables in the lines varies from stanza to stanza. In these instances a stroke has been employed under appropriate syllables of the text to indicate that the singer is to follow the dotted slur at the corresponding point in the music.

It is the right of all to join together in the common act of worship. In the singing of hymns everyone should be able to follow the music. The choir will normally sing in parts, but ought not to avoid the unison. The congregation will normally sing in unison, but the presence of music in the hymn book will invite the worshipper to follow the part that suits his own voice.

The final selection of the tunes was the work of the entire Committee, which was fortunate in having had the assistance of many able musicians and composers.

The Contents

HYMNS IN THE ORDER OF WORSHIP

Hymns in the order of worship

I

ALL CREATURES OF OUR GOD AND KING

LASST UNS ERFREUEN 8 8 8 8 and alleluias   Geistliche Kirchengesänge, Cologne 1623
harmonized by Derek Holman 1931-

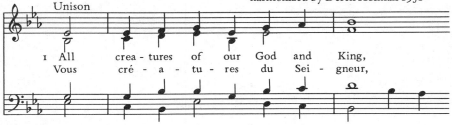

Unison

1 All crea-tures of our God and King,
Vous cré-a-tu-res du Sei-gneur,

lift up your voice and with us sing:
chan-tez tou-jours en son hon-neur,

Harmony

al-le-lu-ia, al-le-lu-ia!
al-lé-lu-ia, al-lé-lu-ia!

Unison

Thou burn-ing sun with gold-en beam,
Car c'est lui seul qu'il faut lou-er,

thou sil-ver moon with soft-er gleam,
il donne au so-leil sa clar-té,

Harmony

O praise him, O praise him,
ren - dez gloi - re, ren - dez gloi - re,

al - le - lu - ia, al - le - lu - ia, al - le - lu - ia!
al - lé - lu - ia, al - lé - lu - ia, al - lé - lu - ia!

2 Thou rushing wind that art so strong,
ye clouds that sail in heaven along,
O praise him, alleluia!
Thou rising morn, in praise rejoice;
ye lights of evening, find a voice:
O praise him, alleluia!

3 Dear mother earth, who day by day
unfoldest blessings on our way:
O praise him, alleluia!
The flowers and fruits that in thee grow,
let them his glory also show:
O praise him, alleluia!

4 And all ye men of tender heart,
forgiving others, take your part:
O sing ye, alleluia!
Ye who long pain and sorrow bear,
praise God and on him cast your care:
O praise him, alleluia!

5 Let all things their Creator bless,
and worship him in humbleness:
O praise him, alleluia!
Praise, praise the Father, praise the Son,
and praise the Spirit, three in one:
O praise him, alleluia!

St Francis of Assisi 1184-1226
tr. William Henry Draper 1855-1933

2 Dieu, sois loué pour le soleil,
pour ce grand frère sans pareil,
alléluia, alléluia!
Et pour la lune et sa lueur,
pour chaque étoile notre sœur,
rendons gloire, alléluia!

3 Loué sois-tu pour sire feu,
vivant, robuste, glorieux,
alléluia, alléluia!
La terre, en maternelle sœur,
nous comble de ses mille fleurs,
rendons gloire, alléluia!

4 Heureux les artisans de paix,
leur nom soit béni à jamais,
alléluia, alléluia!
Ceux qui ont souffert et pâti,
ils te remettent leurs soucis,
à toi montent leurs louanges, alléluia!

5 Dieu trois fois saint, nous te louons,
nous te chantons, nous t'adorons,
alléluia, alléluia!
Gloire au Père et louange au Fils,
et loué soit le Saint-Esprit,
rendons gloire, alléluia!

tr. revue par J-J Bovet 1904
for a lower setting see 7

LET ALL THE WORLD IN EVERY CORNER SING

LUCKINGTON 10 4 6 6 6 6 10 4 FIRST TUNE   Basil Harwood 1859-1949

1 Let all the world in ev - ery cor-ner sing, my God and King!

The heavens are not too high, his praise may thi - ther fly;

the earth is not too low, his prais - es there may grow.

Let all the world in ev - ery cor-ner sing, my God and King!

2 Let all the world in every corner sing,
    my God and King!
    The church with psalms must shout,
    no door can keep them out;
    but above all, the heart
    must bear the longest part.
    Let all the world in every corner sing,
    my God and King!

                                        George Herbert 1593-1633

Unison

1 Let all the world in ev-ery cor-ner sing, my God and King!

The heavens are not too high, his praise may thi-ther fly;

the earth is not too low, his prais-es there may grow.

Let all the world in ev-ery cor-ner sing, my God and King!

2 Let all the world in every corner sing,
   my God and King!
   The church with psalms must shout,
   no door can keep them out;
   but above all, the heart
   must bear the longest part.
   Let all the world in every corner sing,
   my God and King!

George Herbert 1593-1633

3

FROM ALL THAT DWELL BELOW THE SKIES

ILLSLEY 8 8 8 8   John Bishop c1665-1737

1 From all that dwell be - low the skies let the Cre - a - tor's praise a - rise:

let the Re - deem - er's name be sung through ev - ery land, in ev - ery tongue.

2 Eternal are thy mercies, Lord: Isaac Watts 1674-1748
  eternal truth attends thy word;   based on Psalm 117
  thy praise shall sound from shore to shore, This may be sung to Lasst uns
  till suns shall rise and set no more.   erfreuen 1 or 7

4

YE GATES, LIFT UP YOUR HEADS

ST GEORGE'S, EDINBURGH   melody by Andrew Mitchell Thompson 1778-1831
8 6 8 6 D and coda   harmonized by Frederick R C Clarke 1931-

1 Ye gates, lift up your heads on high; ye doors that last for aye,

be lift - ed up, that so the King of glo - ry en - ter may.

But who of glo-ry is the King? The migh-ty Lord is this,

Even that same Lord that great in might and strong in bat-tle is,

even that same Lord that great in might and strong in bat-tle is.

Hal - le-lu - jah, hal - le - lu - jah, hal - le - lu - jah, hal - le - lu - jah,

hal - le-lu - jah. A - men, a - men, a - men.

2 Ye gates, lift up your heads on high;
ye doors that last for aye,
be lifted up, that so the King
of glory enter may.
But who is he that is the King
of glory? Who is this?

The Lord of hosts, and none but he
the King of glory is.
Hallelujah. Amen.

Scottish Psalter 1650
based on Psalm 24

5

SING ALLELUIA FORTH

MARTINS 10 10 7

Percy Carter Buck 1871-1947

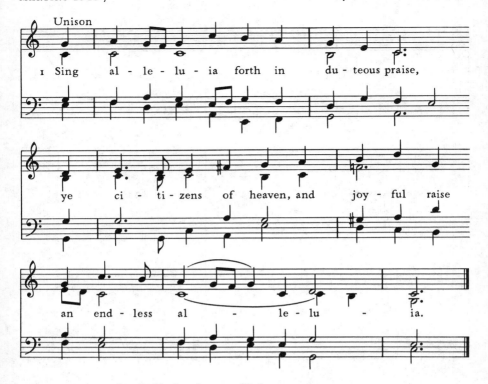

Unison

1 Sing al - le - lu - ia forth in du - teous praise,
ye ci - ti - zens of heaven, and joy - ful raise
an end - less al - le - lu - ia.

2 Ye powers, who stand before the eternal light,
in hymning choirs re-echo to the height
an endless alleluia.

3 Thus in one great acclaim shall ever ring
the strains which tell the honour of your King,
an endless alleluia.

4 Thee, O Creator of the world, we praise
for ever, and tell out in joyous lays
an endless alleluia.

5 To thee, O Lord, our grateful hearts we bring:
O Holy Spirit, jubilant we sing
an endless alleluia.

from the Latin 10th century
tr. John Ellerton 1826-1893

6

CROFT'S 136th 6 6 6 6 4 4 4 4   William Croft 1678-1727

1 Ye ho-ly an-gels bright, who stand be-fore God's throne and dwell in glo-rious light, praise ye the Lord each one. As-sist our song, or else the theme too high doth seem for mor-tal tongue.

2 You blessed souls at rest,
that see your Saviour's face,
whose glory, even the least,
is far above our grace.
God's praises sound,
as in his sight
with sweet delight
you do abound.

3 All nations of the earth,
extol the world's great King:
with melody and mirth
his glorious praises sing.
In him rejoice,
and there proclaim
his holy name
with sounding voice.

4 My soul, bear thou thy part:
triumph in God above,
and with a well-tuned heart
sing thou the songs of love.
And all my days,
let no distress
nor fears suppress
his joyful praise.

Richard Baxter 1615-1691
This may be sung to Darwall 44

7

YE WATCHERS AND YE HOLY ONES

LASST UNS ERFREUEN 8 8 8 8 and alleluias

Geistliche Kirchengesänge, Cologne 1623
harmonized by Derek Holman 1931-

1 Ye watch - ers and ye ho - ly ones,
bright ser - aphs, cher - u - bim and thrones,
raise the glad strain: al - le - lu - ia!
Cry out, do - min - ions, prince - doms, powers,
vir - tues, arch - an - gels, an - gels' choirs:
al - le - lu - ia, al - le - lu - ia,

al - le - lu - ia, al - le - lu - ia, al - le - lu - - ia!

2 O higher than the cherubim,
   more glorious than the seraphim,
   lead their praises: alleluia!
   Thou bearer of the eternal word,
   most gracious, magnify the Lord:
   alleluia!

3 Respond, ye souls in endless rest,
   ye patriarchs and prophets blest:
   alleluia, alleluia!
   Ye holy twelve, ye martyrs strong,
   all saints triumphant, raise the song:
   alleluia!

4 O friends, in gladness let us sing,
   supernal anthems echoing:
   alleluia, alleluia!
   To God the Father, God the Son,
   and God the Spirit, three in one,
   alleluia!

Athelstan Riley 1858-1945
for a higher setting see 1

O ALL YE FAR-SPREADING LAKES

ALGONQUIN irregular   Derek Holman 1931–

1 O all ye far-spreading lakes, praise ye the Lord.
O all ye deep blue waters, praise ye the Lord.
O all ye little shining waves, praise ye the Lord.
O all ye far-off gleaming birch trees, praise ye the Lord.

2 O all ye sands and burly rocks, praise ye the Lord.
O all ye islands and little hills, praise ye the Lord.
O all ye winding trails and beaten roads, praise ye the Lord.
O all ye battling winter creeks, praise ye the Lord.

3 O all ye keen airs and shouting winds, praise ye the Lord.
O all ye clear skies and couching clouds, praise ye the Lord.
O all men with thankful voice, praise ye the Lord.
O all ye debtors to his love, praise ye the Lord.   Alfred Robert George 1878–1961

9

O PRAISE YE THE LORD

LAUDATE DOMINUM 10 10 11 11   Charles Hubert Hastings Parry 1848-1918

1 O praise ye the Lord! praise him in the height;
re - joice in his word, ye an - gels of light;
ye hea - vens, a - dore him by whom ye were made,
and wor - ship be - fore him in bright - ness ar - rayed.

2   O praise ye the Lord! praise him upon earth,
in tuneful accord, ye sons of new birth;
praise him who hath brought you his grace from above,
praise him who hath taught you to sing of his love.

3   O praise ye the Lord, all things that give sound;
each jubilant chord re-echo around;
loud organs, his glory forth tell in deep tone,
and sweet harp, the story of what he hath done.

4   O praise ye the Lord! thanksgiving and song
to him be outpoured all ages along;
for love in creation, for heaven restored,   Henry Williams Baker 1821-1877
for grace of salvation, O praise ye the Lord!   based on Psalm 150

10

PRAISE THE LORD! YE HEAVENS, ADORE HIM

REX GLORIAE 8 7 8 7 D   Henry Thomas Smart 1813-1879

1 Praise the Lord! ye heavens a - dore him; praise him, an - gels in the height;
sun and moon re - joice be - fore him; praise him, all ye stars and light.
Praise the Lord! for he hath spo - ken; worlds his migh - ty voice o - beyed;
laws which ne - ver shall be bro - ken for their guid - ance hath he made.

2 Praise the Lord! for he is glorious;
never shall his promise fail;
God hath made his saints victorious;
sin and death shall not prevail.
Praise the God of our salvation!
Hosts on high, his power proclaim;
heaven and earth and all creation
laud and magnify his name.

Foundling Hospital Collection 1796
author unknown
based on Psalm 148
This may be sung to Austria 155

II

PRAISE THE LORD! HIS GLORIES SHOW

GWALCHMAI 7 7 7 7 and alleluias — Joseph David Jones 1827-1870

1 Praise the Lord! his glo - ries show, Al - le - lu - ia!

saints with - in his courts be - low, Al - le - lu - ia!

an - gels round his throne a - bove, Al - le - lu - ia!

all that see and share his love. Al - le - lu - ia!

2 Earth to heaven, and heaven to earth,
tell his wonders, sing his worth;
age to age, and shore to shore
praise him, praise him evermore.

3 Praise the Lord, his mercies trace;
praise his providence and grace;
all that he for man hath done,
all he sends us through his Son.

Henry Francis Lyte 1793-1847
based on Psalm 150

4 Strings and voices, hands and hearts,
in the concert bear your parts;
all that breathe, your Lord adore;
praise him, praise him evermore.

This hymn may be sung in the manner of
a versicle and a response, by using
the Alleluia throughout as the response.

12

ALL PEOPLE THAT ON EARTH DO DWELL

OLD 100th 8 8 8 8   melody from Genevan Psalter 1551

1 Vous, qui sur la terre habitez,
All people that on earth do dwell,

chantez à haute voix, chantez;
sing to the Lord with cheerful voice,

Réjouissez-vous au Seigneur,
him serve with mirth, his praise forth tell;

par un saint hymne à son honneur.
come ye before him and rejoice.

Original form of melody in last line:

2   Sachez qu'il est le Souverain,
    qu'il nous a formés de sa main,
    nous, le peuple qu'il veut chérir,
    et le troupeau qu'il veut nourrir.

3   Entrez dans son temple aujourd'hui;
    prosternez-vous tous devant lui,
    et, de concert avec les cieux,
    célébrez son nom glorieux.

4   C'est un Dieu rempli de bonté,
    d'une éternelle vérité,
    toujours propice à nos souhaits,
    et sa grâce dure à jamais.

Théodore de Bèze 1519-1605
et d'autres

2   Know that the Lord is God indeed;
    without our aid he did us make;
    we are his folk, he doth us feed,
    and for his sheep he doth us take.

3   O enter then his gates with praise,
    approach with joy his courts unto;
    praise, laud, and bless his name always,
    for it is seemly so to do.

4   For why, the Lord our God is good;
    his mercy is for ever sure;
    his truth at all times firmly stood,
    and shall from age to age endure.

Scottish Psalter 1650
based on Psalm 100

13

BEFORE JEHOVAH'S AWFUL THRONE
OLD 100th 8 8 8 8

1   Before Jehovah's awful throne,
    ye nations, bow with sacred joy;
    know that the Lord is God alone;
    he can create, and he destroy.

2   His sovereign power, without our aid,
    made us of clay, and formed us men;
    and when like wandering sheep we strayed,
    he brought us to his fold again.

3   We'll crowd thy gates with thankful songs,
    high as the heavens our voices raise;
    and earth with her ten thousand tongues
    shall fill thy courts with sounding praise.

4   Wide as the world is thy command,
    vast as eternity thy love;
    firm as a rock thy truth shall stand,
    when rolling years shall cease to move.

Isaac Watts 1674-1748
John Wesley 1703-1791
based on Psalm 100

14

O SING A NEW SONG TO THE LORD

JACKSON 8 6 8 6   Thomas Jackson c1715-1781

1 O sing a new song to the Lord for won-ders he hath done:
his right hand and his ho-ly arm him vic-to-ry hath won.

2 He mindful of his grace and truth
to Israel's house hath been;
and the salvation of our God
all ends of the earth have seen.

3 Let all the earth unto the Lord
send forth a joyful noise;
lift up your voice aloud to him,
sing praises, and rejoice.

4 With harp, with harp, and voice of psalms
unto Jehovah sing:
with trumpets, cornets, gladly sound
before the Lord the King.

5 Let seas and all their fullness roar,
the world, and dwellers there;
let floods clap hands, and let the hills
together joy declare.

6 To judge the earth Jehovah comes,
in righteousness comes he;
in justice he will judge the world,
the people uprightly.

Scottish Psalter 1650
based on Psalm 98

15

O COME, LET US SING TO THE LORD

MONTROSE 8 6 8 6   melody from Gilmour's 'Psalm Singer's Assistant' 1793
harmonized by Frederick R C Clarke 1931-

1 O come, let us sing to the Lord,

to him our voi - ces raise;
with joy - ful noise let us the Rock
of our sal - va - tion praise.

2 Let us before his presence come
   with praise and thankful voice;
   let us sing psalms to him with grace,
   and make a joyful noise.

3 For God's a great God and great King;
   above all gods he is.
   The depths of earth are in his hand,
   the heights of hills are his.

4 To him the spacious sea belongs,
   for he the same did make;
   the dry land also from his hands
   its form at first did take.

5 O come, and let us worship him;
   bow down, ye people all,
   and on our knees before the Lord   Scottish Psalter 1650
   our Maker let us fall.   based on Psalm 95

16

GOD REVEALS HIS PRESENCE

ARNSBERG 6 6 8 D 3 3 6 6   Joachim Neander 1650-1680

1 God re-veals his pres - ence: let us now a - dore him
   God is in his tem - ple: all with-in keep si - lence,

and with awe ap - pear be - fore him. Him a-lone God we own,
pros-trate lie with deep - est re - verence.

him our God and Sav - iour: praise his name for ev - er.

2 God reveals his presence:
hear the harps resounding;
see the crowds the throne surrounding.
'Holy, holy, holy!'
Hear the hymn ascending,
angels, saints, their voices blending.
Bow thine ear
to us here;
hearken, O Lord Jesus,
to our meaner praises.

3 O thou Fount of blessing,
purify my spirit
trusting only in thy merit;
like the holy angels
who behold thy glory,
may I ceaselessly adore thee.
Let thy will
ever still
rule thy church terrestrial,
as the hosts celestial.

Gerhard Tersteegen 1697-1769
tr. Frederick William Foster 1760-1835
John Miller 1756-1810
William Mercer 1811-1873

17

WITH JOY WE GO UP TO THE HOUSE OF THE LORD

WISBECH 11 8 11 8   Alfred Whitehead 1887–

1 With joy we go up to the house of the Lord, and en-ter his gates with a song, to stand in a ci-ty re-newed by his word, the ci-ty where all men be-long.

2   To offer their thanks to his glorious name
    the peoples are summoned by God;
    his throne he has set his decrees to proclaim,
    his judgements are gone out abroad.

3   For peace in the city thou buildest anew,
    for courage and faith in this day,
    for wisdom to seek out the good and the true,
    O Lord of the nations, we pray.

John Webster Grant 1919–
based on Psalm 122

18

I JOYED WHEN TO THE HOUSE OF GOD

ST PAUL 8 6 8 6

from Chalmer's Collection, Aberdeen 1749
harmonized by Stanley L Osborne 1907–

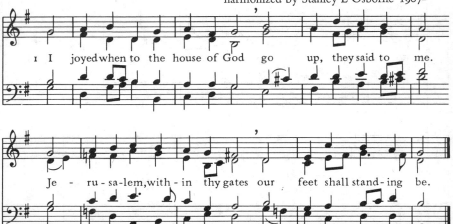

I joyed when to the house of God go up, they said to me.
Je - ru - sa - lem, with - in thy gates our feet shall stand - ing be.

2 Jerusalem our city is
firm built and strongly stands;
unto that place the tribes go up,
pilgrims from all her lands.

3 Pray that Jerusalem may have
peace and felicity:
let them that love thee and thy peace
have still prosperity.

4 Therefore I wish that peace may still
within thy walls remain,
and ever may thy palaces
prosperity retain.

5 Now for my friends' and brethren's sakes
'Peace be in thee,' I'll say;
and for the house of God our Lord
I'll seek thy good alway.

Scottish Psalter 1650
based on Psalm 122
for a lower setting, see 31

19

JOYFUL, JOYFUL WE ADORE THEE

HYMN TO JOY 8 7 8 7 D

melody from Ludwig van Beethoven 1770-1827
arranged by Edward Hodges 1796-1867

I Joy-ful, joy-ful we a-dore thee, God of glo-ry, Lord of love;

hearts un-fold like flowers be-fore thee, o-pening to the sun a-bove.

Melt the clouds of sin and sad-ness, drive the dark of doubt a-way;

giv-er of im-mor-tal glad-ness, fill us with the light of day.

2　All thy works with joy surround thee,
　　earth and heaven reflect thy rays;
　　stars and angels sing around thee,
　　centre of unbroken praise.
　　Field and forest, vale and mountain,
　　flowery meadow, flashing sea,
　　chanting bird and flowing fountain,
　　call us to rejoice in thee.

3　Thou art giving and forgiving,
　　ever blessing, ever blest,
　　well-spring of the joy of living,
　　ocean depth of happy rest!
　　Thou our Father, Christ our Brother,
　　all who live in love are thine;
　　teach us how to love each other,
　　lift us to the joy divine.

Henry van Dyke 1852-1933

20

HOW SHALL I SING THAT MAJESTY

MOLESWORTH 8 6 8 6 D FIRST TUNE   Derek Holman 1931-

1 How shall I sing that ma-jes-ty which an-gels do ad - mire?
Let dust in dust and si - lence lie; sing, sing, ye heaven-ly choir!
Thou-sands of thou-sands stand a - round thy throne, O God most high;
ten thou- sand times ten thou-sand sound thy praise; but who am I?

2 Thy brightness unto them appears,
whilst I thy footsteps trace;
a sound of God comes to my ears,
but they behold thy face.
They sing because thou art their sun;
Lord, send a beam on me;
for where heaven is but once begun
there hallelujahs be.

3 How great a being, Lord, is thine,
which doth all beings keep!
Thy knowledge is the only line
to sound so vast a deep:
thou art a sea without a shore,
a sun without a sphere;
thy time is now and evermore,
thy place is everywhere.

John Mason c1645-1694

1 How shall I sing that ma-jes-ty which an-gels do ad-mire?

Let dust in dust and si-lence lie; sing, sing, ye heaven-ly choir!

Thou-sands of thou-sands stand a-round thy throne, O God most high;

ten thou-sand times ten thou-sand sound thy praise; but who am I?

2 Thy brightness unto them appears,
whilst I thy footsteps trace;
a sound of God comes to my ears,
but they behold thy face.
They sing because thou art their sun;
Lord, send a beam on me;
for where heaven is but once begun
there hallelujahs be.

3 How great a being, Lord, is thine,
which doth all beings keep!
Thy knowledge is the only line
to sound so vast a deep:
thou art a sea without a shore,
a sun without a sphere;
thy time is now and evermore,
thy place is everywhere.

John Mason c1645-1694

21

LO, GOD IS HERE

VATER UNSER 8 8 8 8 8 8

from 'Geistliche Lieder', Leipzig 1539

harmonized by Johann Sebastian Bach 1685-1750

Lo, God is here! let us a-dore and own how awe-some is this place;

let all with-in us feel his power and si-lent bow be-fore his face;

who know his power, his grace who prove, serve him with awe, with re-ver-ence love.

2 Lo, God is here! him day and night
united choirs of angels sing;
to him, enthroned above all height,
heaven's host their noblest praises bring;
disdain not, Lord, our meaner song,
who praise thee with a stammering tongue.

3 Being of beings, may our praise
thy courts with grateful fragrance fill;
still may we stand before thy face,
still hear and do thy sovereign will;
to thee may all our thoughts arise,
ceaseless, accepted sacrifice.

Gerhard Tersteegen 1696-1769
tr. John Wesley 1703-1791

22

PRAISE TO THE LIVING GOD

FOREST HILL 6 6 8 4 D

Derek Holman 1931-

Unison

1 Praise to the liv-ing God! All prais-ed be his name,

who was, and is, and is to be, for aye the same!

The one e-ter-nal God ere aught that now ap-pears,

the first, the last, be-yond all thought his time-less years!

2 Formless, all lovely forms
   declare his loveliness;
   holy, no holiness of earth
   can his express.
   Lo, he is Lord of all!
   Creation speaks his praise,
   and everywhere, above, below,
   his will obeys.

3 His Spirit floweth free,
   high surging where it will;
   in prophet's word he spake of old:
   he speaketh still.
   Established is his law,
   and changeless it shall stand,
   deep writ upon the human heart,
   on sea, on land.

4 Eternal life hath he
   implanted in the soul;
   his love shall be our strength and stay
   while ages roll.
   Praise to the living God!
   All praised be his name,
   who was and is and is to be,
   for aye the same.

based on the Yigdal of
Daniel Ben Judah, 14th century
tr. Max Landsberg 1845-1928
Newton Mann 1836-1926

This may be sung to Leoni 23

23

THE GOD OF BETHLEHEM PRAISE

LEONI 6 6 8 4 D from a melody for the Yigdal, transcribed by Meyer Lyon 1751-1797
adapted by Thomas Olivers 1725-1799

1 The God of Beth-lehem praise, who sent his Son to earth,
and chose King Her-od's dan-gerous days to grant him birth,
who poured in-to his youth all mer-cy, love and truth,
dis-played through-out his life's short span the per-fect man.

2 The God of Jordan praise,
who willed him live for all
and chose John Baptist's greatest days
to seal his call,
whose mission then began
to every sort of man;
the kingdom's grace was then defined
for all mankind.

3 The God of Calvary praise,
who took the servant's part
and chose poor Pilate's cruelest days
to bare his heart.
Spread-eagled there above,
his death proclaimed his love,
declared the Saviour's crucial plea –
he died for me.

4   The God of Easter praise:
    he knew our feeble plight
    and chose the most effectual ways
    to prove his might;
    he shattered death's grim hold
    and back the tombstone rolled:
    the Lord was loosed, the Lord is free,
    he lives for me.   Richard Granville Jones 1926–

24

PRAISE THE LORD WITH JOYFUL CRY

NORTHAMPTON 7 7 7 7   Charles John King 1859–1934

1 Praise the Lord with joy-ful cry; let the mood of praise run high.

Praise him who with migh-ty deeds hu-man great-ness far ex-ceeds.

2   Praise him with the sound that swings,
    with percussion, brass and strings.
    Let the world at every chance
    praise him with a song and dance.

3   Praise with life and voice the Lord,
    him who speaks in deed and word,   Frederik Herman Kaan 1929–
    who to life the world ordained: based on Psalm 150
    let our praise be unrestrained!   This may be sung to Monkland 28

25

ETERNAL, UNCHANGING, WE SING TO THY PRAISE

ST BASIL 11 11 11 11   Healey Willan 1880-1968

1 E - ter - nal, Un - chang - ing, we sing to thy praise:
thy mer - cies are end - less, and right - eous thy ways;
thy ser - vants pro - claim the re - nown of thy name
who rul - est om - ni - po - tent, ev - er the same.

2   Again we rejoice in the world thou hast made,
    thy mighty creation in beauty arrayed,
    we thank thee for life, and we praise thee for joy,
    for love and for hope that no power can destroy.

3   We praise thee for Jesus, our Master and Lord,
    the might of his Spirit, the truth of his word,
    his comfort in sorrow, his patience in pain,   Robert B Y Scott 1899–
    the faith sure and steadfast that Jesus shall reign.   This may be sung to St Denio 139

26

IMMORTAL, INVISIBLE, GOD ONLY WISE

MONTGOMERY 11 11 11 11   probably by Samuel Jarvis c1762

1 Im - mor - tal, in - vi - si - ble, God on - ly wise, in light in - ac - cess - i - ble hid from our eyes, most bless - ed, most glo - rious, the An - cient of days, al - migh - ty, vic - tor - ious, thy great name we praise.

2 Unresting, unhasting, and silent as light,
  nor wanting, nor wasting, thou rulest in might;
  thy justice like mountains high soaring above
  thy clouds which are fountains of goodness and love.

3 To all life thou givest, to both great and small;
  in all life thou livest, the true life of all;
  we blossom and flourish as leaves on the tree,
  and wither and perish – but nought changeth thee.

4 Great Father of glory, pure Father of light,
  thine angels adore thee, all veiling their sight;
  all laud we would render: O help us to see
  'tis only the splendour of light hideth thee.

Walter Chalmers Smith 1824-1908
based on 1 Timothy 1:17
This may be sung to St Denio 139
or St Basil 25

27
O WORSHIP THE KING

HANOVER 10 10 11 11

probably by William Croft 1678-1727

1 O worship the King, all glorious above;
O gratefully sing his power and his love;
our Shield and Defender, the Ancient of days,
pavilioned in splendour and girded with praise.

2 O tell of his might, O sing of his grace,
whose robe is the light, whose canopy space;
his chariots of wrath the deep thunder-clouds form,
and dark is his path on the wings of the storm.

3 The earth with its store of wonders untold,
Almighty, thy power hath founded of old,
hath stablished it fast by a changeless decree,
and round it hath cast, like a mantle, the sea.

4 Thy bountiful care what tongue can recite?
It breathes in the air, it shines in the light;
it streams from the hills, it descends to the plain,
and sweetly distils in the dew and the rain.

5   Frail children of dust, and feeble as frail,
in thee do we trust, nor find thee to fail;
thy mercies how tender, how firm to the end,
our Maker, Defender, Redeemer, and Friend.

6   O measureless Might, ineffable Love,
while angels delight to hymn thee above,
the humbler creation, though feeble their lays,
with true adoration shall sing to thy praise.

Robert Grant 1779-1838
based on paraphrase of Psalm 104
by William Kethe c1530-1593

28

LET US WITH A GLADSOME MIND

MONKLAND 7 7 7 7   Johann Anastasius Freylinghausen 1670-1739
arranged by John Bernard Wilkes 1785-1869

1 Let us with a glad-some mind praise the Lord, for he is kind:
for his mer-cies aye en-dure, ev - er faith-ful, ev-er sure.

2   Let us blaze his name abroad,
for of gods he is the God:
for his mercies aye endure,
ever faithful, ever sure.

3   He with all-commanding might
filled the new-made world with light:
for his mercies aye endure,
ever faithful, ever sure.

4   He hath with a piteous eye
looked upon our misery:
for his mercies aye endure,
ever faithful, ever sure.

5   All things living he doth feed,
his full hand supplies their need:
for his mercies aye endure,
ever faithful, ever sure.

6   Let us then with gladsome mind
praise the Lord, for he is kind:
for his mercies aye endure,
ever faithful, ever sure.

John Milton 1608-1674
based on Psalm 136

PRAISE TO THE LORD, THE ALMIGHTY

LOBE DEN HERREN 14 14 4 7 8   Stralsund Gesangbuch 1665

1 Praise to the Lord, the Al - migh-ty, the King of cre - a - tion;
O my soul, praise him, for he is thy health and sal - va - tion:
all ye who hear, bro-thers and sis - ters draw near,
praise him in glad a - dor - a - tion.

2 Praise to the Lord, who o'er all things so wondrously reigneth,
shelters thee under his wings, yea, so gently sustaineth:
hast thou not seen
how thy entreaties have been
granted in what he ordaineth?

3 Praise to the Lord, who doth prosper thy work and defend thee;
surely his goodness and mercy here daily attend thee:
ponder anew
what the Almighty can do,
if with his love he befriend thee.

4 Praise to the Lord, who, when tempests their warfare are waging,
who, when the elements madly around thee are raging,

biddeth them cease,
turneth their fury to peace,
whirlwinds and waters assuaging.

5 Praise to the Lord, who when darkness of sin is abounding,
who when the godless do triumph, all virtue confounding,
sheddeth his light,
chaseth the horrors of night,
saints with his mercy surrounding.

6 Praise to the Lord! O let all that is in me adore him!
All that hath life and breath come now with praises before him!
Let the Amen
sound from his people again:
gladly for aye we adore him.

Joachim Neander 1650–1680
tr. Catherine Winkworth 1829–1878 and others
based on Psalms 103 and 150

30

PRAISE, MY SOUL, THE KING OF HEAVEN

PRAISE, MY SOUL 878787   John Goss 1800–1880

1 Praise, my soul, the King of hea - ven; to his feet thy tri-bute bring;
ran-somed, healed, re-stored, for-gi - ven, who like thee his praise should sing?
Praise him, praise him, al - le - lu - ia, praise the ev - er - last-ing King.

2 Praise him for his grace and fa - vour to our fa - thers in dis - tress;

praise him, still the same for ev - er, slow to chide and swift to bless;

praise him, praise him, al - le - lu - ia, glo - rious in his faith - ful - ness.

3 Fa - ther-like he tends and spares us; well our fee - ble frame he knows;

in his hands he gent - ly bears us, res - cues us from all our foes:

praise him, praise him, al - le - lu - ia, wide - ly as his mer - cy flows.

Henry Francis Lyte 1793-1847
based on Psalm 103

Harmony

4 Frail as sum-mer's flower we flou-rish; blows the wind and it is gone;

but, while mor-tals rise and per-ish, God en-dures un-chang-ing on:

praise him, praise him, al - le - lu - ia, praise the high e - ter-nal one.

Unison

5 An-gels, help us to a-dore him, ye be-hold him face to face;

sun and moon bow down be-fore him: dwell-ers all in time and space,

praise him, praise him, al - le - lu - ia, praise with us the God of grace.

31

O THOU MY SOUL

ST PAUL 8686

Chalmer's Collection, Aberdeen 1749
harmonized by Stanley L Osborne 1907-

1 O thou my soul, bless God the Lord; and all that in me is

be stir-red up, his ho-ly name to mag-ni-fy and bless.

2 Bless, O my soul, the Lord thy God,
and not forgetful be
of all his gracious benefits
he hath bestowed on thee:

3 all thine iniquities who doth
most graciously forgive;
who thy diseases all and pains
doth heal, and thee relieve;

4 who doth redeem thy life, that thou
to death may'st not go down;
who thee with loving-kindness doth
and tender mercies crown:

5 who with abundance of good things
doth satisfy thy mouth,
so that, even as the eagle's age,
renewed is thy youth.

Scottish Psalter 1650
based on Psalm 103
for a higher setting see 18

32

THE LORD IS KING

DEUS TUORUM MILITUM 8888

Grenoble 'Antiphoner' 1753
harmonized by Stanley L Osborne 1907-

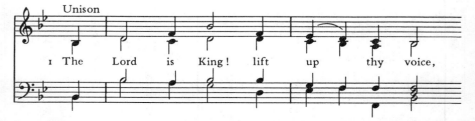

Unison

1 The Lord is King! lift up thy voice,

O earth, and all ye heavens, re - joice;
from world to world the joy shall ring.
'The Lord Om - ni - po - tent is King!'

2 He reigns! ye saints, exalt your strains;
   your God is King, your Father reigns;
   and he is at the Father's side,
   the Man of love, the Crucified.

3 Come, make your wants, your burdens known;
   he will present them at the throne;
   and angel bands are waiting there
   his messages of love to bear.

4 One Lord, one empire, all secures;
   he reigns, and life and death are yours:
   through earth and heaven one song shall ring,
   'The Lord Omnipotent is King!'

Josiah Conder 1789-1855
based on Revelation 19:6
for a higher setting see 78

33

WORSHIP THE LORD IN THE BEAUTY OF HOLINESS

ÜTTINGEN 12 10 12 10   Johann H Rheinhardt's 'Choralbuch', Üttingen 1754

1 Wor-ship the Lord in the beau-ty of ho-li-ness; bow down be-fore him, his glo-ry pro-claim; gold of o-be-dience and in-cense of low-li-ness bring, and a-dore him: the Lord is his name!

2 Low at his feet lay thy burden of carefulness;
high on his heart he will bear it for thee,
comfort thy sorrows, and answer thy prayerfulness,
guiding thy steps as may best for thee be.

3 Fear not to enter his courts, in the slenderness
of the poor wealth thou canst reckon as thine;
truth in its beauty and love in its tenderness,
these are the offerings to lay on his shrine.

4 These though we bring them in trembling and fearfulness,
he will accept for the Name that is dear,
mornings of joy give for evenings of tearfulness,
trust for our trembling, and hope for our fear.

5 Worship the Lord in the beauty of holiness;
   bow down before him, his glory proclaim;
   gold of obedience and incense of lowliness
   bring, and adore him: the Lord is his name!

   John Samuel Bewley Monsell 1811-1875

34

O LORD, THOU ART MY GOD

BROCKHAM 8 8 8 8   Jeremiah Clark 1670-1707

1 O Lord, thou art my God and King; thee will I mag-ni-fy and praise.

I will thee bless, and glad-ly sing un-to thy ho-ly name al-ways.

2 Each day I rise I will thee bless,
   and praise thy name time without end.
   Much to be praised and great God is;
   his greatness none can comprehend.

3 Race shall thy works praise unto race,
   the mighty acts show done by thee,
   I will speak of the glorious grace
   and honour of thy majesty.

4 Thy wondrous works I will record;
   by men the might shall be extolled
   of all thy dreadful acts, O Lord,
   and I thy greatness will unfold.

5 They utter shall abundantly
   the memory of thy goodness great;
   and shall sing praises cheerfully,
   whilst they thy righteousness relate.

Scottish Psalter 1650
based on Psalm 145
This may be sung to Duke Street 164

35

YE SERVANTS OF GOD

PADERBORN 10 10 11 11   Paderborn Gesangbuch 1765

1 Ye ser - vants of God, your Mas - ter pro - claim,
and pub - lish a - broad his won - der - ful name;
the name all vic - tor - ious of Je - sus ex - tol;
his king - dom is glo - rious, and rules o - ver all.

2   God ruleth on high, almighty to save,
   and still he is nigh, his presence we have;
   the great congregation his triumph shall sing,
   ascribing salvation to Jesus our King.

3   Salvation to God, who sits on the throne!
   Let all cry aloud, and honour the Son:
   the praises of Jesus the angels proclaim,
   fall down on their faces, and worship the Lamb.

4   Then let us adore and give him his right,
   all glory and power, all wisdom and might,
   all honour and blessing, with angels above,
   and thanks never ceasing, and infinite love.

Charles Wesley 1707-1788
This may be sung to
Laudate Dominum 9

SONGS OF PRAISE THE ANGELS SANG

CULBACH 7 7 7 7   Scheffler's 'Heilige Seelenlust' 1657

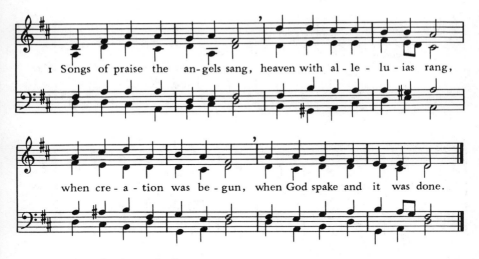

2 Songs of praise awoke the morn
   when the Prince of peace was born;
   songs of praise arose when he
   captive led captivity.

3 Heaven and earth must pass away,
   songs of praise shall crown that day;
   God will make new heavens and earth,
   songs of praise shall hail their birth.

4 And will man alone be dumb
   till that glorious kingdom come?
   No, the church delights to raise
   psalms and hymns and songs of praise.

5 Saints below, with heart and voice,
   still in songs of praise rejoice;
   learning here, by faith and love,
   songs of praise to sing above.

6 Hymns of glory, songs of praise,
   Father, unto thee we raise.
   Jesus, glory unto thee,
   with the Spirit, ever be.

James Montgomery 1771-1854
This may be sung to Orientis partibus 386

TO THE NAME OF OUR SALVATION

ORIEL 8 7 8 7 8 7   C Ett's 'Cantica Sacra', Munich 1840

1 To the name of our sal-va-tion laud and hon-our let us pay,

which for many a gen-er-a-tion hid in God's fore-know-ledge lay,

but with ho-ly ex-ul-ta-tion we may sing a-loud to-day.

2 Jesus is the name exalted
over every other name;
in this name, whene'er assaulted,
we can put our foes to shame;
strength to them who else had halted,
eyes to blind, and feet to lame.

3 'Tis the name that whoso preaches
finds its music in his ear;
who in prayer that name beseeches
finds its comfort ever near;
who its perfect wisdom reaches
heavenly joy possesses here.

4 Praise and honour to the Father,
praise and honour to the Son,
praise and honour to the Spirit,
ever three and ever one;
one in might and one in glory,
while unending ages run.

from the Nevers Breviary
tr. John Mason Neale 1818-1866

38

SING YE PRAISES TO THE FATHER   adapted from a Welsh melody

ARFON (major) 8 7 8 7 D   harmonized by Stanley L Osborne 1907-

1 Sing ye prais-es to the Fa-ther, sing ye prais-es to the Son,

sing ye prais-es to the Spir-it, liv-ing and e-ter-nal One.

God has made us, God has blessed us, God has called us to be true;

he is Lord of all cre-a-tion, dai-ly mak-ing all things new.

2 Join the praise of every creature,
sing with singing birds at dawn;
when the stars shine forth at nightfall,
hear their heavenly antiphon.
Praise him for the light of summer,
autumn glories, winter snows,
for the coming of the springtime
and the life of all that grows.

3 Praise God on our days of gladness
for his summons to rejoice,
praise him in our times of sadness
for the comfort of his voice.
God our Father, strong and loving,
Christ our Saviour, Leader, Lord,
living God, Creator Spirit—
be thy holy name adored!

Robert B Y Scott 1899-

39

AT THE NAME OF JESUS

KING'S WESTON 11 11 11 11 FIRST TUNE   Ralph Vaughan Williams 1872-1958

1 At the name of Je - sus ev-ery knee shall bow,

ev-ery tongue con - fess him King of glo - ry now;

'tis the Fa- ther's plea - sure we should call him Lord,

who from the be - gin - ning was the migh - ty Word.

3 Name him, bro-thers, name him, with

e - ver to be wor - shipped, trust-ed, and a - dored.

2 Humbled for a season to receive a name
from the lips of sinners unto whom he came,
faithfully he bore it, spotless to the last,
brought it back victorious when from death he passed.

3 Name him, brothers, name him, with love strong as death,
   but with awe and wonder, and with bated breath;
   he is God the Saviour, he is Christ the Lord,
   ever to be worshipped, trusted, and adored.

4 In your hearts enthrone him; there let him subdue
   all that is not holy, all that is not true;
   crown him as your Captain in temptation's hour;
   let his will enfold you in its light and power.

5 Brothers, this Lord Jesus shall return again,
   with his Father's glory, with his angel train;
   for all wreaths of empire meet upon his brow,
   and our hearts confess him King of glory now.

Caroline Maria Noel
1817-1877
based on Philippians 2:5-11

EVELYNS 11 11 11 11   SECOND TUNE

William Henry Monk 1823-1889

1 At the name of Je - sus   ev - ery knee shall   bow,

ev - ery tongue con - fess   him   King   of glo - ry   now;

'tis   the Fa - ther's plea - sure   we   should call   him   Lord,

who from   the   be - gin - ning   was   the migh - ty   Word.

40

1 Praise to the Ho - liest in the height,
and in the depth be praise,
in all his words most won - der - ful,
most sure in all his ways.

2 O loving wisdom of our God!
When all was sin and shame,
a second Adam to the fight
and to the rescue came.

3 O wisest love! that flesh and blood,
which did in Adam fail,
should strive afresh against the foe,
should strive and should prevail;

4 and that a higher gift than grace
should flesh and blood refine,
God's presence, and his very self,
and essence all-divine.

5   O generous love! that he who smote
     in Man for man the foe,
     the double agony in Man
     for man should undergo;

6   and in the garden secretly,
     and on the cross on high,
     should teach his brethren, and inspire
     to suffer and to die.

7   Praise to the Holiest in the height,
     and in the depth be praise,
     in all his words most wonderful,   John Henry Newman 1801-1890
     most sure in all his ways.   This may be sung to Richmond 147

CHORUS ANGELORUM 8 6 8 6   SECOND TUNE   Arthur Somervell 1863-1937

1 Praise to the Ho - liest in the height, and in the depth be praise, in all his words most won - der - ful, most sure in all his ways.

41

THINE IS THE GLORY

MACCABAEUS 5 5 6 5 6 5 6 5 and refrain

George Frederick Handel 1685-1759

1 A   toi   la   gloi - re,   O   Res - sus - ci - té!
Thine is   the   glo - ry,   ri - sen, con - quering Son:

A   toi   la   vic - toi - re   pour l'é - ter - ni - té!
end - less is   the   vic - tory   thou o'er death hast   won.

Bril - lant de   lu - miè - re,   l'ange est des - cen - du,
An - gels in bright rai - ment   rolled the stone a - way,

il   rou - le   la   pier - re   du tom - beau vain - cu.
kept the fold - ed grave-clothes where the bo - dy   lay.

A   toi   la   gloi - re,   O   Res - sus - ci - té!
Thine is   the   glo - ry,   ri - sen, con - quering Son:

A toi la vic - toi - re pour l'é - ter - ni - té !
end - less is the vic - tory thou o'er death hast won.

2 Vois-le paraître:
  c'est lui, c'est Jésus,
  ton Saveur, ton Maître!
  Oh! ne doute plus;
  sois dans l'allégresse,
  peuple du Seigneur,
  et redis sans cesse
  que Christ est vainqueur!
  A toi la gloire . . .

2 Lo, Jesus meets us,
  risen from the tomb!
  Lovingly he greets us,
  scatters fear and gloom.
  Let his church with gladness
  hymns of triumph sing,
  for her Lord now liveth:
  death has lost its sting.
  Thine is the glory . . .

3 Craindrais-je encore?
  Il vit à jamais,
  celui que j'adore,
  le Prince de paix;
  il est ma victoire,
  mon puissant soutien,
  ma vie et ma gloire:
  non, je ne crains rien!
  A toi la gloire . . .

3 No more we doubt thee,
  glorious Prince of life;
  life is nought without thee:
  aid us in our strife;
  make us more than conquerors,
  through thy deathless love;
  bring us safe through Jordan
  to thy home above.
  Thine is the glory . . .

Edmond Louis Budry 1854-1932   tr. Richard Birch Hoyle 1875-1939

42

ALL HAIL THE POWER OF JESUS' NAME

LADYWELL 8686D FIRST TUNE   William Harold Ferguson 1874-1950

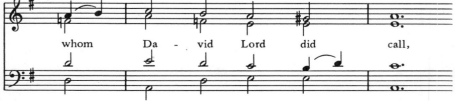

1 All hail the power of Jesus' name!
Let angels prostrate fall;
bring forth the royal diadem
to crown him Lord of all.
Hail him, ye heirs of David's line,
whom David Lord did call,

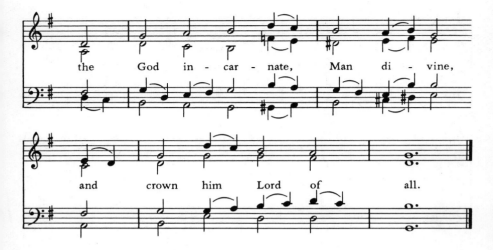

the God in - car - nate, Man di - vine, and crown him Lord of all.

2 Crown him, ye martyrs of your God,
who from his altar call;
extol him in whose path ye trod,
and crown him Lord of all.
Sinners, whose love can ne'er forget
the wormwood and the gall,
go, spread your trophies at his feet,
and crown him Lord of all.

3 Let every tongue and every tribe,
responsive to the call,
to him all majesty ascribe,
and crown him Lord of all.
O that, with yonder sacred throng,
we at his feet may fall,
join in the everlasting song,
and crown him Lord of all!

Edward Perronet 1726-1792
and others

ALL HAIL THE POWER OF JESUS' NAME

MILES LANE 8686 and repeat SECOND TUNE William Shrubsole 1760–1806

1 All hail the power of Je - sus' name! Let an - gels pros-trate fall;

bring forth the roy - al di - a - dem to crown him, crown him,

crown him, crown him Lord of all.

2 Hail him, ye heirs of David's line,
whom David Lord did call,
the God incarnate, Man divine,
and crown him Lord of all.

3 Crown him, ye martyrs of your God,
who from his altar call;
extol him in whose path ye trod,
and crown him Lord of all.

4 Sinners, whose love can ne'er forget
the wormwood and the gall,
go, spread your trophies at his feet,
and crown him Lord of all.

5 Let every tongue and every tribe,
responsive to the call,
to him all majesty ascribe,
and crown him Lord of all.

6 O that, with yonder sacred throng,
we at his feet may fall,
join in the everlasting song,
and crown him Lord of all!

Edward Perronet 1726–1792
and others

43

BRIGHT THE VISION THAT DELIGHTED

REDHEAD No. 46 8 7 8 7   Richard Redhead 1820-1901

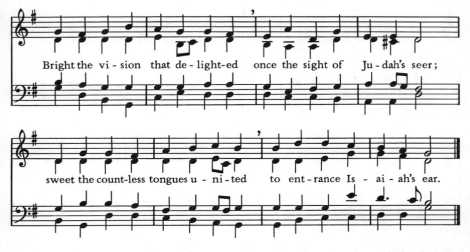

Bright the vi-sion that de-light-ed once the sight of Ju-dah's seer; sweet the count-less tongues u-ni-ted to ent-rance Is-ai-ah's ear.

2 Round the Lord in glory seated
cherubim and seraphim
filled his temple, and repeated
each to each the alternate hymn:

3 'Lord, thy glory fills the heaven;
earth is with its fullness stored;
unto thee be glory given,
holy, holy, holy, Lord.'

4 Heaven is still with glory ringing,
earth takes up the angels' cry,
'Holy, holy, holy,' singing,
'Lord of hosts, the Lord most high.'

5 With his seraph train before him,
with his holy church below,
thus unite we to adore him,
bid we thus our anthem flow:

6 'Lord, thy glory fills the heaven;
earth is with its fullness stored;
unto thee be glory given,
holy, holy, holy, Lord.'

Richard Mant 1776-1848
based on Isaiah 6:1-3

Descant by Francis Jackson 1917-

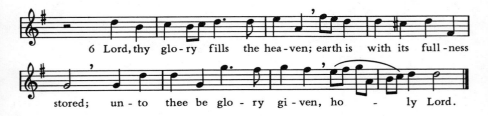

6 Lord, thy glo-ry fills the hea-ven; earth is with its full-ness stored; un-to thee be glo-ry gi-ven, ho - ly Lord.

44

REJOICE, THE LORD IS KING

GOPSAL 666688 FIRST TUNE George Frederick Handel 1685-1759

1 Re - joice, the Lord is King; your Lord and King a - dore;
re - joice, give thanks and sing and tri - umph ev - er - more:
lift up your heart, lift up your voice: Re - joice; a - gain I say, Re - joice.

2 Jesus the Saviour reigns,
the God of truth and love;
when he had purged our stains,
he took his seat above:
lift up your heart, lift up your voice:
Rejoice; again I say, Rejoice.

3 His kingdom cannot fail;
he rules o'er earth and heaven;
the keys of death and hell
are to our Jesus given:
lift up your heart...

4 He sits at God's right hand
till all his foes submit,
and bow to his command,
and fall beneath his feet:
lift up your heart...

5 Rejoice in glorious hope;
Jesus, the Judge, shall come
and take his servants up
to their eternal home:
we soon shall hear the archangel's voice;
the trump of God shall sound, Rejoice.

Charles Wesley 1707-1788

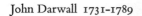

1 Re - joice, the Lord is King; your Lord and King a - dore;

re - joice, give thanks and sing and tri - umph ev - er - more:

lift up your heart, lift up your voice:

Re - joice; a - gain I say, Re - joice.

45

STAND UP AND BLESS THE LORD

ST THOMAS 6 6 8 6   Aaron Williams 1731-1776

1 Stand up and bless the Lord, ye people of his choice; stand up and bless the Lord your God with heart and soul and voice.

2 Though high above all praise,
above all blessing high,
who would not fear his holy name,
and laud and magnify?

3 O for the living flame
from his own altar brought,
to touch our lips, our minds inspire,
and wing to heaven our thought!

4 God is our strength and song,
and his salvation ours;
then be his love in Christ proclaimed
with all our ransomed powers.

5 Stand up and bless the Lord;
the Lord your God adore;
stand up and bless his glorious name
henceforth for evermore.

James Montgomery 1771-1854

46

FAIREST LORD JESUS

CRUSADERS' HYMN 5 6 8 10 8   'Schlesische Volkslieder' 1842
harmonized by James Hopkirk 1908–

1 Fair - est Lord Je - sus, rul - er of all na - ture,

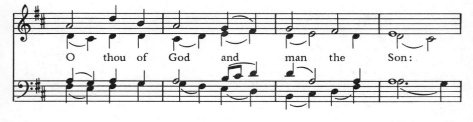

O thou of God and man the Son:

thee will I cher - ish, thee will I hon - our,

thou my soul's glo - ry, joy, and crown.

2 Fair are the meadows,
   fairer still the woodlands,
   robed in the blooming garb of spring;
   Jesus is fairer, Jesus is purer,
   who makes the troubled heart to sing.

3 Fair is the sunshine,
   fairer still the moonlight,
   and fair the twinkling, starry host;
   Jesus shines brighter, Jesus shines purer,
   than all the angels heaven can boast.

4 All fairest beauty
   heavenly and earthly,
   wondrously, Jesus, is found in thee;
   none can be nearer, fairer or dearer,
   than thou, my Saviour, art to me.

from the German, 17th century
tr. in 'Church Chorals and Choir Studies' 1850

47

COME, LET US JOIN OUR CHEERFUL SONGS

NATIVITY 8686   Henry Lahee 1826-1912

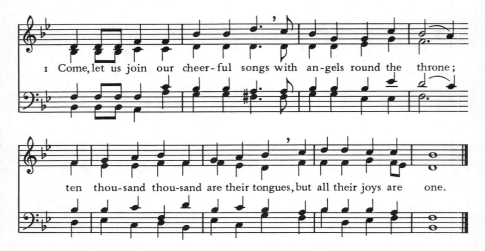

1 Come, let us join our cheer-ful songs with an-gels round the throne; ten thou-sand thou-sand are their tongues, but all their joys are one.

2 'Worthy the Lamb that died,' they cry,
  'to be exalted thus!'
  'Worthy the Lamb!' our lips reply,
  'for he was slain for us.'

3 Jesus is worthy to receive
  honour and power divine;
  and blessings, more than we can give,
  be, Lord, for ever thine!

4 The whole creation join in one
  to bless the sacred name
  of him that sits upon the throne,
  and to adore the Lamb!

Isaac Watts 1674-1748
based on Revelation 5:11-12

O FOR A THOUSAND TONGUES TO SING

LOBT GOTT, IHR CHRISTEN 8 6 8 6 and repeat   adapted from N Herman 1480-1561
harmonized by Johann Sebastian Bach 1685-1750

1 O for a thou-sand tongues to sing my dear Re-deem-er's praise,
the glo-ries of my God and King, the tri-umphs of his grace,
the tri-umphs of his grace.

2 Jesus! the name that charms our fears,
that bids our sorrows cease,
'tis music in the sinner's ears,
'tis life, and health, and peace.

3 He speaks, and listening to his voice,
new life the dead receive,
the mournful broken hearts rejoice,
the humble poor believe.

4 Hear him, ye deaf, his praise, ye dumb,
your loosened tongues employ;
ye blind, behold your Saviour come;
and leap, ye lame, for joy!

5 My gracious Master and my God,
assist me to proclaim,
to spread through all the earth abroad
the honours of thy name.

Charles Wesley 1707-1788
This may be sung to Richmond 147

49

ALLELUIA! SING TO JESUS!

HYFRYDOL 8 7 8 7 D

melody by Rowland Hugh Pritchard 1811-1887

harmonized by Hugh J McLean 1930-

1 Al - le - lu - ia! sing to Je - sus!

his the scep - tre, his the throne;

al - le - lu - ia! his the tri - umph,

his the vic - to - ry a - lone.

Hark! the songs of peace - ful Si - on

thun - der like a migh - ty flood;

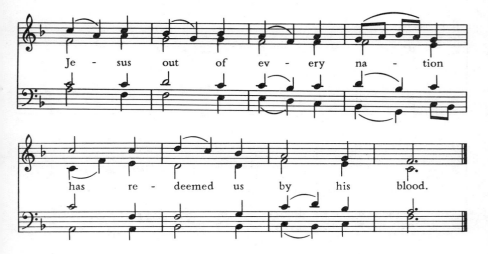

Je - sus out of ev - ery na - tion has re - deemed us by his blood.

2   Alleluia! not as orphans
    are we left in sorrow now;
    alleluia! he is near us,
    faith believes, nor questions how.
    Though the cloud from sight received him
    when the forty days were o'er,
    shall our hearts forget his promise,
    'I am with you evermore'?

3   Alleluia! King eternal,
    thee the Lord of lords we own;
    alleluia! born of Mary,
    earth thy footstool, heaven thy throne.
    Thou within the veil hast entered,
    robed in flesh, our great High Priest;
    thou on earth both Priest and Victim
    in the eucharistic feast.

4   Alleluia! sing to Jesus!
    his the sceptre, his the throne;
    alleluia! his the triumph,
    his the victory alone.
    Hark! the songs of peaceful Sion
    thunder like a mighty flood:
    Jesus out of every nation
    has redeemed us by his blood.

William Chatterton Dix 1837–1898

50

HOLY, HOLY, HOLY, LORD GOD ALMIGHTY

NICÆA irregular   John Bacchus Dykes 1823-1876

Ho - ly, ho - ly, ho - ly, Lord God al - migh - ty!

ear - ly in the morn - ing our song shall rise to thee;

ho - ly, ho - ly, ho - ly, mer - ci - ful and migh - ty,

God in three per - sons, bless - ed Tri - ni - ty!

2 Holy, holy, holy! all the saints adore thee,
  casting down their golden crowns around the glassy sea,
  cherubim and seraphim falling down before thee,
  which wert, and art, and evermore shalt be.

3 Holy, holy, holy! though the darkness hide thee,
  though the eye of sinful man thy glory may not see,
  only thou art holy; there is none beside thee,
  perfect in power, in love, and purity.

4 Holy, holy, holy, Lord God almighty!
  All thy works shall praise thy name in earth and sky and sea;
  holy, holy, holy, merciful and mighty,
  God in three persons, blessed Trinity!

Reginald Heber 1783-1826
based on Revelation 4:8-11

descant by Godfrey Hewitt 1909-

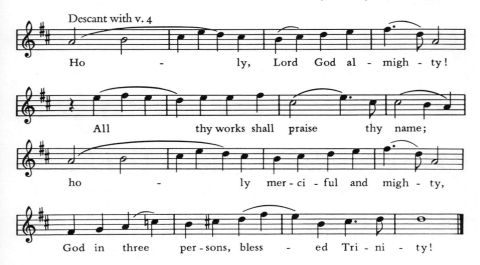

51
I'LL PRAISE MY MAKER
PSALM 36 888888 D

Matthäus Greiter c1500–1552
harmonized by Frederick R C Clarke 1931–

1 I'll praise my Ma-ker while I've breath, and when my voice is lost in death,

praise shall em-ploy my no-bler powers; my days of praise shall ne'er be past,

while life, and thought, and be-ing last, or im-mor-tal-i-ty en-dures.

Hap-py the man whose hopes re-ly on Is-rael's God; he made the sky,

and earth, and seas, with all their train; his truth for ev-er stands se-cure,

he saves the op-prest, he feeds the poor, and none shall find his pro-mise vain.

2 The Lord pours eyesight on the blind;
the Lord supports the fainting mind;
he sends the labouring conscience peace;
he helps the stranger in distress,
the widow and the fatherless,
and grants the prisoner sweet release.
I'll praise him while he lends me breath;
and when my voice is lost in death,
praise shall employ my nobler powers;
my days of praise shall ne'er be past,
while life, and thought, and being last,
or immortality endures.

Isaac Watts 1674-1748
John Wesley 1703-1791
based on Psalm 146

52

TO GOD THE ONLY WISE

ST MICHAEL 6686

from the Genevan Psalter 1551
adapted by William Crotch 1775-1847

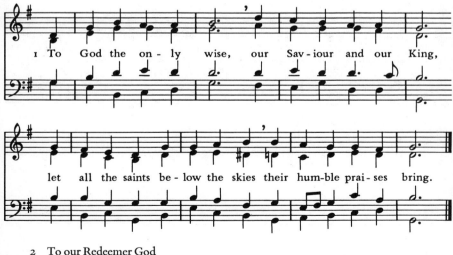

1 To God the on-ly wise, our Sav-iour and our King,

let all the saints be-low the skies their hum-ble prai-ses bring.

2 To our Redeemer God
wisdom and power belong,
immortal crowns of majesty,
and everlasting song.

Isaac Watts 1674-1748

53
ALL HONOUR AND PRAISE

OLD 104th 10 10 11 11

Ravenscroft's Psalter 1621

All hon-our and praise, do-min-ion and might,
to God, three in one, e-ter-nal-ly be,
who round us has shed his own mar-vel-lous light,
and called us from dark-ness his glo-ry to see.

Original form of last line:

Jean Baptiste de Santeuil 1630-1697
tr. Isaac Williams 1802-1865

54

NOW TO THE KING OF HEAVEN

ST JOHN 666688   melody from the 'Parish Choir' 1851

Now to the King of heaven your cheer-ful voi-ces raise;
to him be glo-ry given, all ma-jes-ty and praise;
wide as he reigns his name be sung by ev-ery tongue in end-less strains.

Philip Doddridge 1702-1751
Isaac Watts 1674-1748

55
PRAISE GOD FROM WHOM ALL BLESSINGS FLOW

OLD 100th 8 8 8 8   Genevan Psalter 1551

La grâ - ce de no - tre Sau - veur,
Praise God from whom all bless - ings flow;

l'a - mour du Père et sa fa - veur,
praise him, all crea - tures here be - low;

et l'onc - ti - on du Saint - Es - prit,
praise him a - bove, ye heaven - ly host;

soient a - vec nous par Jé - sus - Christ!
praise Fa - ther, Son and Ho - ly Ghost.

Psautier, 16e siècle
Thomas Ken 1637-1711

56

O SEND THY LIGHT FORTH

ABBEY 8686   based on a melody from the Scottish Psalter 1615

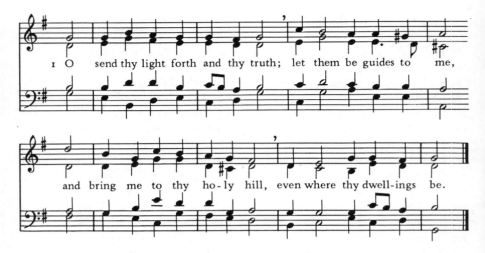

1 O send thy light forth and thy truth; let them be guides to me, and bring me to thy ho-ly hill, even where thy dwell-ings be.

2 Then will I to God's altar go,
to God my chiefest joy;
yea, God, my God, thy name to praise
my harp I will employ.

3 Why art thou then cast down, my soul?
What should discourage thee?
And why with vexing thoughts art thou
disquieted in me?

4 Still trust in God; for him to praise
good cause I yet shall have:
he of my countenance is the health,
my God that doth me save.

Scottish Psalter 1650
based on Psalm 43

57

GOD OF ETERNITY

LIEBSTER IMMANUEL 11 10 11 10   Himmels-Lust, Jena 1679
harmonized by Johann Sebastian Bach 1685-1750

1 God of e - ter - ni - ty, Lord of the a - ges,

Fa - ther and Spir - it and Sav - iour of men:
thine is the glo - ry of time's num - bered pa - ges;
thine is the power to re - vive us a - gain.

2 Thankful, we come to thee, Lord of the nations,
praising thy faithfulness, mercy and grace
shown to our fathers in past generations,
pledge of thy love to each people and race.

3 Where'er our homes may be, sundered by oceans,
Zion is builded and God is adored.
Lift we our hearts in united devotions!
Ends of the earth, join in praise to the Lord!

4 Pardon our sinfulness, God of all pity;
call to remembrance thy mercies of old;
strengthen thy church to abide as a city
set on a hill for a light to thy fold.

5 Head of the church on earth, risen, ascended,
thine is the honour that dwells in this place:
as thou hast blessed us through years that have ended,
still lift upon us the light of thy face.

Ernest Northcroft Merrington 1876-c1960

58

BLEST ARE THE PURE IN HEART Johann Balthasar König 1691-1758

FRANCONIA 6 6 8 6 adapted by William Henry Havergal 1793-1870

1 Blest are the pure in heart, for they shall see our God;
the sec-ret of the Lord is theirs, their soul is Christ's a - bode.

2 The Lord, who left the heavens
our life and peace to bring,
to dwell in lowliness with men,
their pattern and their King,

4 Lord, we thy presence seek;
may ours this blessing be:
give us a pure and lowly heart,
a temple meet for thee.

3 still to the lowly soul
he doth himself impart,
and for his dwelling and his throne
chooseth the pure in heart.

John Keble 1792-1866
and others

Derek Holman 1931-

Descant

4 Lord, we thy pres - ence seek; may ours this bless - ing be:
give us a pure and low - ly heart, a tem-ple meet for thee.

59

BEHOLD US, LORD, A LITTLE SPACE

ST FLAVIAN 8 6 8 6 adapted from Day's Psalter, 1562

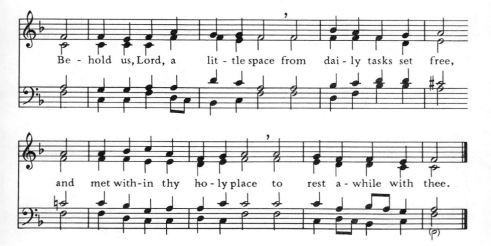

Be - hold us, Lord, a lit - tle space from dai - ly tasks set free,

and met with-in thy ho - ly place to rest a - while with thee.

2 Around us rolls the ceaseless tide
   of business, toil, and care;
   and scarcely can we turn aside
   for one brief hour of prayer.

3 Yet these are not the only walls
   wherein thou mayst be sought;
   on homeliest work thy blessing falls
   in truth and patience wrought.

4 Thine is the loom, the forge, the mart,
   the wealth of land and sea,
   the worlds of science and of art,
   revealed and ruled by thee.

5 Then let us prove our heavenly birth
   in all we do and know;
   and claim the kingdom of the earth
   for thee, and not thy foe.

6 Work shall be prayer, if all be wrought
   as thou wouldst have it done;
   and prayer, by thee inspired and taught,
   itself with work be one.

John Ellerton 1826–1893
for a higher setting see 322

60

SPIRIT DIVINE, ATTEND OUR PRAYERS

GRAFENBERG 8 6 8 6   Johann Crüger 1598–1662

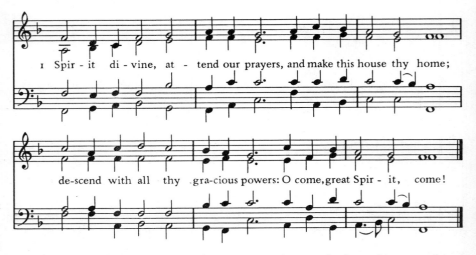

1 Spir-it di-vine, at - tend our prayers, and make this house thy home;

de-scend with all thy gra-cious powers: O come, great Spir - it, come!

2 Come as the light: to us reveal
our emptiness and woe;
and lead us in those paths of life
where all the righteous go.

3 Come as the wind: sweep clean away
what dead within us lies,
and search and freshen all our souls
with living energies.

4 Come as the fire: and purge our hearts
like sacrificial flame;
let our whole soul an offering be
to our Redeemer's name.

5 Spirit divine, attend our prayers:
make a lost world thy home;
descend with all thy gracious powers:
O come, great Spirit, come!

Andrew Reed 1787–1862

61

HOLY FATHER

CONFUCIAN TEMPLE CHANT 5 5 5 5 D

a Chinese melody

harmonized by Stanley L Osborne 1907–

1 Holy Father, thou, thee we worship now;
thou providest rain, givest ripened grain,
spring's sun, warm and bright, autumn's cool delight,
year by year the same: praise thy holy name.

2 Christ in thy great love
sent from heaven above,
come to this poor heart;
enter, never part.
Truth's great strength inspire,
make my soul entire,
clear the world's dim sight,
share thy holy light.

T C Chao
John Wesley Stinson 1910–

62

COME, THOU ALMIGHTY KING

SERUG 664 6664
composer unknown
from Samuel Sebastian Wesley's 'European Psalmist' 1872

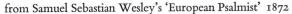
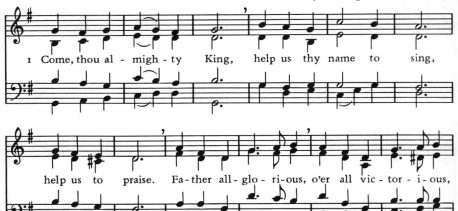

1 Come, thou al - migh - ty King, help us thy name to sing, help us to praise. Fa - ther all - glo - ri - ous, o'er all vic - tor - i - ous, come and reign o - ver us, An - cient of days.

2 Come, thou incarnate Word,
gird on thy mighty sword,
our prayer attend;
come, and thy people bless,
come, give thy word success;
stablish thy righteousness,
Saviour and friend!

3 Come, holy Comforter,
thy sacred witness bear
in this glad hour;
thou who almighty art,
rule thou in every heart,
never from us depart,
Spirit of power!

4 To thee, great one in three,
eternal praises be
hence evermore;
thy sovereign majesty
may we in glory see,
and to eternity
love and adore!

anonymous 18th century

63

DEAR LORD, WHOSE LOVING EYES CAN SEE

MONT RICHARD 8 8 8 8   Percy Carter Buck 1871–1947

1 Dear Lord, whose lov-ing eyes can see each troub-led mind with-out, with-in, we bring our week of life to thee, all soiled and worn and marred with sin.

2   We bring our bitterness of heart,
    our hate and want of charity:
    help us to choose the better part,
    and learn to love, dear Lord, like thee.

3   We bring our care for daily bread,
    the fear that turns the heart to stone;
    we cry to thee: lift up our head
    and show us we are not alone.

4   We bring the faith that over all,
    though faint and feeble, flickers still:
    increase it, Lord, that at thy call
    we may our daily task fulfil.

5   Lord, make us pure; enrich our life
    with heavenly love for evermore;
    give us thy strength to face the strife,
    and serve thee better than before.

Edwin Gilbert 1859–c1935

64

DEAR SHEPHERD OF THY PEOPLE

ROCHESTER 8 6 8 6   Charles Hylton Stewart 1884-1932

1 Dear Shep - herd of thy peo - ple, hear;

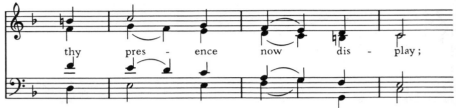

thy pres - ence now dis - play;

as thou hast given a place for prayer,

so give us hearts to pray.

2 Within these walls let holy peace
and love and concord dwell;
here give the troubled conscience ease,
the wounded spirit heal.

3 May we in faith receive thy word,
in faith present our prayers,
and in the presence of our Lord
disburden all our cares.

4 The hearing ear, the seeing eye,
the humbled mind, bestow;
and shine upon us from on high
to make our graces grow.

John Newton 1725-1807

65

JESUS, WHERE'ER THY PEOPLE MEET

WARRINGTON 8 8 8 8   Ralph Harrison 1748-1810

1 Je - sus, wher - e'er thy peo - ple meet,
there they be - hold thy mer - cy - seat;
wher - e'er they seek thee thou art found,
and ev - ery place is hal - lowed ground.

2 For thou, within no walls confined,
inhabitest the humble mind;
such ever bring thee where they come,
and going take thee to their home.

3 Here may we prove the power of prayer
to strengthen faith and sweeten care,
to teach our faint desires to rise,
and bring all heaven before our eyes.

4 Lord, we are few, but thou art near;
nor short thine arm, nor deaf thine ear;
O rend the heavens, come quickly down,
and make a thousand hearts thine own.

William Cowper 1731-1800
for a lower setting see 361

FATHER OF HEAVEN

SONG 5   8 8 8 8   FIRST TUNE

Orlando Gibbons 1583-1625

1 Father of heaven, whose love profound
a ransom for our souls hath found,
before thy throne we sinners bend;
to us thy pardoning love extend.

2 Almighty Son, incarnate Word,
our Prophet, Priest, Redeemer, Lord,
before thy throne we sinners bend;
to us thy saving grace extend.

3 Eternal Spirit, by whose breath
the soul is raised from sin and death,
before thy throne we sinners bend;
to us thy quickening power extend.

4 All-holy Father, Spirit, Son,
mysterious Godhead, three in one,
before thy throne we sinners bend;
grace, pardon, life to us extend.

Edward Cooper 1770-1833

1 Father of heaven, whose love profound
a ransom for our souls hath found,
before thy throne we sinners bend;
to us thy pardoning love extend.

2 Almighty Son, incarnate Word,
   our Prophet, Priest, Redeemer, Lord,
   before thy throne we sinners bend;
   to us thy saving grace extend.

3 Eternal Spirit, by whose breath
   the soul is raised from sin and death,
   before thy throne we sinners bend;
   to us thy quickening power extend.

4 All-holy Father, Spirit, Son,
   mysterious Godhead, three in one,
   before thy throne we sinners bend;
   grace, pardon, life to us extend.

Edward Cooper 1770-1833

67

COME DOWN, O LOVE DIVINE

DOWN AMPNEY 6 6 11 D

Ralph Vaughan Williams 1872-1958

1 Come down, O love di - vine, seek thou this soul of mine,

and vis - it it with thine own ar - dour glow - ing.

O Com-fort - er, draw near, with - in my heart ap - pear,

and kin - dle it, thy ho - ly flame be - stow - ing.

2 O let it freely burn,
   till earthly passions turn
   to dust and ashes in its heat consuming;
   and let thy glorious light
   shine ever on my sight,
   and clothe me round, my onward path illuming.

3 Let holy charity
   mine outward vesture be,
   and lowliness become mine inner clothing,
   true lowliness of heart,
   which takes the humbler part,
   and o'er its own shortcomings weeps with loathing.

4 And so the yearning strong
with which the soul will long
shall far outpass the power of human telling;
for none can guess its grace,
till he become the place
wherein the Holy Spirit makes his dwelling.

Bianco da Siena ?–1434
tr. Richard Frederick Littledale 1833–1890

68

I BIND UNTO MYSELF TODAY

ST PATRICK irregular

ancient Irish hymn melody
arranged by Charles Villiers Stanford 1852–1924

1 I bind un - to my - self to - day the strong name
of the Tri - ni - ty, by in - vo - ca - tion of the
same, the three in one, and one in three.

vv. 2, 3, 4, 6

2 I bind this day to me for ev-er, by power of
faith, Christ's in - car - na-tion, his bap - tism in Jor-dan
ri - ver, his death on cross for my sal - va-tion, his
burst - ing from the spi - ced tomb, his rid - ing
up the heaven-ly way, his com - ing at the day of
doom, I bind un - to my - self to - day.

3 I bind unto myself today
the virtues of the star-lit heaven,
the glorious sun's life-giving ray,
the whiteness of the moon at even,
the flashing of the lightning free,
the whirling wind's tempestuous shocks,
the stable earth, the deep salt sea
around the old eternal rocks.

4 I bind unto myself today
the power of God to hold and lead,
his eye to watch, his might to stay,
his ear to hearken to my need,
the wisdom of my God to teach,
his hand to guide, his shield to ward,
the word of God to give me speech,
his heavenly host to be my guard.

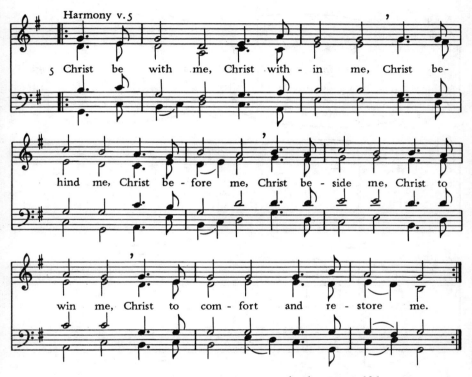

Harmony v. 5

5 Christ be with me, Christ with-in me, Christ be-hind me, Christ be-fore me, Christ be-side me, Christ to win me, Christ to com-fort and re-store me.

...

5 Christ beneath me, Christ above me,
Christ in quiet, Christ in danger,
Christ in hearts of all that love me,
Christ in mouth of friend and stranger.

6 I bind unto myself the name,
the strong name of the Trinity,
by invocation of the same,
the three in one, and one in three,
of whom all nature hath creation,
eternal Father, Spirit, Word.
Praise to the Lord of my salvation;
salvation is of Christ the Lord.

ascribed to St Patrick 372-466
tr. Cecil Frances Alexander 1818-1895

69

GOD BE IN MY HEAD

GOD BE IN MY HEAD irregular

Henry Walford Davies 1869-1941

God be in my head, and in my un-der-stand-ing;

God be in mine eyes, and in my look-ing;

God be in my mouth, and in my speak-ing;

God be in my heart, and in my think-ing;

God be at mine end, and at my de-part-ing.

from the Book of Hours 1514

70

APPROACH, MY SOUL, THE MERCY-SEAT

STRACATHRO 8686

melody by Charles Hutcheson 1792-1860
harmonized by Geoffrey Turton Shaw 1879-1943

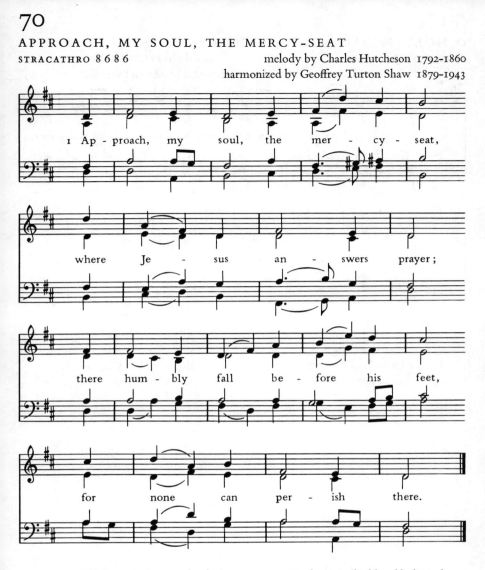

1 Ap - proach, my soul, the mer - cy - seat,
where Je - sus an - swers prayer;
there hum - bly fall be - fore his feet,
for none can per - ish there.

2 Thy promise is my only plea,
with this I venture nigh:
thou callest burdened souls to thee,
and such, O Lord, am I.

3 Bowed down beneath a load of sin,
by Satan sorely pressed,
by war without, and fears within,
I come to thee for rest.

4 Be thou my shield and hiding place,
that, sheltered near thy side,
I may my fierce accuser face
and tell him thou hast died.

5 O wondrous love, to bleed and die,
to bear the cross and shame,
that guilty sinners, such as I,
might plead thy gracious name!

John Newton 1725-1807
This may be sung to Abridge 182

71

O HOLY SPIRIT, LORD OF GRACE

EPWORTH 8 6 8 6

melody from Charles Wesley 1757-1834
harmonized by Martin Fallas Shaw 1875-1958

O Ho-ly Spir-it, Lord of grace, e-ter-nal fount of love,

in-flame, we pray, our in-most hearts with fire from heaven a - bove.

2 As thou in bond of love dost join
the Father and the Son,
so fill us all with mutual love,
and knit our hearts in one.

3 All glory to the Father be,
all glory to the Son,
all glory, Holy Ghost, to thee,
while endless ages run.

Charles Coffin 1676-1749
tr. John Chandler 1806-1876

COME, LET US TO THE LORD OUR GOD

BELMONT 8 6 8 6   adapted from William Gardiner 1770-1853
Gardiner's 'Sacred Melodies' 1812

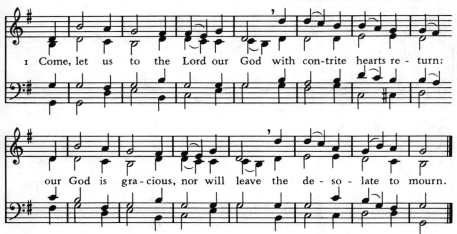

1 Come, let us to the Lord our God with con-trite hearts re - turn:

our God is gra - cious, nor will leave the de - so - late to mourn.

2 His voice commands the tempest forth,
and stills the stormy wave;
and though his arm be strong to smite,
'tis also strong to save.

3 Long hath the night of sorrow reigned,
the dawn shall bring us light;
God shall appear, and we shall rise
with gladness in his sight.

4 Our hearts, if God we seek to know,
shall know him, and rejoice;
his coming like the morn shall be,
like morning songs his voice.

5 As dew upon the tender herb
diffusing fragrance round,
as showers that usher in the spring
and cheer the thirsty ground,

6 so shall his presence bless our souls
and shed a joyful light,
that hallowed morn shall chase away
the sorrows of the night.

John Morison c 1750-1798
Scottish Paraphrases 1781
based on Hosea 6:1-4

AND THE FOLLOWING

73

TURN BACK, O MAN

OLD 124th 10 10 10 10 10

Genevan Psalter 1551

1 Turn back, O man, for-swear thy fool-ish ways.
Old now is earth, and none may count her days;
yet thou, her child, whose head is crowned with flame,
still wilt not hear thine in-ner God pro-claim,
'Turn back, O man, for-swear thy fool-ish ways.'

2 Earth might be fair and all men glad and wise.
Age after age their tragic empires rise,
built while they dream, and in that dreaming weep:
would man but wake from out his haunted sleep,
earth might be fair and all men glad and wise.

3 Earth shall be fair, and all her people one:
  nor till that hour shall God's whole will be done.
  Now, even now, once more from earth to sky
  peals forth in joy man's old undaunted cry,
  'Earth shall be fair, and all her folk be one!'   Clifford Bax 1886-1962

74

FORGIVE OUR SINS AS WE FORGIVE
ST MARY 8 6 8 6   Playford's Psalter 1677

1 'For-give our sins as we for-give', you taught us, Lord, to pray;

but you a-lone can grant us grace to live the words we say.

2 How can your pardon reach and bless
  the unforgiving heart
  that broods on wrongs, and will not let
  old bitterness depart?

3 In blazing light your cross reveals
  the truth we dimly knew,
  how small the debts men owe to us,
  how great our debt to you!

4 Lord, cleanse the depths within our souls
  and bid resentment cease;
  then reconciled to God and man,
  our lives will spread your peace.

                                          Rosamond E Herklots 1905-

75
BLOW, WINDS OF GOD
CAITHNESS 8 6 8 6   Scottish Psalter 1635

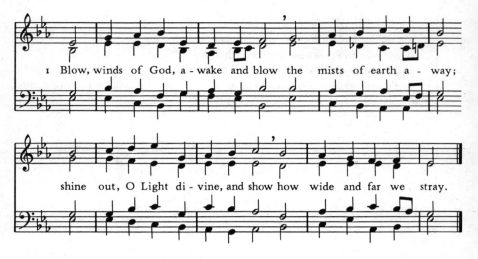

1 Blow, winds of God, a-wake and blow the mists of earth a-way; shine out, O Light di-vine, and show how wide and far we stray;

2 We may not climb the heavenly steeps
   to bring the Lord Christ down;
   in vain we search the lowest deeps,
   for him no depths can drown.

3 To thee our full humanity,
   its joys and pains, belong;
   the wrong of man to man on thee
   inflicts a deeper wrong.

4 The healing of thy seamless dress
   is by our beds of pain;
   we touch thee in life's throng and press,
   and we are whole again.

5 The letter fails, the systems fall,
   and every symbol wanes;
   the Spirit over-brooding all,
   eternal Love, remains.

John Greenleaf Whittier 1807-1892

76

THERE'S A WIDENESS IN GOD'S MERCY

GOTT WILL'S MACHEN 8 7 8 7   Johann Ludwig Steiner 1688-1761

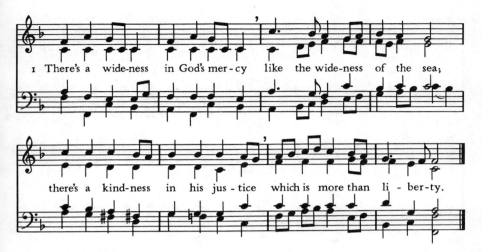

1 There's a wide-ness in God's mer-cy like the wide-ness of the sea;
there's a kind-ness in his jus-tice which is more than li-ber-ty.

2 There is no place where earth's sorrows
are more felt than up in heaven;
there is no place where earth's failings
have such kindly judgement given.

3 There is plentiful redemption
in the blood that has been shed;
there is joy for all the members
in the sorrows of the Head.

4 Souls of men, why will ye scatter
like a crowd of frightened sheep?
Foolish hearts, why will ye wander
from a love so true and deep?

5 For the love of God is broader
than the measures of man's mind,
and the heart of the Eternal
is most wonderfully kind.

Frederick William Faber 1814-1863
This may be sung to Stuttgart 389

Descant by Stanley L Osborne 1907-

5 For the love of God is broad-er than the mea-sures of man's mind,
and the heart of the E-ter-nal is most won-der-ful-ly kind.

77

JESUS, LOVER OF MY SOUL

ABERYSTWYTH 7 7 7 7 D FIRST TUNE

Joseph Parry 1841–1903

1 Jesus, lover of my soul, let me to thy bosom fly, while the nearer waters roll, while the tempest still is high. Hide me, O my Saviour, hide, till the storm of life is past; safe into the haven guide, O receive my soul at last.

2 Other refuge have I none;
   hangs my helpless soul on thee.
   Leave, ah! leave me not alone;
   still support and comfort me.
   All my trust on thee is stayed,
   all my help from thee I bring;
   cover my defenceless head
   with the shadow of thy wing.

3 Thou, O Christ, art all I want;
   more than all in thee I find!
   Raise the fallen, cheer the faint,
   heal the sick, and lead the blind.
   Just and holy is thy name,
   I am all unrighteousness:
   false and full of sin I am,
   thou art full of truth and grace.

John Bacchus Dykes 1823–1876

Je - sus, lov- er of my soul, let me to thy bo - som fly,

while the near-er wa - ters roll, while the tem-pest still is high.

Hide me, O my Sav-iour, hide, till the storm of life is past;

safe in - to the ha - ven guide, O re-ceive my soul at last.

4 Plenteous grace with thee is found,
grace to cover all my sin;
let the healing streams abound;
make and keep me pure within.
Thou of life the fountain art,
freely let me take of thee;
spring thou up within my heart;
rise to all eternity.

Charles Wesley 1707-1788

78

WE WORSHIP THEE

DEUS TUORUM MILITUM 8 8 8 8

Grenoble church melody
harmonized by Stanley L Osborne 1907-

1 We wor - ship thee, great sov - 'reign Lord,
whose might the a - ges doth con - trol,
who hast made all things by thy word,
and car - est for each hu - man soul.

2　From lives made wretched by our pride
　　we look to thee, ashamed within;
　　from thy pure sight we cannot hide
　　the misery of human sin.

3　O God, have pity on a race
　　so torn with hate, suspicion, greed,
　　for which in holy love and grace
　　thy Son upon his cross did bleed.

4　Our only hope is in thy plan,
　　which thou in Christ wilt yet fulfil
　　to raise rebellious, fallen man
　　and bind him to thy perfect will.

5　Then teach us our eternal worth,
　　that we may love and serve thee more,
　　and sing thy praises here on earth,
　　and with thy saints in heaven adore.

A. Leonard Griffith 1920-
for a lower setting see 32

79

ROCK OF AGES

REDHEAD No. 76 7 7 7 7 7 7

Richard Redhead 1820-1901

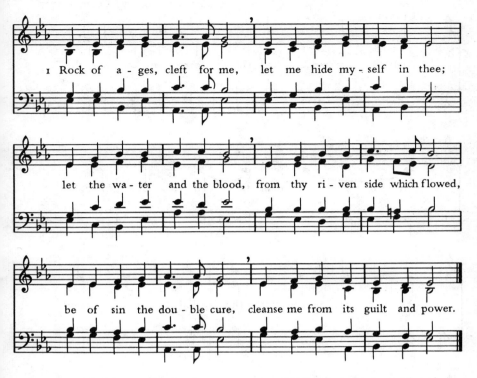

1 Rock of a-ges, cleft for me, let me hide my-self in thee;
let the wa-ter and the blood, from thy ri-ven side which flowed,
be of sin the dou-ble cure, cleanse me from its guilt and power.

2 Not the labours of my hands
can fulfil thy law's demands;
could my zeal no respite know,
could my tears for ever flow,
all for sin could not atone:
thou must save, and thou alone.

3 Nothing in my hand I bring,
simply to thy cross I cling;
naked, come to thee for dress;
helpless, look to thee for grace;
foul, I to the fountain fly;
wash me, Saviour, or I die.

4 While I draw this fleeting breath,
when mine eyelids close in death,
when I soar through tracts unknown,
see thee on thy judgement throne,
Rock of ages, cleft for me,
let me hide myself in thee.

Augustus Montague Toplady
1740-1778

GOD WHO CREATED THIS GARDEN OF EARTH

QUEDLINBURG 10 10 10 10   melody by Johann Christian Kittel 1732–1809
harmonized by Stanley L Osborne 1907–

1 God who cre - a - ted this gar - den of earth,
giv - ing in A - dam to all of us birth,
what have we done with the dan - ger - ous tree?
Lord, for - give A - dam, for A - dam is me.

2   Adam's ambitious, he wants to be wise,
casts out obedience, then lusts with his eyes,
grasps his sweet fruit: 'As God I shall be.'
Lord, forgive Adam, for Adam is me.

3   Thirst after power is this sin of my shame,
pride's ruthless thrust after status and fame,
turning and stealing and cowering from thee;
Lord, forgive Adam, for Adam is me.

4   Cursed is the earth through this cancerous crime,
symbol of man through all passage of time.
Put it all right, Lord! Let Adam be free.
Do it for Adam, for Adam is me.

5   Glory to God! What is this that I see?
    Man made anew, second Adam is he,
    bleeding his love on another fine tree.
    Dies second Adam, young Adam for me.

6   Rises that Adam the master of death,
    pours out his spirit in holy new breath;
    sheer liberation! With him I am free!
    Live, second Adam, in mercy in me!

Richard Granville Jones 1926–

81

I SING THE MIGHTY POWER
OLD 81st 8 6 8 6 D

Day's Psalmes 1562

1 I sing the migh-ty power of God that made the moun-tains rise,
that spread the flow-ing seas a-broad, and built the lof-ty skies.
I sing the wis-dom that or-dained the sun to rule the day;
the moon shines full at his com-mand and all the stars o - bey.

2 I sing the goodness of the Lord
that filled the earth with food;
he formed the creatures with his word,
and then pronounced them good.
Lord, how thy wonders are displayed
where'er I turn my eye;
if I survey the ground I tread,
or gaze upon the sky!

3 There's not a plant or flower below
but makes thy glories known;
and clouds arise, and tempests blow,
by order from thy throne;
while all that borrows life from thee
is ever in thy care,
and everywhere that man can be,
thou, God, art present there.

This may be sung to St Stephen 151 or 207   Isaac Watts 1674-1748

82

THIS IS MY FATHER'S WORLD

TERRA BEATA 6 6 8 6 D irregular

English traditional melody

1 This is my Fa-ther's world, and to my listen-ing ears all na-ture sings, and round me rings the mu-sic of the spheres. This is my Fa-ther's world; I rest me in the thought— of rocks and trees, of skies and seas, his hand the won-ders wrought.

2 This is my Father's world:
the birds their carols raise;
the morning light, the lily white,
declare their Maker's praise.
This is my Father's world:
he shines in all that's fair;
in the rustling grass I hear him pass,
he speaks to me everywhere.

3 This is my Father's world:
O let me ne'er forget
that though the wrong seems oft so strong,
God is the ruler yet.
This is my Father's world:
the battle is not done;
Jesus, who died, shall be satisfied,
and earth and heaven be one.

Maltbie Davenport Babcock 1858-1901

83

O LORD OF EVERY SHINING CONSTELLATION

ERWIN II IO II IO   Herbert Howells 1892–

1 O Lord of ev - ery shin - ing con - stel - la - tion
that wheels in splen - dour through the mid - night sky:
grant us thy Spir - it's true il - lu - mi - na - tion
to read the sec - rets of thy work on high.

2 And thou who mad'st the atom's hidden forces,
whose laws its mighty energies fulfil:
teach us, to whom thou giv'st such rich resources,
in all we use, to serve thy holy will.

3 O Life, awaking life in cell and tissue,
from flower to bud, from beast to brain of man:
O help us trace, from birth to final issue,
the sure unfolding of thine ageless plan.

4 Thou who hast stamped thine image on thy creatures,
and though they marred that image, lov'st them still:
uplift our eyes to Christ, that in his features
we may discern the beauty of thy will.

5 Great Lord of nature, shaping and renewing,
 who mad'st us more than nature's sons to be:
 help us to tread, thy grace our souls enduing,
 the road to life and immortality.

Albert Frederick Bayly 1901-
Northbrook 212 is commended for this hymn.

84

HE'S GOT THE WHOLE WORLD

NEGRO MELODY irregular   traditional

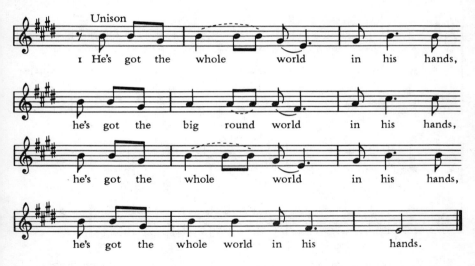

Unison

1 He's got the whole world in his hands,

he's got the big round world in his hands,

he's got the whole world in his hands,

he's got the whole world in his hands.

He's got the wind and the rain in his hands,
he's got the sun and the moon in his hands,
he's got the wind and the rain in his hands,
he's got the whole world in his hands.

He's got the tiny little baby in his hands,
he's got the big round world in his hands,
he's got the tiny little baby in his hands,
he's got the whole world in his hands,

4 He's got you and me, brother, in his hands,
he's got the big round world in his hands,
he's got you and me, brother, in his hands,
he's got the whole world in his hands.

5 He's got everybody in his hands,
he's got the big round world in his hands,
he's got everybody in his hands,
he's got the whole world in his hands.

Negro spiritual

85

THE SPACIOUS FIRMAMENT

CREATION 8 8 8 8 FIRST TUNE · adapted from Franz Joseph Haydn 1732-1809

1 The spa - cious fir - ma - ment on high,
with all the blue e - the - real sky,
and span - gled heavens, a shin - ing frame,
their great O - rig - i - nal pro - claim.

2 The unwearied sun from day to day
does his Creator's power display,
and publishes to every land
the work of an almighty hand.

3 Soon as the evening shades prevail,
the moon takes up the wondrous tale,
and nightly to the listening earth
repeats the story of her birth,

4 while all the stars that round her burn,
and all the planets in their turn
confirm the tidings, as they roll,
and spread the truth from pole to pole.

5 What though in solemn silence all
move round the dark terrestrial ball,
what though no real voice, nor sound,
amidst their radiant orbs be found;

6 in reason's ear they all rejoice,
and utter forth a glorious voice,
for ever singing, as they shine,
'The hand that made us is divine'.

Joseph Addison 1672-1719
based on Psalm 19

1 The spa-cious fir-ma-ment on high, with all the blue e - the-real sky,

and span-gled heavens, a shin-ing frame, their great O - rig - i - nal pro-claim.

2 The un-wea-ried sun from day to day does his Cre-a - tor's power dis-play,

and pub-lish-es to ev-ery land the work of an al - migh-ty hand,

the work of an al - migh - ty hand.

86

ALL THINGS BRIGHT AND BEAUTIFUL — English traditional melody

ROYAL OAK 7676 and refrain — arranged by Martin Fallas Shaw 1875-1958

1 All things bright and beau-ti-ful, all crea-tures great and small,

all things wise and won-der-ful, the Lord God made them all.

vv. 2, 3, 4, 5, 6

Each lit-tle flower that o-pens, each lit-tle bird that sings,

he made their glow-ing col-ours, he made their ti-ny wings.

D.C. al Fine

3 The purple-headed mountain,
the river running by,
the sunset, and the morning
that brightens up the sky,

4 the cold wind in the winter,
the pleasant summer sun,
the ripe fruits in the garden,
he made them every one.

5 The tall trees in the greenwood,
the meadows where we play,
the rushes by the water
we gather every day,

6   he gave us eyes to see them,
    and lips that we might tell
    how great is God almighty,
    who has made all things well.

7   All things bright and beautiful,   Cecil Frances Alexander 1823-1895
    all creatures great and small,
    all things wise and wonderful,   If desired, the first stanza may be sung at
    the Lord God made them all.   the beginning and the end only.

87

THY MERCY, LORD
LONDON NEW 8686   Scottish Psalter 1635

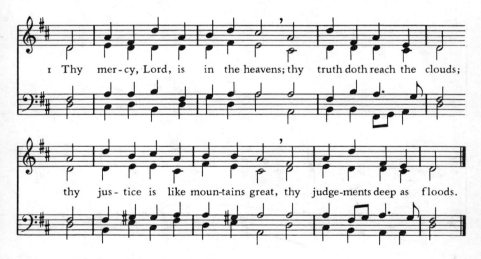

1 Thy mer-cy, Lord, is in the heavens; thy truth doth reach the clouds;

thy jus-tice is like moun-tains great, thy judge-ments deep as floods.

2   Lord, thou preservest man and beast:
    how precious is thy grace!
    Therefore in shadow of thy wings
    men's sons their trust shall place.

3   Their hunger thou shalt satisfy
    with good things from thy store:
    from rivers of thy pleasures they
    shall drink and thirst no more.

4   With thee the fountain is of life
    and from thy presence flows;   Scottish Psalter 1650
    and brightness from thy dwelling place   based on Psalm 36
    out to all people goes.   for a higher setting see 159

88

GOD WHO GIVES TO LIFE ITS GOODNESS

ABBOT'S LEIGH 8 7 8 7 D

Cyril Vincent Taylor 1907-

God who gives to life its good-ness,

God cre - a - tor of all joy,

God who gives to man his free - dom,

God who bless - es tool and toy:

teach us now to laugh and praise you,

deep with - in your prais - es sing,

till the whole cre - a - tion dan - ces
for the good - ness of its King.

2   God who fills the earth with beauty,
    God who binds each friend to friend,
    God who names man co-creator,
    God who wills that chaos end:
    grant us now creative spirits,
    minds responsive to your mind,
    hearts and wills your rule extending,
    all our acts by Love refined.

Walter Henry Farquharson 1936–

89

O WORLD OF GOD
JERUSALEM 8 8 8 8 D

Charles Hubert Hastings Parry 1848-1918
arranged by Gordon P S Jacob 1895-

Unison

1 O world of God, so vast and strange, pro-found and

won-der-ful and fair, be-yond the ut - most reach of

thought - but not be - yond a Fa - ther's care! We are not

stran - gers on this earth whirl-ing a - mid the suns of

space; we are God's child - ren, this our home, with men of ev-ery clime and

race.

2 O world of men where life is lived,
  so strangely mingling joy and pain,
  so full of evil and of good,
  so needful that the good shall reign!
  It is this world that God has loved,
  and goodness was its Maker's plan,
  the promise of God's triumph is
  his coming in a Son of Man.

3 O world of time's far-stretching years!
  There was a day when time stood still,
  a central moment when there rose
  a cross upon a cruel hill;
  in pain and death love's power was seen,
  the mystery of time revealed,
  the wisdom of the ways of God,
  the grace through which man's hurt is healed.

Robert B. Y. Scott 1899-

Ending for final stanza

healed.

90

GOD OF CONCRETE

CONCRETE 777777

Frederick R C Clarke 1931-

1 God of con-crete, God of steel, God of pis-ton and of wheel, God of py-lon, God of steam, God of gir-der and of beam, God of a-tom, God of mine: all the world of power is thine. A-men.

2 Lord of cable, Lord of rail,
Lord of freeway and of mail,
Lord of rocket, Lord of flight,
Lord of soaring satellite,
Lord of lightning's flashing line:
all the world of speed is thine.

3 Lord of science, Lord of art,
Lord of map and graph and chart,
Lord of physics and research,
Word of bible, Faith of church,
Lord of sequence and design:
all the world of truth is thine.

4 God whose glory fills the earth,
gave the universe its birth,
loosed the Christ with Easter's might,
saves the world from evil's blight,
claims us all by grace divine:
all the world of love is thine.

Richard Granville Jones 1926-

AND THE FOLLOWING

27 O worship the King
28 Let us with a gladsome mind
38 Sing ye praises to the Father
46 Fairest Lord Jesus
199 For the beauty of the earth
203 We thank you, God
204 We praise you for the sun

91

THE HEAVENS DECLARE THY GLORY

SAMSON 8888

adapted from George Frederick Handel 1685-1759
by Frederick R C Clarke 1931-

1 The heavens declare thy glory, Lord, in every star thy wisdom shines; but when our eyes behold thy word, we read thy name in fairer lines.

2 The rolling sun, the changing light,
and night and day thy power confess;
but the blest volume thou hast writ
reveals thy justice and thy grace.

3 Sun, moon, and stars convey thy praise
round the whole earth, and never stand;
so when thy truth began its race,
it touched and glanced on every land.

4 Nor shall thy spreading gospel rest
till through the world thy truth has run,
till Christ has all the nations blest
that see the light or feel the sun.

5 Thy gospel makes the simple wise;
thy laws are pure, thy judgements right.
Great Sun of righteousness, arise,
bless the dark world with heavenly light!

Isaac Watts 1674-1748
based on Psalm 19

92

THE LORD ALMIGHTY SPOKE THE WORD

SYDENHAM STREET 8 8 4 4 6   Frederick R C Clarke 1931-

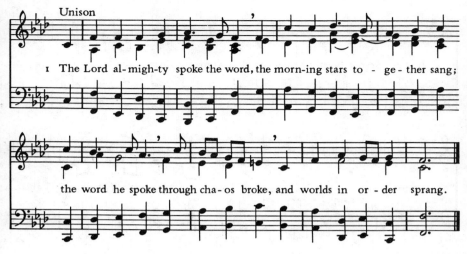

1 The Lord al-migh-ty spoke the word, the morn-ing stars to - ge - ther sang;

the word he spoke through cha-os broke, and worlds in or - der sprang.

2 The Lord almighty gave the word
    that came to us in flesh to dwell;
    the word he gave
    broke through the grave,
    and vanquished sin and hell.

3 O Lord almighty, living Word,
    and Spirit blest, we worship thee:
    thy word proclaim,
    and in thy name
    the kingdom that shall be.

Charles E. Watson 1869-1942

93

THE SPIRIT BREATHES UPON THE WORD

TIVERTON 8686 FIRST TUNE

? Grigg, c1790

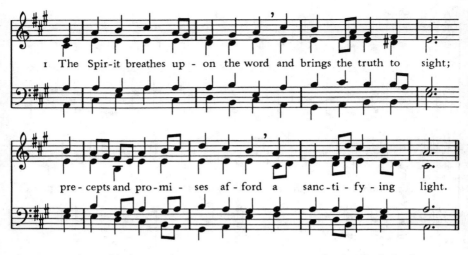

1 The Spir-it breathes up - on the word and brings the truth to sight; pre-cepts and pro-mi - ses af-ford a sanc-ti-fy - ing light.

2 A glory gilds the sacred page,
   majestic like the sun:
   it gives a light to every age;
   it gives, but borrows none.

3 The hand that gave it still supplies
   the gracious light and heat;
   his truths upon the nations rise;
   they rise, but never set.

4 Let everlasting thanks be thine,
   for such a bright display
   as makes a world of darkness shine
   with beams of heavenly day.

5 My soul rejoices to pursue
   the steps of him I love,
   till glory breaks upon my view
   in brighter worlds above.

William Cowper 1731-1800

THIS ENDRIS NYGHT 8686 SECOND TUNE   English traditional melody, c15th century

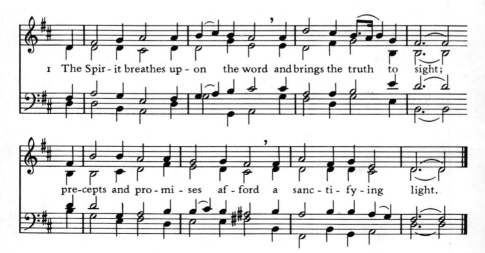

1 The Spir- it breathes up - on the word and brings the truth to sight; pre-cepts and pro-mi - ses af-ford a sanc-ti-fy - ing light.

94

THANKS TO GOD

KINGLEY VALE 87 87 47

Hugh Percy Allen 1869-1946

Unison

1 Thanks to God whose word was spo-ken in the deed that made the earth.

His the voice that called a na-tion, his the fires that tried her worth.

God has spo-ken: praise him for his o-pen word.

2 Thanks to God whose word incarnate
glorified the flesh of man.
Deeds and words and death and rising
tell the grace in heaven's plan.
God has spoken:
praise him for his open word.

3 Thanks to God whose word was written
in the Bible's sacred page,
record of the revelation
showing God to every age.
God has spoken:
praise him for his open word.

4 Thanks to God whose word is answered
by the Spirit's voice within.
Here we drink of joy unmeasured,
life redeemed from death and sin.
God is speaking:
praise him for his open word.

Reginald Thomas Brooks 1918-
This may be sung to St Osmund 323

95

GOD WHO SPOKE IN THE BEGINNING

KENSINGTON 878787

Herbert Howells 1892–

Unison

God who spoke in the be - gin - ning, form-ing rock and shap-ing spar,

set all life and growth in mo-tion, earth-ly world and dis - tant star;

he who calls the earth to or-der is the ground of what we are.

2 God who spoke through men and nations,
through events long past and gone,
showing still today his purpose,
speaks supremely through his Son;
he who calls the earth to order
gives his word and it is done.

3 God whose speech becomes incarnate –
Christ is servant, Christ is Lord! –
calls us to a life of service,
heart and will to action stirred;
he who uses man's obedience
has the first and final word.

Frederik Herman Kaan 1929–

96

NOT FAR BEYOND THE SEA

CORNWALL 8 8 6 D

Samuel Sebastian Wesley 1810-1876

1 Not far be-yond the sea nor high a - bove the heavens, but ve - ry nigh thy voice, O God, is heard. For each new step of faith we take thou hast more truth and light to break forth from thy ho - ly word.

2 Rooted and grounded in thy love,
with saints on earth and saints above
we join in full accord
to grasp the breadth, length, depth, and height,
the crucified and risen might
of Christ, the incarnate Word.

3 Help us to press toward that mark,
and, though our vision now is dark,
to live by what we see.
So, when we see thee face to face,
thy truth and light our dwelling-place
for evermore shall be.

George Bradford Caird 1917–
based on Ephesians 3 :14-19

97

SPEAK FORTH YOUR WORD

DURROW 7676D

Irish traditional melody
harmonized by William France 1912–

1 Speak forth your word, O Fa - ther, men's hun - gry minds to feed: the peo-ple starve and per - ish, and can-not name their need; for so, Lord, you have made us that not a - lone by bread, but by your word of com - fort our hun-ger must be fed.

2 The secrets of the atom,
the universe of light,
all wonders of creation
proclaim your boundless might;
but only through the witness
from man to man passed on
do you reveal in fullness
the gospel of your Son.

3 To each man in his language,
to each man in his home,
by many paths and channels
the faith of Christ may come:

the printed word on paper,
the wave that spans the air,
the screen, the stage, the picture,
may all its truth declare.

4 How shall men hear your message
if there are none to preach?
How shall they learn your lesson
if there are none to teach?
Take us, then, Lord, and use us
to tell what we have heard,
and all the minds of millions
shall feed upon your word.

Charles Jeffries c1925-

98

LORD, BE THY WORD MY GUIDE

KINGSLAND 6666

William Boyce 1710-1779

1 Lord, be thy word my guide, in it may I re-joice:

thy glo-ry be my aim, thy ho-ly will my choice,

2 thy promises my hope,
thy providence my guard,
thine arm my strong support,
thyself my great reward.

Christopher Wordsworth 1807-1885

99

GOD, WHO HAST CAUSED TO BE WRITTEN

CAUSA DIVINA 14 14 4 7 8

Frederick R C Clarke 1931–

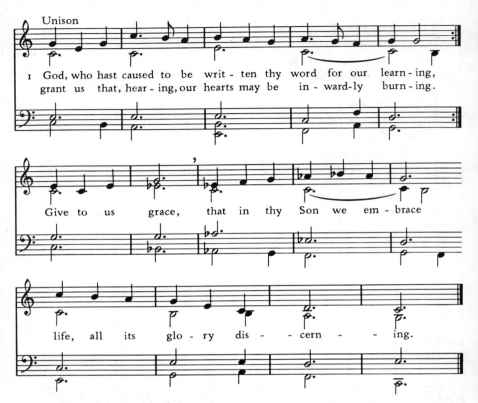

1 God, who hast caused to be writ-ten thy word for our learn-ing,
grant us that, hear-ing, our hearts may be in-ward-ly burn-ing.
Give to us grace, that in thy Son we em-brace
life, all its glo-ry dis - - cern - - ing.

2 Now may our God give us joy, and his peace in believing
all things were written in truth for our thankful receiving.
As Christ did preach,
from man to man love must reach:
grant us each day love's achieving.

3 Lord, should the powers of the earth and the heavens be shaken,
grant us to see thee in all things, our vision awaken.
Help us to see,
though all the earth cease to be,
thy truth shall never be shaken.

T Herbert O'Driscoll 1928–

AND THE FOLLOWING

100

O LOVE, HOW DEEP
PUER NOBIS NASCITUR 8888

melody from Michael Praetorius 1571-1621
harmonized by G R Woodward 1848-1935

1 O love, how deep! how broad! how high! It fills the heart with ec-sta-sy, that God, the Son of God, should take our mor-tal form for mor-tals' sake.

2 He sent no angel to our race
   of higher or of lower place,
   but wore the robe of human frame
   himself, and to this lost world came.

3 For us he was baptized, and bore
   his holy fast, and hungered sore;
   for us temptations sharp he knew;
   for us the tempter overthrew.

4 For us he prayed, for us he taught,
   for us his daily works he wrought,
   by words and signs, and actions, thus
   still seeking not himself but us.

5 For us to wicked men betrayed,
scourged, mocked, in purple robe arrayed,
he bore the shameful cross and death;
for us at length gave up his breath.

6 For us he rose from death again,
for us he went on high to reign,
for us he sent his Spirit here
to guide, to strengthen, and to cheer.

7 To him whose boundless love has won
salvation for us through his Son,
to God the Father, glory be
both now and through eternity.

from the Latin, 15th century
tr. Benjamin Webb 1820-1885
for another setting see 310

101

THE RE IS A GREEN HILL FAR AWAY
HORSLEY 8 6 8 6   William Horsley 1774-1858

1 There is a green hill far a - way, out - side a ci - ty wall,
where the dear Lord was cru - ci - fied who died to save us all.

2 We may not know, we cannot tell,
what pains he had to bear;
but we believe it was for us
he hung and suffered there.

3 He died that we might be forgiven,
he died to make us good,
that we might go at last to heaven,
saved by his precious blood.

4 There was no other good enough
to pay the price of sin;
he only could unlock the gate
of heaven, and let us in.

5 O dearly, dearly has he loved,
and we must love him too,
and trust in his redeeming blood,
and try his works to do.

Cecil Frances Alexander 1823-1895

102

FATHER, LONG BEFORE CREATION

MILLER CHAPEL 878787

David Hugh Jones 1900–

1 Fa-ther, long be-fore cre-a-tion thou hadst cho-sen us in love;

and that love so deep, so mov-ing, draws us close to Christ a-bove.

Still it keeps us, still it keeps us firm-ly fixed in Christ a-lone.

2 God's compassion is my story,
 is my boasting all the day;
 mercy free and never failing
 moves my will, directs my way.
 God so loved us
 that his only Son he gave.

3 Though the world may change its fashion,
 yet our God is e'er the same;
 his compassion and his covenant
 through all ages will remain.
 God's own children
 must for ever praise his name.

from the Chinese, anonymous c1952
tr. Francis Price Jones 1890–

103

HERALD! SOUND THE NOTE OF JUDGEMENT

NEANDER 8 7 8 7 8 7

Joachim Neander 1650–1680

1 Her-ald! Sound the note of judge-ment! warn-ing men of right and wrong, turn-ing them from sin and sad-ness, till once more they sing the song: Sound the trum-pet! Tell the mess-age! Christ the Sav-iour King has come!

2 Herald! Sound the note of gladness!
Tell the news that Christ is here;
make a pathway through the desert
for the one who brings God near:
Sound the trumpet! Tell the message!
Christ the Saviour King has come!

3 Herald! Sound the note of pardon!
Those repenting are forgiven;
God receives his wayward children,
and to all new life is given:
Sound the trumpet! Tell the message!
Christ the Saviour King has come!

4 Herald! Sound the note of triumph!
Christ has come to share our life,
bringing God's own love and power,
granting victory in our strife:
Sound the trumpet! Tell the message!
Christ the Saviour King has come!

Moir A J Waters 1906–

104

WE MEET YOU, O CHRIST

SHERSTON 10 10 11 11

Walter Kendall Stanton 1891-

1 We meet you, O Christ, in man-y a guise;
your im-age we see in sim-ple and wise,
You live in a pal-ace, ex-ist in a shack.
We see you, the gar-dener, a tree on your back.

2 In millions alive, away and abroad,
  involved in our life you live down the road.
  Imprisoned in systems you long to be free.
  We see you, Lord Jesus, still bearing your tree.

3 We hear you, O man, in agony cry.
  For freedom you march, in riots you die.
  Your face in the papers we read and we see.
  The tree must be planted by human decree.

4 You choose to be made at one with the earth;
  the dark of the grave prepares for your birth.
  Your death is your rising, creative your word;
  the tree springs to life and our hope is restored.

Frederik Herman Kaan 1929-

105

MEN GO TO GOD

SURSUM CORDA 10 10 10 10   Alfred Morton Smith 1879-

1 Men go to God when they are sore-ly placed,
pray him for suc-cour, for his peace, for bread,
for mer-cy, for them sin-ning, sick or dead.
All men do so in faith or un-be-lief.

2 Men go to God when he is sorely placed,
   find him poor, scorned, unsheltered, without bread,
   whelmed under weight of evil, weak or dead.
   Christians stand by God in his hour of grief.

3 God goes to man when he is sorely placed,
   body and spirit feeds he with his bread.
   For every man, he as a man hangs dead:
   forgiven life he gives men through his death.

Dietrich Bonhöffer
Walter Henry Farquharson 1936-

LORD OF THE DANCE

LORD OF THE DANCE irregular   Sydney Carter 1915–

Unison

1 I danced in the morn-ing when the world was be-gun,

and I danced in the moon and the stars and the sun;

and I came down from hea-ven and I danced on the earth -

at Beth - le - hem I had my birth.

Refrain

Dance then wher - ev - er you may be;

I am the Lord of the Dance, said he;

I'll lead you all wher-ev-er you may be,
I will lead you all in the dance, said he.

2   I danced for the scribe and the pharisee,
    but they would not dance and they wouldn't follow me;
    I danced for the fishermen, for James and John;
    they came with me and the dance went on.
    Dance then wherever you may be ...

3   I danced on the Sabbath and I cured the lame;
    the holy people said it was a shame;
    they whipped and they stripped and they hung me high,
    and they left me there on a cross to die.
    Dance then wherever you may be ...

4   I danced on a Friday when the sky turned black –
    it's hard to dance with the devil on your back;
    they buried my body and they thought I'd gone –
    but I am the dance and I still go on.
    Dance then wherever you may be ...

5   They cut me down and I leap up high:
    I am the life that'll never, never die;
    I'll live in you if you'll live in me –
    I am the Lord of the Dance, said he.
    Dance then wherever you may be ...   Sydney Carter 1915-

The small notes are for v. 5

The stanzas may be sung by a soloist
and the refrain by the people.

107

ALL PRAISE TO THEE

SINE NOMINE 10 10 10 4

Ralph Vaughan Williams 1872-1958

Unison

1 All praise to thee, for thou, O King di - vine,
didst yield the glo - ry that of right was thine,
that in our dark - ened hearts thy grace might shine:
al - le - lu - ia, al - le - lu - ia!

2 Thou cam'st to us in lowliness of thought;
by thee the outcast and the poor were sought,
and by thy death was God's salvation wrought:
alleluia!

3 Let this mind be in us which was in thee,
who wast a servant that we might be free,
humbling thyself to death on Calvary:
alleluia!

4 Wherefore, by God's eternal purpose, thou
art high exalted o'er all creatures now,

and given the name to which all knees shall bow:
alleluia!

5 Let every tongue confess with one accord
   in heaven and earth that Jesus Christ is Lord;
   and God the Father be by all adored:
   alleluia!

Francis Bland Tucker 1895-
based on Philippians 2.5-11
for a higher setting see 501

108

THE HEAD THAT ONCE WAS CROWNED
ST MAGNUS 8 6 8 6

Jeremiah Clark 1659-1707

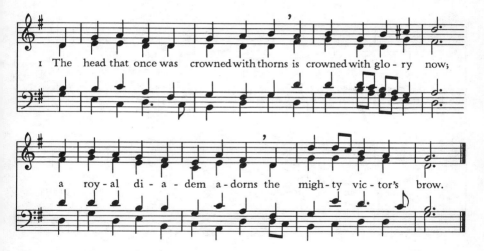

1 The head that once was crowned with thorns is crowned with glo-ry now;
a roy-al di-a-dem a-dorns the migh-ty vic-tor's brow.

2 The highest place that heaven affords
   is his, is his by right,
   the King of kings and Lord of lords,
   and heaven's eternal light,

3 the joy of all who dwell above,
   the joy of all below,
   to whom he manifests his love
   and grants his name to know.

4 To them the cross, with all its shame,
   with all its grace, is given,
   their name an everlasting name,
   their joy the joy of heaven.

5 They suffer with their Lord below,
   they reign with him above,
   their profit and their joy to know
   the mystery of his love.

6 The cross he bore is life and health,
   though shame and death to him,
   his people's hope, his people's wealth,
   their everlasting theme.

Thomas Kelly 1769-1854
based on Hebrews 2:10

109

WHEN I SURVEY THE WONDROUS CROSS

ROCKINGHAM 8 8 8 8

adapted by Edward Miller 1731-1807

1 When I sur-vey the won-drous cross on which the Prince of glo-ry died, my rich-est gain I count but loss, and pour con-tempt on all my pride.

2 Forbid it, Lord, that I should boast
save in the death of Christ, my God:
all the vain things that charm me most,
I sacrifice them to his blood.

3 See from his head, his hands, his feet,
sorrow and love flow mingled down!
Did e'er such love and sorrow meet,
or thorns compose so rich a crown?

4 Were the whole realm of nature mine,
that were a present far too small:
love so amazing, so divine,
demands my soul, my life, my all.

Isaac Watts 1674-1748
based on Galatians 6:14

110

WE SING THE PRAISE OF HIM WHO DIED

BOW BRICKHILL 8 8 8 8 Sydney Hugo Nicholson 1875–1947

1 We sing the praise of him who died,
of him who died upon the cross;
the sinner's hope let men deride,
for this we count the world but loss.

2 Inscribed upon the cross we see
in shining letters 'God is love';
he bears our sins upon the tree;
he brings us mercy from above.

3 The cross – it takes our guilt away;
it holds the fainting spirit up;
it cheers with hope the gloomy day,
and sweetens every bitter cup;

4 it makes the coward spirit brave,
and nerves the feeble arm for fight;
it takes the terror from the grave,
and gilds the bed of death with light;

5 the balm of life, the cure of woe,
the measure and the pledge of love,
the sinner's refuge here below,
the angel's theme in heaven above.

Thomas Kelly 1769–1854
based on Galatians 6:14
This may be sung to Fulda 303

III

FATHER OF PEACE

CHICHESTER 8 6 8 6

Ravenscroft's Psalter 1621

1 Father of peace and God of love, we own thy power to save, that power by which our Shepherd rose victorious o'er the grave.

2 Him from the dead thou brought'st again,
   when by his sacred blood
   confirmed and sealed for evermore
   the eternal covenant stood.

3 O may thy Spirit seal our souls,
   and mould them to thy will,
   that our weak hearts no more may stray,
   but keep thy precepts still;

4 that to perfection's sacred height
   we nearer still may rise,
   and all we think, and all we do,
   be pleasing in thine eyes.

Philip Doddridge 1702-1751
William Cameron 1751-1811
based on Hebrews 13: 20-21

II2

ONCE IN ROYAL DAVID'S CITY

IRBY 8 7 8 7 7 7 irregular

melody by Henry John Gauntlett 1805-1876
harmonized by Arthur Henry Mann 1850-1928

1 Once in royal David's city stood a lowly cattle-shed,

where a mo-ther laid her ba-by in a man-ger for his bed.

Ma-ry was that mo-ther mild, Je-sus Christ her lit-tle child.

2 He came down to earth from heaven
  who is God and Lord of all,
  and his shelter was a stable,
  and his cradle was a stall.
  With the poor and mean and lowly
  lived on earth our Saviour holy.

3 And through all his wondrous childhood
  he would honour and obey,
  love, and watch the lowly maiden
  in whose gentle arms he lay.
  Christian children all should be
  kind, obedient, good as he.

4 Not in that poor lowly stable,
  with the oxen standing by,
  we shall see him, but in heaven,
  set at God's right hand on high,
  when, like stars, his children crowned
  all in white shall gather round.

Cecil Frances Alexander 1823-1895

113

IN THE CROSS OF CHRIST I GLORY
CROSS OF JESUS 8 7 8 7

John Stainer 1840-1901

1 In the cross of Christ I glo-ry, tower-ing o'er the wrecks of time; all the light of sac-red sto-ry gath-ers round its head sub-lime.

2 When the woes of life o'ertake me,
   hopes deceive, and fears annoy,
   never shall the cross forsake me;
   lo! it glows with peace and joy.

3 When the sun of bliss is beaming
   light and love upon my way,
   from the cross the radiance streaming
   adds more lustre to the day.

4 Bane and blessing, pain and pleasure,
   by the cross are sanctified;
   peace is there that knows no measure,
   joys that through all time abide.

5 In the cross of Christ I glory,
   towering o'er the wrecks of time;
   all the light of sacred story
   gathers round its head sublime.

John Bowering 1792-1872
based on Galatians 6:14

114

WHAT A FRIEND WE HAVE IN JESUS
FRIENDSHIP 8 7 8 7 D

melody by Charles Crozat Converse 1832-1918
harmonized by Stanley L Osborne 1907-

Unison

1 What a friend we have in Je - sus, all our sins and griefs to

bear! What a pri-vi-lege to car - ry ev - ery thing to God in prayer! O what peace we of-ten for - feit, O what need-less pain we bear, all be-cause we do not car - ry ev - ery thing to God in prayer!

2 Have we trials or temptations?
Is there trouble anywhere?
We should never be discouraged;
take it to the Lord in prayer.
Can we find a friend so faithful,
who will all our sorrows share?
Jesus knows our every weakness;
take it to the Lord in prayer.

3 Are we weak and heavy-laden,
cumbered with a load of care?
Christ the Saviour is our refuge;
take it to the Lord in prayer.
Do our friends despise, forsake us?
Are we tempted to despair?
Jesus' strength will shield our weakness,
and we'll find new courage there.

Joseph Scriven 1820-1886

115

I HEARD THE VOICE OF JESUS

KINGSFOLD 8 6 8 6 D   Traditional melody of England and Ireland

1 I heard the voice of Je-sus say, 'Come un-to me and rest;
lay down, thou wea-ry one, lay down thy head up-on my breast'.
I came to Je-sus as I was, wea-ry and worn and sad;
I found in him a rest-ing place, and he has made me glad.

In stanzas 2 and 3, lines 5 and 6 follow this:

2 I heard the voice of Jesus say,
'Behold, I freely give
the living water; thirsty one,
stoop down, and drink, and live'.
I came to Jesus, and I drank
of that life-giving stream;
my thirst was quenched, my soul revived,
and now I live in him.

3 I heard the voice of Jesus say,
'I am this dark world's light;
look unto me, thy morn shall rise,
and all thy day be bright'.
I looked to Jesus, and I found
in him my star, my sun;
and in that light of life I'll walk
till travelling days are done.

Horatius Bonar 1808-1889
for a higher setting see 202

116

HOW SWEET THE NAME OF JESUS SOUNDS

ST PETER 8 6 8 6   Alexander Robert Reinagle 1799-1877

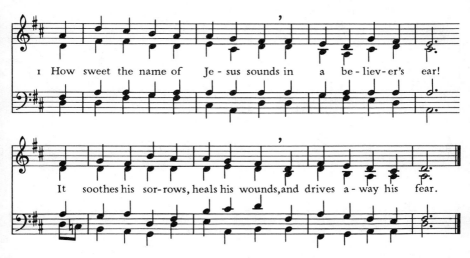

1 How sweet the name of Je-sus sounds in a be-liev-er's ear!

It soothes his sor-rows, heals his wounds, and drives a-way his fear.

2 It makes the wounded spirit whole,
and calms the troubled breast;
'tis manna to the hungry soul,
and to the weary rest.

3 Dear Name! the rock on which I build,
my shield and hiding-place,
my never-failing treasury, filled
with boundless stores of grace.

4 Jesus, my Shepherd, Brother, Friend,
my Prophet, Priest and King,
my Lord, my Life, my Way, my End,
accept the praise I bring.

5 Weak is the effort of my heart,
and cold my warmest thought;
but when I see thee as thou art,
I'll praise thee as I ought.

John Newton 1725-1807

117

HOW BRIGHTLY BEAMS THE MORNING STAR!

WIE SCHÖN LEUCHTET 887 D 888   Philipp Nicolai 1556–1608

1 How bright-ly beams the morn-ing star!

What sud-den ra-diance from a-far

doth cheer us with its shin-ing?

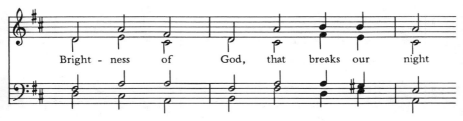

Bright-ness of God, that breaks our night

and fills the dark-ened souls with light,

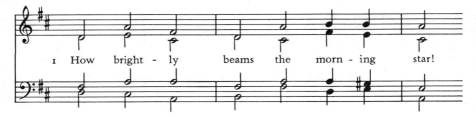

who long for truth were pin-ing!

Newly, truly, God's word feeds us,
rightly leads us, life bestowing.
Praise, O praise such love o'erflowing!

2 All praise to him who came to save,
who conquered death and scorned the grave;
each day new praise resoundeth
to him, the life who once was slain,
the friend whom none shall trust in vain,
whose grace for aye aboundeth;
sing then, ring then, tell the story
of his glory, till his praises
flood with light earth's darkest mazes!

Johann Adolf Schlegel 1721-1793
tr. Catherine Winkworth 1829-1898
and others

118

JESUS, THY BLOOD AND RIGHTEOUSNESS

O JESU CHRISTE, WAHRES LICHT 8 8 8 8   Nürnberg Gesangbuch 1676

1 Je - sus, thy blood and right - eous - ness
my beau - ty are, my glo - rious dress;
'midst flam - ing worlds, in these ar - rayed,
with joy shall I lift up my head.

2   Bold shall I stand in thy great day;
for who aught to my charge shall lay?
Fully absolved through these I am
from sin and fear, from guilt and shame.

3   Jesus, be endless praise to thee,
whose boundless mercy hath for me –
for me a full atonement made,
an everlasting ransom paid.

4   O let the dead now hear thy voice;
now bid thy banished ones rejoice;
their beauty this, their glorious dress,
Jesus, thy blood and righteousness.

Nikolaus Ludwig Zinzendorf
1700-1760
tr. John Wesley 1703-1791

119

CHRIST IS THE WORLD'S LIGHT

CHRISTUS URUNKNAK 10 11 11 6 — Hungarian carol arranged by Thomas Lagrady
harmonized by Robert L Sanders 1906-

1 Christ is the world's light, he and none o - ther;
born in our dark - ness, he be - came our bro - ther;
if we have seen him, we have seen the Fa - ther;
glo - ry to God on high.

2 Christ is the world's peace, he and none other;
no man can serve him and despise his brother;
who else unites us, one in God the Father?
Glory to God on high.

3 Christ is the world's life, he and none other;
sold once for silver, murdered here, our brother –
he, who redeems us, reigns with God the Father:
glory to God on high.

4 Give God the glory, God and none other!
Give God the glory, Spirit, Son and Father!
Give God the glory, God in man my brother!
Glory to God on high.

Frederick Pratt Green 1903-

120

JESUS, THE VERY THOUGHT OF THEE

ST BOTOLPH 8686 FIRST TUNE   Gordon Archibald Slater 1895-

1 Jesus, the very thought of thee with sweetness fills my breast; but sweeter far thy face to see, and in thy presence rest.

2 No voice can sing, no heart can frame,
nor can the memory find
a sweeter sound than Jesus' name,
the Saviour of mankind.

3 O hope of every contrite heart,
O joy of all the meek,
to those who ask how kind thou art,
how good to those who seek!

4 But what to those who find? Ah, this
no tongue nor pen can show;
the love of Jesus, what it is
none but his loved ones know.

5 Jesus, our only joy be thou,
as thou our prize wilt be;
in thee be all our glory now,
and through eternity.

Bernard of Clairvaux 12th century
tr. Edward Caswall 1814-1878

ST PAUL'S, KINGSTON 8686 SECOND TUNE   Graham George 1912-

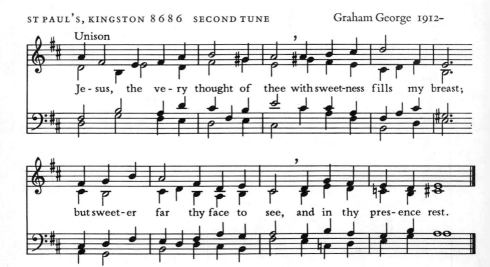

Jesus, the very thought of thee with sweetness fills my breast; but sweeter far thy face to see, and in thy presence rest.

121

O JESUS, KING MOST WONDERFUL

METZLER'S REDHEAD 8686   FIRST TUNE   Richard Redhead 1820-1901

1 O Je - sus, King most won-der-ful, thou con-quer-or re - nowned,

thou sweet-ness most in - ef - fa - ble, in whom all joys are found:

2 when once thou visitest the heart,
   then truth begins to shine;
   then earthly vanities depart,
   then kindles love divine.

3 O Jesus, light of all below,
   thou fount of living fire,
   surpassing all the joys we know,
   and all we can desire:

4 Jesus, may all confess thy name,
   thy wondrous love adore,
   and seeking thee, their hearts inflame
   to seek thee more and more.

5 Thee, Jesus, may our voices bless,
   thee may we love alone,
   and ever in our lives express
   the image of thine own.

Bernard of Clairvaux 12th century
tr. Edward Caswall 1814-1878

ST AGNES, DURHAM 8686   SECOND TUNE   John Bacchus Dykes 1823-1876

1 O Je - sus, King most won-der - ful, thou con-quer-or re - nowned,

thou sweet-ness most in - ef - fa - ble, in whom all joys are found:

122

WISE MEN SEEKING JESUS

EUDOXIA 6 5 6 5

Sabine Baring-Gould 1834-1924

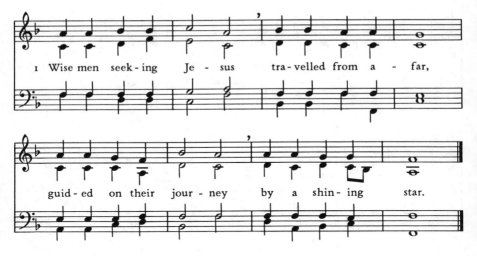

1 Wise men seek-ing Je - sus tra-velled from a - far,
guid-ed on their jour-ney by a shin-ing star.

2 But if we desire him,
   he is close at hand;
   for our native country
   is our Holy Land.

3 Each of us may find him
   by our quiet lakes,
   meet him on our hillsides
   when the morning breaks.

4 In our fertile wheatfields
   while the sheaves are bound,
   in our busy markets,
   Jesus may be found.

5 Fishermen talk with him
   by the great north sea,
   as the first disciples
   did in Galilee.

6 Every town and city
   in our land might be
   made by Jesus' presence
   like sweet Bethany.

7 He is more than near us
   if we love him well;
   Christ comes seeking ever
   in our hearts to dwell.

James Thomas East 1860-1937

123

JESUS LOVES ME

JESUS LOVES ME 7 7 7 7 and refrain

melody from
William Batchelder Bradbury 1816-1868
harmonized by Stanley L Osborne 1907-

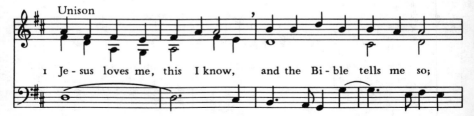

Unison

1 Je - sus loves me, this I know, and the Bi - ble tells me so;

lit - tle ones to him be - long, in his love we shall be strong.

Refrain

Yes, Je - sus loves me, yes, Je - sus loves me,

yes, Je - sus loves me, the Bi - ble tells me so.

2 Jesus loves me, this I know,
   as he loved so long ago,
   taking children on his knee,
   saying, 'Let them come to me'.

3 Jesus loves me still today,
   walking with me on my way,
   wanting as a friend to give
   light and love to all who live.

Anna Bartlett Warner c1822–c1915
David Rutherford McGuire 1929–

If desired, the refrain may be sung at the end
of the last verse only.

124

JESUS IS THE MAN

CWM RHONDDA 10 7 10 7 8 7 7

John Hughes 1873-1932

1 Jesus is the man who cares for others, Jesus is the man for me!
Jesus calls mankind to be his brothers, gives the world his unity,
braves all dangers, loves all strangers, tends the helpless refugee:
Jesus is the man for me!

2 Jesus is the man for liberation,
Jesus is the man for me,
brings release to every generation,
challenges all tyranny,
bears aggression, breaks oppression,
gives the slave his liberty:
Jesus is the man for me!

3 Jesus is the man for celebration,
Jesus is the man for me,
brings the gospel's joyful exultation,
purges life of misery,

pardon granted, peace implanted,
conscience new and clean and free:
Jesus is the man for me!

4 Jesus is the man for resurrection,
Jesus is the man for me!
Crucified he suffered man's rejection,
yet he lives eternally,
death transcended, fate is ended,
now he makes man's destiny:
Jesus is the man for me!

Richard Granville Jones 1926-

125
SING WE OF THE MODERN CITY

GENEVA 8 7 8 7 D

George Henry Day 1915–

Unison

1 Sing we of the mo-dern ci - ty, scene a-like of joy and stress;

sing we of its name-less peo - ple in their ur - ban wil-der-ness.

In - to end-less rows of hous-es life is set a mil - lion-fold,

life ex-pressed in hu - man be-ings dai-ly born and grow-ing old.

2 In the city full of people,
world of speed and hectic days,
in the ever-changing setting
of the latest trend and craze,
Christ is present, and among us;
in the crowd we see him stand.
In the bustle of the city
Jesus Christ is every man.

3 God is not remote in heaven,
but on earth to share our shame,
changing graph and mass and numbers
into persons with a name.
Christ has shown, beyond statistics,
human life with glory crowned,
by his timeless presence proving
people matter, people count!

Frederik Herman Kaan 1929–
This may be sung to Alleluia 280

126

COME, LET US SING OF A WONDERFUL LOVE
WONDERFUL LOVE 10 8 10 7 8 10

Adam Watson 1845-1912

1 Come, let us sing of a won-der-ful love, ten-der and true, ten-der and true,
out of the heart of the Fa-ther a-bove, stream-ing to me and to you:
won-der-ful love, won-der-ful love dwells in the heart of the Fa-ther a-bove.

2 Jesus the Saviour this gospel to tell
joyfully came –
came with the helpless and hopeless to dwell,
sharing their sorrow and shame,
seeking the lost,
saving, redeeming at measureless cost.

3 Jesus is seeking the wanderers yet;
why do they roam?
Love only waits to forgive and forget;
home, weary wanderers, home!
Wonderful love
dwells in the heart of the Father above.

4 Come to my heart, O thou wonderful love!
Come and abide,
lifting my life till it rises above
envy and falsehood and pride:
seeking to be
lowly and humble, a learner of thee.

Robert Walmsley 1831-1905

127

LORD, WHEN THOU DIDST THYSELF UNDRESS

TRANSLATION 8 8 8 8 irreg.

Derek Holman 1931-

1 Lord, when thou didst thy-self un-dress, lay-ing by thy robes of glo-ry,

v.5 only

to make us more thou wouldst be less, and be-camst a woe-ful sto-ry.

2 To put on clouds instead of light,
   and clothe the morning star with dust,
   was a translation of such height
   as, but in thee, was ne'er expressed;

3 brave worms, and earth! that thus could have
   a God enclosed within your cell,
   your maker pent up in a grave,
   life locked in death, heav'n in a shell.

4 Ah, my dear Lord! what couldst thou spy
   in this impure, rebellious clay,
   that made thee thus resolve to die
   for those that kill thee every day?

5 O what strange wonders could thee move
   to slight thy precious blood, and breath!
   Sure it was love, my Lord; for love
   is only stronger far than death.

Henry Vaughan 1622-1695

AND THE FOLLOWING

128

I TO THE HILLS WILL LIFT MINE EYES

GLOUCESTER 8 6 8 6   FIRST TUNE

Ravenscroft's Psalter 1621
harmonized by John Tomkins 1586-1638

1 I to the hills will lift mine eyes; from whence doth come mine aid?

My safe-ty com-eth from the Lord, who heaven and earth hath made.

2 Thy foot he'll not let slide, nor will
   he slumber that thee keeps.
   Behold, he that keeps Israel,
   he slumbers not, nor sleeps.

3 The Lord thee keeps, the Lord thy shade
   on thy right hand doth stay:
   the moon by night thee shall not smite,
   nor yet the sun by day.

4 The Lord shall keep thy soul; he shall
   preserve thee from all ill.
   Henceforth thy going out and in
   God keep for ever will.

Scottish Psalter 1650
based on Psalm 121

DUNDEE 8 6 8 6   SECOND TUNE

Scottish Psalter 1615

1 I to the hills will lift mine eyes; from whence doth come mine aid?

My safe-ty com-eth from the Lord, who heaven and earth hath made.

129

UNTO THE HILLS AROUND · melody by Charles Purday 1799–1885
SANDON 10 4 10 4 10 10 · harmonized by Frederick R C Clarke 1931–

1 Un-to the hills a-round do I lift up my long-ing eyes:

O whence for me shall my sal-va-tion come, from whence a - rise?

From God the Lord doth come my cer-tain aid,

from God the Lord who heaven and earth hath made.

2 He will not suffer that thy foot be moved:
safe shalt thou be.
No careless slumber shall his eyelids close
who keepeth thee.
Behold, he sleepeth not, he slumbereth ne'er,
who keepeth Israel in his holy care.

3 Jehovah is himself thy keeper true,
thy changeless shade;
Jehovah thy defence on thy right hand
himself hath made.
And thee no sun by day shall ever smite;
no moon shall harm thee in the silent night.

4 From every evil shall he keep thy soul,
from every sin:
Jehovah shall preserve thy going out,
thy coming in.
Above thee watching, he whom we adore
shall keep thee henceforth, yea, for evermore.

John Campbell 1845–1914
based on Psalm 121

130

GOD IS OUR REFUGE

YORK 8 6 8 6

Scottish Psalter 1615

1 God is our re-fuge and our strength, in straits a pres-ent aid;
there - fore, al-though the earth re-move, we will not be a - fraid,

2 though hills amidst the seas be cast;
though waters roaring make
and troubled be; yea, though the hills
by swelling seas do shake.

3 A river is, whose streams make glad
the city of our God,
the holy place, wherein the Lord
Most High has his abode.

4 God in the midst of her doth dwell,
and nothing shall her move;
the Lord to her an helper will,
and that right early, prove.

Scottish Psalter 1650
based on Psalm 46
This may be sung to Winchester Old 405

131

THE LORD'S MY SHEPHERD

CRIMOND 8686

melody by Jesse Irvine 1836–1887
harmonized by Hugh J McLean 1930–

1 The Lord's my shep - herd, I'll not want:
he makes me down to lie
in pas - tures green; he lead - eth me
the qui - et wa - ters by.

2 My soul he doth restore again,
   and me to walk doth make
   within the paths of righteousness,
   even for his own name's sake.

3 Yea, though I walk through death's dark vale,
   yet will I fear no ill;
   for thou art with me, and thy rod
   and staff me comfort still.

4 My table thou hast furnished
   in presence of my foes;
   my head thou dost with oil anoint,
   and my cup overflows.

5 Goodness and mercy all my life
   shall surely follow me,
   and in God's house for evermore
   my dwelling-place shall be.

Scottish Psalter 1650
based on Psalm 23

132

THE KING OF LOVE
ST COLUMBA 8787 FIRST TUNE

ancient Irish hymn melody

1 The King of love my shep - herd is,
whose good - ness fail - eth nev - er;
I no - thing lack if I am his
and he is mine for ev - er.

2 Where streams of living water flow
my ransomed soul he leadeth,
and where the verdant pastures grow
with food celestial feedeth.

3 Perverse and foolish oft I strayed;
but yet in love he sought me,
and on his shoulder gently laid,
and home rejoicing brought me.

1 The King of love my shep-herd is whose good-ness fail-eth nev-er;

I no-thing lack if I am his and he is mine for ev-er.

(P)

4   In death's dark vale I fear no ill
    with thee, dear Lord, beside me;
    thy rod and staff my comfort still,
    thy cross before to guide me.

5   Thou spread'st a table in my sight;
    thy unction grace bestoweth;
    and O what transport of delight
    from thy pure chalice floweth!

6   And so through all the length of days
    thy goodness faileth never:
    good shepherd, may I sing thy praise   Henry Williams Baker 1821-1877
    within thy house for ever!   based on Psalm 23

133

O GOD, OUR HELP IN AGES PAST

ST ANNE 8 6 8 6   probably by William Croft 1678–1727

1 O God, our help in a-ges past, our hope for years to come, our shel-ter from the storm-y blast, and our e-ter-nal home:

2 under the shadow of thy throne
thy saints have dwelt secure;
sufficient is thine arm alone,
and our defence is sure.

3 Before the hills in order stood,
or earth received her frame,
from everlasting thou art God,
to endless years the same.

4 A thousand ages in thy sight
are like an evening gone,
short as the watch that ends the night
before the rising sun.

5 Time like an ever-rolling stream
bears all its sons away;
they fly forgotten, as a dream
dies at the opening day.

6 O God, our help in ages past,
our hope for years to come,
be thou our guard while troubles last,
and our eternal home.

Isaac Watts 1674–1748
based on Psalm 90

134

ALL MY HOPE ON GOD IS FOUNDED

MICHAEL 8 7 8 7 3 3 7

Herbert Howells 1892–

Unison

1 All my hope on God is found - ed; he doth still my trust re - new:
me through change and chance he guid eth, on - ly good and on - ly true.
God un-known, he a - lone calls my heart to be his own.

2 Pride of man and earthly glory,
   sword and crown, betray man's trust;
   what with care and toil he buildeth,
   tower and temple, fall to dust.
   But God's power,
   hour by hour,
   is my temple and my tower.

3 Daily doth the almighty giver
   bounteous gifts on us bestow;
   his desire our soul delighteth,
   pleasure leads us where we go.
   Love doth stand
   at his hand;
   joy doth wait on his command.

4 God's great goodness aye endureth,
   deep his wisdom, passing thought:
   splendour, light and life attend him,
   beauty springeth out of naught.
   Evermore
   from his store
   new-born worlds rise and adore.

Joachim Neander 1650–1680
tr. Robert Bridges 1844–1930
based on 1 Timothy 6:17

135
OUR GOD'S A FORTRESS

EIN' FESTE BURG 8 7 8 7 66667

melody by Martin Luther 1483-1546
harmonized by Johann Sebastian Bach 1685-1750

1 Our God's a fort-ress firm and sure, a strong de-fence a - round us.

With him we know our cause se-cure, though griefs and pains sur - round us.

Our old mal - i - cious foe is set to work us woe:

both force and sly de - ceit he'll use for our de - feat:

no earth - ly power can match him.

2 Our human strength alone must fail
when evil's hosts invade us,
yet shall the one true Man prevail,
whom God has sent to aid us.
You ask who that may be:
Christ Jesus, none but he,
Lord Sabaoth alone,
of gods the mighty one –
he must maintain the battle.

3 With demons did this wide world swarm,
all eager to devour us,
we need not fear their threatened harm,
they shall not overpower us.
The leader of our foes,
though fiercely he oppose,
his kingdom shall not last;
for judgement's on him passed –
a simple word shall fell him.

4 That word all hell shall leave to stand,
nor is it by their merit:
the Lord is with us, his right hand
pours out his gifts and Spirit.
Our foes may take our life,
goods, honour, child and wife:
by faith we let them go,
they gain no victory so:
all's ours with Jesus' kingdom.

Martin Luther 1483-1546
tr. Jay Macpherson 1931-
based on Psalm 46

136

MY GOD, THE SPRING OF ALL MY JOYS

CLONARD 8 6 8 6   William McClelland 1909–

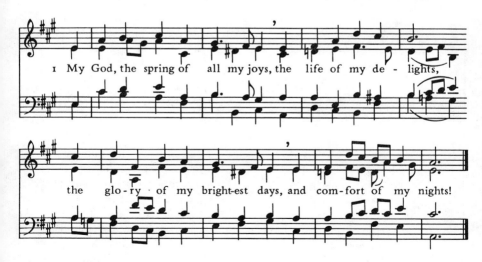

1 My God, the spring of all my joys, the life of my de - lights,

the glo-ry of my bright-est days, and com-fort of my nights!

2 In darkest shades, if thou appear,
my dawning is begun;
thou art my soul's bright morning star,
and thou my rising sun.

Isaac Watts 1674-1748

137

THROUGH ALL THE CHANGING SCENES OF LIFE

WILTSHIRE 8 6 8 6

George Thomas Smart 1776-1867

1 Through all the chang-ing scenes of life, in trou-ble and in joy, the prais-es of my God shall still my heart and tongue em-ploy.

2 O magnify the Lord with me,
with me exalt his name;
when in distress to him I called,
he to my rescue came.

3 The hosts of God encamp around
the dwellings of the just;
deliverance he affords to all
who on his succour trust.

4 O make but trial of his love;
experience will decide
how blest are they, and only they,
who in his truth confide.

5 Fear him, ye saints, and you will then
have nothing else to fear;
make you his service your delight,
your wants shall be his care.

6 To Father, Son, and Holy Ghost,
the God whom we adore,
be glory, as it was, is now,
and shall be evermore.

Tate and Brady 1696
based on Psalm 34

138

TO MERCY, PITY, PEACE, AND LOVE

BISHOPS 8 6 8 6

John Joubert 1927–

3 For Mercy has a human heart,
   Pity a human face,
   and Love, the human form divine,
   and Peace, the human dress.

4 Then every man of every clime
   that prays in his distress,
   prays to the human form divine,
   Love, Mercy, Pity, Peace.

William Blake 1757–1827

139

HOW FIRM A FOUNDATION
ST DENIO 11 11 11 11

Welsh hymn melody

1 How firm a foun - da - tion, ye saints of the Lord,
is laid for your faith in his ex - cel - lent word!
What more can he say than to you he hath said,
to you who to Je - sus for re - fuge have fled?

2 'Fear not, I am with thee; O be not dismayed!
 For I am thy God and will still give thee aid;
 I'll strengthen thee, help thee, and cause thee to stand,
 upheld by my righteous omnipotent hand.

3 'When through the deep waters I call thee to go,
 the rivers of woe shall not thee overflow;
 for I will be with thee, thy troubles to bless,
 and sanctify to thee thy deepest distress.

4 'When through fiery trials thy pathway shall lie,
 my grace, all-sufficient, shall be thy supply:
 the flame shall not hurt thee; I only design
 thy dross to consume, and thy gold to refine.

5 'The soul that on Jesus hath leaned for repose
    I will not – I will not desert to his foes;
    that soul, though all hell should endeavour to shake,
    I'll never – no, never – no, never forsake!'

R. Keen c1787

140

ART THOU WEARY, HEAVY LADEN?

STEPHANOS 8 5 8 3   melody by Henry Williams Baker 1821-1877
                                                  harmonized by Stanley L Osborne 1907-

1 Art thou wea-ry, hea-vy la-den? Art thou sore dis-tressed?

'Come to me', saith one, 'and com-ing be at rest.'

2   Hath he marks to lead me to him,
    if he be my guide?
    In his feet and hands are wound-prints,
    and his side.

3   Is there diadem as monarch,
    that his brow adorns?
    Yea, a crown, in very surety,
    but of thorns.

4   If I find him, if I follow,
    what his guerdon here?
    Many a sorrow, many a labour,
    many a tear!

5   If I still hold closely to him,
    what hath he at last?
    Sorrow vanquished, labour ended,
    Jordan passed.

6   If I ask him to receive me,
    will he say me nay?
    Not till earth, and not till heaven
    pass away.

7   Finding, following, keeping, struggling,
    is he sure to bless?
    Saints, apostles, prophets, martyrs,
    answer, Yes!

St Stephen of Mar Saba 725-794
tr. John Mason Neale 1818-1866

141

MY GOD, HOW ENDLESS IS THY LOVE

O JESU CHRIST 8 8 8 8   P Reinigius c1587

1 My God, how end-less is thy love! Thy gifts are ev - ery even-ing new,

and morn-ing mer-cies from a - bove gent-ly dis-til, like ear - ly dew.

2 Thou spread'st the curtains of the night,
  great Guardian of my sleeping hours;
  thy sovereign word restores the light,
  and quickens all my drowsy powers.

3 I yield my powers to thy command;
  to thee I consecrate my days:
  perpetual blessings from thy hand
  demand perpetual songs of praise.   Isaac Watts 1674-1748

142

ALL THE WAY MY SAVIOUR LEADS ME

ALL THE WAY 8 7 8 7 D   Robert Lowry 1826-1899
                                   harmonized by Stanley L Osborne 1907-

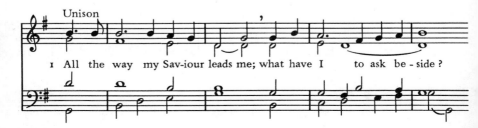

1 All the way my Sav-iour leads me; what have I to ask be - side?

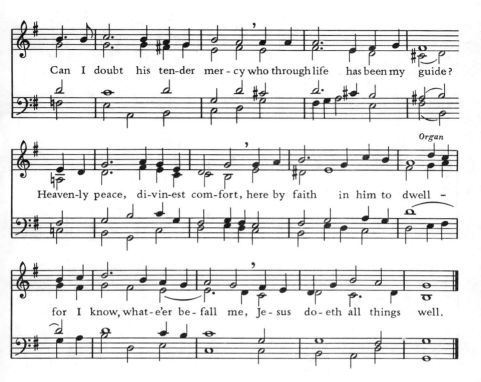

Can I doubt his ten-der mer - cy who through life has been my guide?

Heaven-ly peace, di-vin-est com-fort, here by faith in him to dwell –

for I know, what-e'er be-fall me, Je - sus do-eth all things well.

Organ

2 All the way my Saviour leads me,
   cheers each winding path I tread,
   gives me grace for every trial,
   feeds me with the living bread.
   Though my weary steps may falter,
   and my soul athirst may be,
   gushing from the rock before me,
   lo, a spring of joy I see!

3 All the way my Saviour leads me:
   O the fullness of his love!
   Perfect rest to me is promised
   in my Father's house above.
   When my spirit, clothed, immortal,
   wings its flight to realms of day,
   this my song through endless ages,
   'Jesus led me all the way!'

Frances Jane Crosby Van Alstyne
1823-1915

AND THE FOLLOWING

143

WHEN ISRAEL WAS IN EGYPT'S LAND

NEGRO MELODY irregular

traditional

Solo ... Chorus
1 When Is-rael was in E-gypt's land, Let my peo-ple go!

Solo ... Chorus
op-pressed so hard they could not stand: Let my peo-ple go!

Go down, Mo-ses, 'way down in E-gypt's land,
Go down

tell old Phar-aoh, let my peo-ple go!
tell old Phar - aoh Let my peo-ple go!

2 We need not always weep and mourn,   Let my people go!
  and wear these slavery chains forlorn: Let my people go!
  Go down, Moses,
  'way down in Egypt's land,
  tell old Pharaoh,
  let my people go!

3 O let us all from bondage flee,   Let my people go!
  and let us all in Christ be free: Let my people go!
  Go down, Moses, ...

Negro spiritual

144

GLORIOUS THINGS OF THEE ARE SPOKEN

RUSTINGTON 8 7 8 7 D   Charles Hubert Hastings Parry 1848-1918

1 Glo - rious things of thee are spo - ken, Zi - on, ci - ty of our God;

he whose word can - not be bro - ken formed thee for his own a - bode.

On the rock of a - ges found - ed, what can shake thy sure re - pose?

With sal - va - tion's walls sur - round - ed, thou mayst smile at all thy foes.

2 See! the streams of living waters,
   springing from eternal love,
   well supply thy sons and daughters
   and all fear of want remove.
   Who can faint, when such a river
   ever flows their thirst to assuage –
   grace, which like the Lord, the giver,
   never fails from age to age?

3 Saviour, if of Zion's city
   I through grace a member am,
   let the world deride or pity,
   I will glory in thy name.
   Fading is the worldling's pleasure,
   all his boasted pomp and show:
   solid joys and lasting treasure
   none but Zion's children know.

John Newton 1725-1807
based on Isaiah 33: 20, 21
This may be sung to Austria 155

145

CHRIST IS MADE THE SURE FOUNDATION

URBS BEATA 8 7 8 7 8 7   FIRST TUNE

Sarum plainsong
harmonized by Margaret Drynan 1915-

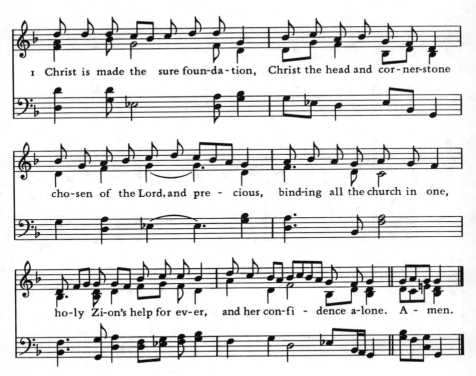

1 Christ is made the sure foun-da-tion, Christ the head and cor-ner-stone cho-sen of the Lord, and pre - cious, bind-ing all the church in one, ho-ly Zi-on's help for ev-er, and her con-fi - dence a-lone. A - men.

2 To this temple where we call thee
   come, O Lord of hosts, today;
   with thy wonted loving-kindness
   hear thy servants as they pray,
   and thy fullest benediction
   shed within its walls alway.

3 Here vouchsafe to all thy servants
   what they ask of thee to gain,
   what they gain from thee for ever
   with the blessed to retain,
   and hereafter in thy glory
   evermore with thee to reign.

4 Laud and honour to the Father,
   laud and honour to the Son,
   laud and honour to the Spirit,
   ever three and ever one,
   one in might, and one in glory,
   while unending ages run.

from the Latin 7th or 8th century
tr. John Mason Neale 1818-1866

WESTMINSTER ABBEY 8 7 8 7 8 7 SECOND TUNE adapted from Henry Purcell 1658-1695

1 Christ is made the sure foun-da-tion, Christ the head and cor-ner-stone
cho-sen of the Lord, and pre-cious, bind-ing all the church in one,
ho-ly Zi-on's help for ev-er, and her con-fi-dence a-lone.

2 To this temple where we call thee
come, O Lord of hosts, today;
with thy wonted loving-kindness
hear thy servants as they pray,
and thy fullest benediction
shed within its walls alway.

3 Here vouchsafe to all thy servants
what they ask of thee to gain,
what they gain from thee for ever
with the blessed to retain,
and hereafter in thy glory
evermore with thee to reign.

4 Laud and honour to the Father,
laud and honour to the Son,
laud and honour to the Spirit,
ever three and ever one,
one in might, and one in glory,
while unending ages run.

from the Latin 7th or 8th century
tr. John Mason Neale 1818-1866

146

THE CHURCH'S ONE FOUNDATION

AURELIA 7676D

Samuel Sebastian Wesley 1810-1876

1 The church's one foun - da - tion is Je - sus Christ her Lord:
L'é - glise u - ni - ver - sel - le a pour roc Jé - sus - Christ;

she is his new cre - a - tion by wa - ter and the word;
elle est l'œu - vre nou - vel - le que sa pa - ro - le fit.

from heaven he came and sought her to be his ho - ly bride;
Ha - bi - tant le ciel mê - me, il vint se l'at - ta - cher,

with his own blood he bought her, and for her life he died.
et, par un don su - prê - me, mou - rut pour la sau - ver!

2 Elect from every nation,
  yet one o'er all the earth,
  her charter of salvation
  one Lord, one faith, one birth,
  one holy name she blesses,
  partakes one holy food,
  and to one hope she presses
  with every grace endued.

3 'Mid toil and tribulation
  and tumult of her war,
  she waits the consummation
  of peace for evermore,
  till with the vision glorious
  her longing eyes are blest,
  and the great church victorious
  shall be the church at rest.

4 Yet she on earth hath union
  with God the three in one,
  and mystic sweet communion
  with those whose rest is won.
  O happy ones and holy!
  Lord, give us grace that we,
  like them, the meek and lowly,
  on high may dwell with thee.

Samuel John Stone 1839-1900

2 L'église en sa prière
  unit à leur Sauveur
  les peuples de la terre
  soumis au seul Seigneur.
  C'est son nom qu'elle acclame,
  son pain qui la nourrit;
  elle verse à toute âme
  l'espoir qui la guérit.

3 Honnie et méconnue,
  menant de durs combats,
  elle attend la venue
  de la paix ici-bas.
  Contemplant par avance
  la fin de son tourment,
  la grande délivrance,
  le repos permanent.

4 Aujourd'hui, sur la terre,
  elle est unie à Dieu,
  et, par un saint mystère,
  aux élus du saint lieu.
  Rends-nous, comme eux, fidèles,
  et reçois-nous, Seigneur,
  dans la vie éternelle,
  dans l'éternel bonheur!

tr. F Barth

147

CITY OF GOD

RICHMOND 8 6 8 6

adapted from Thomas Haweis 1734-1820
and Samuel Webbe c1770-1843

1 City of God, how broad and far
out-spread thy walls sublime!
The true thy chartered freemen are,
of every age and clime.

2 One holy church, one army strong,
one steadfast, high intent;
one working band, one harvest-song,
one King omnipotent.

3 How purely hath thy speech come down
from man's primeval youth!
How grandly hath thine empire grown
of freedom, love and truth!

4 How gleam thy watch-fires through the night
with never-fainting ray!
How rise thy towers, serene and bright,
to meet the dawning day!

5 In vain the surge's angry shock,
in vain the drifting sands:
unharmed upon the eternal rock
the eternal city stands.

Samuel Johnson 1822-1882

148

THE CHURCH IS WHEREVER GOD'S PEOPLE

traditional

OLD CORNISH CAROL 12 10 12 11 · harmonized by Frederick R C Clarke 1931–

Unison

1 The church is wher-ev-er God's peo-ple are prais-ing,
sing-ing his good-ness for joy on this day.
The church is wher-ev-er dis-ci-ples of Je-sus
re-mem-ber his sto-ry and walk in his way.

2 The church is wherever God's people are helping,
caring for neighbours in sickness and need.
The church is wherever God's people are sharing
the words of the Bible in gift and in deed.

Carol Rose Ikeler 1920–

149

IN CHRIST THERE IS NO EAST OR WEST

MCKEE 8 6 8 6 · · · · · · · · · · · · · · · · · · negro melody adapted by Harry T Burleigh 1866-1949

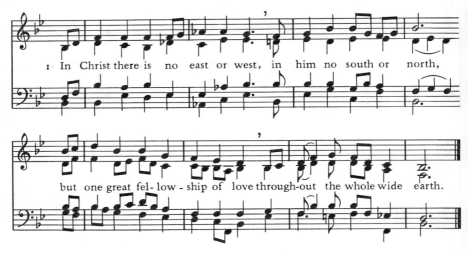

1 In Christ there is no east or west, in him no south or north,
but one great fel-low-ship of love through-out the whole wide earth.

2 In him shall true hearts everywhere
  their high communion find;
  his service is the golden cord
  close-binding all mankind.

3 Join hands, then, brothers of the faith,
  whate'er your race may be;
  who serve my Father as a son
  is surely kin to me.

4 In Christ now meet both east and west,
  in him meet south and north;
  all Christlike souls are one in him
  throughout the whole wide earth.

John Oxenham 1852-1941

150

O GOD OF THE ETERNAL NOW

DETROIT 8 6 8 6 · American traditional melody
harmonized by Stanley L Osborne 1907-

Unison

1 O God of the e-ter-nal now, why is your church so slow?

What is it that pre-vents us all in grace and faith to grow?

2 If, Lord, it is our love of ease
  by which we thwart your plan,
  then call us out, unsettle us,
  and lead us by the hand.

3 May we with courage take the risk
  to leave the past behind,
  to be a people on the move,
  throw caution to the wind.

4 Give us the heart of Abraham,
  for changes make us bold;
  and bless us only so that we
  in turn may bless the world.

Frederik Herman Kaan 1929-

151

BEHOLD THE AMAZING GIFT OF LOVE
ST STEPHEN 8 6 8 6

William Jones 1726-1800

1 Be-hold the a-maz-ing gift of love the Fa-ther hath be-stowed
on us, the sin-ful sons of men, to call us sons of God!

2 Concealed as yet this honour lies,
  by this dark world unknown,
  a world that knew not when he came,
  even God's eternal Son.

3 High is the rank we now possess,
  but higher we shall rise;
  though what we shall hereafter be
  is hid from mortal eyes.

4 Our souls, we know, when he appears
  shall bear his image bright;
  for all his glory full disclosed
  shall open to our sight.

5 A hope so great and so divine
  may trials well endure,
  and purge the soul from sense and sin
  as Christ himself is pure.

Isaac Watts 1674-1748
William Cameron 1751-1811
based on 1 John 3 : 1-3, and Galatians 4 : 6
for another arrangement see 207

152

THY HAND, O GOD, HAS GUIDED

THORNBURY 7676D

Basil Harwood 1859-1949

1 Thy hand, O God, has guid - ed thy flock from age to age;

thy won-drous tale is writ - ten full clear on ev - ery page;

our fa - thers owned thy good - ness, and we their deeds re - cord;

and both of this bear wit - ness,

one church, one faith, one Lord.

2 Thy heralds brought glad tidings
  to greatest as to least;
  they bade men rise and hasten
  to share the great King's feast;
  and this was all their teaching,
  in every deed and word,
  to all alike proclaiming
  one church, one faith, one Lord.

3 When shadows thick were falling,
  and all seemed sunk in night,
  thou, Lord, didst send thy servants,
  thy chosen sons of light.
  On them and on thy people
  thy plenteous grace was poured,
  and this was still their message:
  one church, one faith, one Lord.

4 And we, shall we be faithless?
  Shall hearts fail, hands hang down?
  Shall we evade the conflict,
  and cast away our crown?
  Not so: in God's deep counsels
  some better thing is stored;
  we will maintain unflinching
  one church, one faith, one Lord.

5 Thy mercy will not fail us,
  nor leave thy work undone;
  with thy right hand to help us,
  the victory shall be won;
  and then by men and angels
  thy name shall be adored,
  and this shall be their anthem:
  one church, one faith, one Lord.

Edward Hayes Plumptre 1821-1891

AND THE FOLLOWING

153

THERE'S A VOICE IN THE WILDERNESS

ASCENSION irregular

Henry Hugh Bancroft 1904-

1 & 4 There's a voice in the wil - der - ness cry - ing, a
2 O Zi - on, that bring-est good ti - dings, get thee
3 but the word of our God en - dur - eth, the

call from the ways un - trod: Pre - pare in the de - sert a
up to the heights and sing! Pro - claim to a de - so - late
arm of the Lord is strong; he stands in the midst of

high - way, a high - way for our God! The
peo - ple the com - ing of their King. Like the
na - tions, and he will right the wrong. He shall

val - leys shall be ex - alt - ed, the lof - ty hills brought
flowers of the field they per - ish, the works of men de -
feed his flock like a shep - herd, and fold the lambs to his

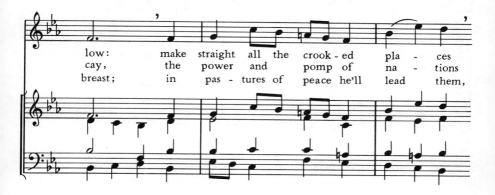

low: make straight all the crook - ed pla - ces
cay, the power and pomp of na - tions
breast; in pas - tures of peace he'll lead them,

where the Lord our God may go!
shall pass like a dream a - way;
and give to the wea - ry rest.

James Lewis Milligan 1876-1961

154

HAIL TO THE LORD'S ANOINTED

CRÜGER 7 6 7 6 D

Johann Crüger 1598-1662

1 Hail to the Lord's a - noint - ed, great Da - vid's great - er Son!
Hail, in the time ap - point - ed, his reign on earth be - gun!

He comes to break op - pres - sion, to set the cap - tive free,

to take a - way trans - gres - sion, and rule in e - qui - ty.

2 He shall come down like showers
upon the fruitful earth,
and love, joy, hope, like flowers
spring in his path to birth.
Before him on the mountains
shall peace the herald go,
and righteousness in fountains
from hill to valley flow.

3 Kings shall fall down before him,
and gold and incense bring;
all nations shall adore him,
his praise all people sing.
To him shall prayer unceasing
and daily vows ascend,
his kingdom still increasing,
a kingdom without end.

4 O'er every foe victorious,
he on his throne shall rest,
from age to age more glorious,
all-blessing and all-blest.
The tide of time shall never
his covenant remove.
His name shall stand for ever:
that name to us is Love.

James Montgomery 1771-1854
based on Psalm 72

155

ZION'S KING SHALL REIGN VICTORIOUS

AUSTRIA 8 7 8 7 D

Franz Josef Haydn 1732–1809

1 Zi - on's King shall reign vic - tor - ious, all the earth shall own his sway;
he will make his king-dom glo-rious, he will reign through end-less day.
Migh-ty King, thine arm re - veal-ing, now thy glo-rious cause main-tain;
bring the na-tions help and heal-ing, make them sub-ject to thy reign.

2 Nations now from God estranged
then shall see a glorious light;
night to day shall then be changed;
heaven shall triumph in the sight.
Mighty King, thine arm revealing,
now thy glorious cause maintain;
bring the nations help and healing,
make them subject to thy reign.

Thomas Kelly 1769–1854
probably based on Zechariah 14

156

MINE EYES HAVE SEEN THE GLORY

BATTLE HYMN 15 15 15 6 and refrain

American Camp Meeting tune

1 Mine eyes have seen the glo-ry of the com-ing of the Lord;
he is tramp-ling out the vin-tage where the grapes of wrath are stored;
he hath loosed the fate-ful light-ning of his ter-ri-ble swift sword:
his truth is march-ing on.

Refrain

Glo-ry, glo-ry, hal-le-lu-jah! Glo-ry, glo-ry, hal-le-lu-jah!
Glo-ry, glo-ry, hal-le-lu-jah! His truth is march-ing on!

2 He hath sounded forth the trumpet that shall never call retreat;
   he is sifting out the hearts of men before his judgement seat.
   O be swift, my soul, to answer him; be jubilant, my feet!
   Our God is marching on!

3 In the beauty of the lilies Christ was born across the sea,
   with a glory in his bosom that transfigures you and me;
   as he died to make men holy, let us live to make men free,
   while God is marching on!

4 He is coming like the glory of the morning on the wave;
   he is wisdom to the mighty, he is succour to the brave;
   so the world shall be his footstool, and the soul of time his slave:
   our God is marching on!

Julia Ward Howe 1819-1910

157

AND DID THOSE FEET IN ANCIENT TIME

JERUSALEM 8 8 8 8 D

Charles Hubert Hastings Parry 1848-1918
arranged by Gordon P S Jacob 1895-

Unison
1 And did those feet in an - cient time walk up-on

ar - rows of de — sire: bring me my spear: O clouds un -
fold! bring me my cha - ri - ot of fire. 4 I will not
cease from men - tal fight nor shall my sword sleep in my
hand, till we have built Je - ru - sa - lem in Eng-land's
green and pleas-ant land.

William Blake 1757-1827

158

GOD WHO STRETCHED THE SPANGLED HEAVENS

CARN BREA 8 7 8 7 D   Derek Holman 1931–

1 God, who stretched the span-gled hea-vens, in-fin-ite in time and place, flung the suns in burn-ing ra-diance through the si - lent fields of space, we thy child-ren, in thy like-ness, share in-ven-tive powers with thee: great Cre-a - tor, still cre-a - ting, teach us what we yet may be.

2 Proudly rise our modern cities,
  stately buildings, row on row;
  yet their windows, blank, unfeeling,
  stare on canyoned streets below,
  where the lonely drift unnoticed
  in the city's ebb and flow,
  lost to purpose and to meaning,
  scarcely caring where they go.

3 We have conquered worlds undreamed of
  since the childhood of our race,
  known the ecstasy of winging
  through unchartered realms of space,
  probed the secrets of the atom,
  yielding unimagined power,
  facing us with life's destruction
  or our most triumphant hour.

4   As thy new horizons beckon,
    Father, give us strength to be
    children of creative purpose,
    thinking thy thoughts after thee,
    till our dreams are rich with meaning,
    each endeavour, thy design:
    great Creator, lead us onward
    till our work is one with thine.

Catherine Bonnell Arnott 1927-

159

GOD MOVES IN A MYSTERIOUS WAY
LONDON NEW 8686

Scottish Psalter 1635

1 God moves in a mys-ter-ious way his won-ders to per-form;
he plants his foot-steps in the sea and rides up-on the storm.

2 Deep in unfathomable mines
  of never-failing skill
  he treasures up his bright designs
  and works his sovereign will.

3 Ye fearful saints, fresh courage take;
  the clouds ye so much dread
  are big with mercy, and shall break
  in blessings on your head.

4 Judge not the Lord by feeble sense,
  but trust him for his grace;
  behind a frowning providence
  he hides a smiling face.

5 His purposes will ripen fast,
  unfolding every hour;
  the bud may have a bitter taste,
  but sweet will be the flower.

6 Blind unbelief is sure to err,
  and scan his work in vain;
  God is his own interpreter,
  and he will make it plain.

William Cowper 1731-1800
for a higher setting see 87

160

O HOLY CITY, SEEN OF JOHN

SANCTA CIVITAS 868686 FIRST TUNE

Herbert Howells 1892-

1 O ho - ly ci - ty, seen of John, where Christ, the Lamb, doth reign,
2 Hark, how from men whose lives are held more cheap than mer - chan-dise,

with - in whose four-square walls shall come no night, nor need, nor pain,
from wo - men strug-gling sore for bread, from lit - tle child-ren's cries,

and where the tears are wiped from eyes that shall not weep a - gain!
there swells the sob-bing hu - man plaint that bids thy walls a - rise.

3 O shame on us who rest content
   while lust and greed for gain
   in street and shop and tenement
   wring gold from human pain,
   and bitter lips in blind despair
   cry, 'Christ hath died in vain!'

4 Give us, O God, the strength to build
   the city that hath stood
   too long a dream, whose laws are love,
   whose ways are brotherhood,
   and where the sun that shineth is
   God's grace for human good.

Descant

5 Al - rea - dy that ci - ty ri - seth fair.

5 Al - rea - dy in the mind of God that ci - ty ri - seth fair.

Its splen-dour chal - len-ges the souls that dare,

Lo, how its splen-dour chal - len - ges the souls that great-ly dare,

yea, bids us seize the whole of life and build its glo-ry there!

yea, bids us seize the whole of life and build its glo - ry there!

Walter Russell Bowie 1882–
based on Revelation 21, 22

O HOLY CITY, SEEN OF JOHN

'The Union Harmony,' Virginia 1848

MORNING SONG 868686 SECOND TUNE harmonized by Winfred Douglas 1867-1944

1 O ho-ly ci-ty, seen of John, where Christ, the Lamb, doth reign, with-in whose four-square walls shall come no night, nor need, nor pain, and where the tears are wiped from eyes that shall not weep a-gain!

2 Hark, how from men whose lives are held
more cheap than merchandise,
from women struggling sore for bread,
from little children's cries,
there swells the sobbing human plaint
that bids thy walls arise.

3 O shame on us who rest content
while lust and greed for gain
in street and shop and tenement
wring gold from human pain,
and bitter lips in blind despair
cry, 'Christ hath died in vain!'

4 Give us, O God, the strength to build
the city that hath stood
too long a dream, whose laws are love,
whose ways are brotherhood,
and where the sun that shineth is
God's grace for human good.

5 Already in the mind of God
that city riseth fair.
Lo, how its splendour challenges
the souls that greatly dare,
yea, bids us seize the whole of life
and build its glory there!

Walter Russell Bowie 1882-
based on Revelation 21, 22

161

CREATION'S LORD, WE GIVE YOU THANKS

WAREHAM 8 8 8 8   William Knapp 1698-1768

1 Cre - a - tion's Lord, we give you thanks

that this your world is in - com - plete;

that bat - tle calls our mar - shalled ranks,

that work a - waits our hands and feet;

2 that you have not yet finished man:
that we are in the making still,
as friends who share the Maker's plan,
as sons who know the Father's will.

3 Beyond the present sin and shame,
wrong's bitter, cruel, scorching blight,
we see the beckoning vision flame,
the blessed kingdom of the right.

4 What though the kingdom long delay,
and still with haughty foes must cope?
It gives us that for which to pray,
a field for toil and faith and hope.

5 Since what we choose is what we are,
and what we love we yet shall be,
the goal may ever shine afar,—
the will to win it makes us free.

William deWitt Hyde 1858-1917
This may be sung to Samson 91
for a lower setting of Wareham
see 233

162

BEHOLD! THE MOUNTAIN OF THE LORD

BISHOPTHORPE 8 6 8 6

Jeremiah Clark 1670-1707

1 Be - hold! the moun - tain of the Lord in lat - ter days shall rise on moun - tain tops a - bove the hills, and draw the won - dering eyes.

2 The beam that shines from Zion hill
shall lighten every land;
the King who reigns in Salem's towers
shall all the world command.

3 Among the nations he shall judge;
his judgements truth shall guide;
his sceptre shall protect the just,
and quell the sinner's pride.

4 No strife shall rage, nor hostile feuds
disturb those peaceful years;
to ploughshares men shall beat their swords,
to pruning-hooks their spears.

5 No longer hosts encountering hosts
shall crowds of slain deplore:
they hang the trumpet in the hall,
and study war no more.

6 Come then, O come from every land
to worship at his shrine;
and, walking in the light of God,
with holy beauties shine.

Scottish Paraphrases 1781
based on Isaiah 2:2-6
for a higher setting see 196

163

GOD'S NAME FOR EVER SHALL ENDURE

WIGTON 8686

Scottish Psalter 1635

1 God's name for ev - er shall en - dure; last like the sun it shall;
men shall be blest in him, and blest all na - tions shall him call.

2 The just shall flourish in his days,
   and prosper in his reign;
   and while the moon endures he shall
   abundant peace maintain.

3 His large and great dominion shall
   from sea to sea extend;
   it from the river shall reach forth
   to earth's remotest end.

4 For he the needy will set free,
   when they on him shall call;
   he'll save the poor and those for whom
   there is no help at all.

5 Now blessed be the Lord our God,
   the God of Israel,
   for he alone doth wondrous works,
   in glory that excel.

Scottish Psalter 1650
based on Psalm 72
This may be sung to Dunfermline 430

164

JESUS SHALL REIGN

DUKE STREET 8 8 8 8

John Hatton   ? -1793

1 Je - sus shall reign wher - e'er the sun

doth his suc - ces - sive jour - neys run;

his king - dom stretch from shore to shore,

till moons shall wax and wane no more.

2 People and realms of every tongue
dwell on his love with sweetest song,
and infant voices shall proclaim
their early blessings on his name.

3 Blessings abound where'er he reigns;
the prisoner leaps to lose his chains;
the weary find eternal rest,
and all the sons of want are blest.

4 Let every creature rise and bring
peculiar honours to our King,
angels descend with songs again,
and earth repeat the loud Amen.

Isaac Watts 1674-1748
based on Psalm 72

165

THOU SHALT ARISE
TRURO 8 8 8 8

Psalmodia Evangelica 1789

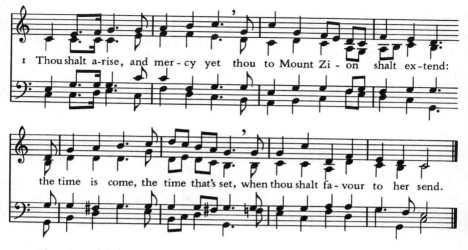

1 Thou shalt a-rise, and mer-cy yet thou to Mount Zi-on shalt ex-tend:
the time is come, the time that's set, when thou shalt fa-vour to her send.

2 Thy saints take pleasure in her stones;
her very dust to them is dear.
All distant lands and kingly thrones
on earth thy glorious name shall fear.

3 God in his glory shall appear,
when Zion he builds and repairs;
he shall regard and lend his ear
unto the needy's humble prayers.

4 The needy's prayer he will not scorn.
All times shall this be on record:
and generations yet unborn
shall praise and magnify the Lord.

5 He from his holy place looked down,
the earth he viewed from heaven on high,
to hear the prisoner's mourning groan,
and free them that are doomed to die;

6 that Zion and Jerusalem too
his name and praise may well record,
when people and the kingdoms do
assemble all to praise the Lord.

Scottish Psalter 1650
based on Psalm 102
This may be sung to Duke Street 164

166

JESUS CALLS US

ST OSWALD 8 7 8 7

John Bacchus Dykes 1823–1876

1 Je - sus calls us; o'er the tu-mult of our life's wild rest - less sea,
day by day his sweet voice sound-eth, say-ing,'Christ-ian, fol-low me',

2 as of old Saint Andrew heard it
by the Galilean lake,
turned from home and toil and kindred,
leaving all for his dear sake.

3 Jesus calls us from the worship
of the vain world's golden store,
from each idol that would keep us,
saying, 'Christian, love me more'.

4 In our joys and in our sorrows,
days of toil and hours of ease,
still he calls, in cares and pleasures,
'Christian, love me more than these'.

5 Jesus calls us: by thy mercies,
Saviour, may we hear thy call,
give our hearts to thine obedience,
serve and love thee best of all.

Cecil Frances Alexander 1823–1895
based on Matthew 4:18, 19

167

ONCE TO EVERY MAN AND NATION

EBENEZER 8 7 8 7 D

Thomas John Williams 1869–1944

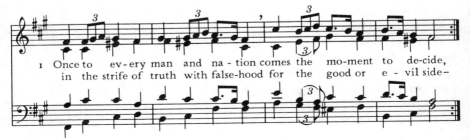

1 Once to ev - ery man and na - tion comes the mo-ment to de-cide,
in the strife of truth with false-hood for the good or e - vil side-

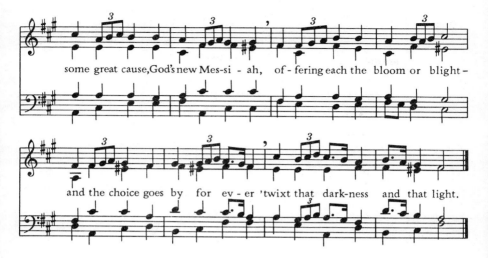

some great cause, God's new Mes-si - ah, of - fering each the bloom or blight—

and the choice goes by for ev - er 'twixt that dark-ness and that light.

2 Then to side with truth is noble,
   when we share her wretched crust,
   ere her cause bring fame and profit
   and 'tis prosperous to be just.
   Then it is the brave man chooses,
   while the coward stands aside
   till the multitude make virtue
   of the faith they had denied.

3 By the light of burning martyrs,
   Christ, thy bleeding feet we track,
   toiling up new Calvaries ever
   with the cross that turns not back.
   New occasions teach new duties,
   time makes ancient good uncouth:
   they must upward still and onward,
   who would keep abreast of truth.

4 Though the cause of evil prosper,
   yet 'tis truth alone is strong,
   though her portion be the scaffold
   and upon the throne be wrong.
   Yet that scaffold sways the future,
   and, behind the dim unknown,
   standeth God within the shadow,
   keeping watch above his own.

adapted from James Russell Lowell 1819-1891
for a lower setting see 484

168

ALL WHO LOVE AND SERVE YOUR CITY

DOMINION-CHALMERS 8 7 8 7   William France 1912–

1 All who love and serve your ci-ty, all who bear its dai-ly stress,
all who cry for peace and jus-tice, all who curse and all who bless:

2 in your day of loss and sorrow,
    in your day of helpless strife,
    honour, peace and love retreating,
    seek the Lord, who is your life.

3 In your day of wealth and plenty,
    wasted work and wasted play,
    call to mind the word of Jesus,
    'I must work while it is day'.

4 For all days are days of judgement,
    and the Lord is waiting still,
    drawing near to men who spurn him,
    offering peace and Calvary's hill.

5 Risen Lord! shall yet the city
    be the city of despair?
    Come today, our Judge, our Glory;
    be its name, 'The Lord is there!'

Erik Routley 1917–
This may be sung to
Gott des Himmels 260

169

BEHOLD, A STRANGER AT THE DOOR!

BIRLING 8 8 8 8   melody from a 19th century English manuscript
                      harmonized by Charles Peaker 1900–

1 Be-hold, a stran-ger at the door!

He gent-ly knocks, has knocked be - fore,
has wait-ed long, is wait - ing still:
we treat no o - ther friend so ill.

2 If we will open, see, he stands
   with loving heart and laden hands;
   O matchless kindness! and he shows
   this matchless kindness to his foes.

3 Admit him, for the human breast
   ne'er entertained so kind a guest;
   no mortal tongue their joys can tell
   with whom he condescends to dwell.

4 Sovereign of souls, thou Prince of peace,
   O may thy gentle reign increase!
   Throw wide the door, each willing mind,
   and be his empire all mankind.   Joseph Grigg 1721-1768

170

FROM THE SLAVE PENS OF THE DELTA

OMNI DIE 8 7 8 7 D

German Proper melody

1 'From the slave pens of the Del-ta, from the ghet-toes on the Nile,

let my peo-ple seek their free-dom in the wil-der-ness a-while':

so God spake from out of Si-nai, so he spake and it was done,

and his peo-ple crossed the wa-ters toward the ri-sing of the sun.

2 'From the aging shrines and structures,
   from the cloister and the aisle,
   let my people seek their freedom
   in the wilderness awhile':
   so the Son of God has spoken,
   and the storm-clouds are unfurled,
   for his people must be scattered
   to be servants in the world.

3 When we murmur on the mountains
   for the old Egyptian plains,
   when we miss our ancient bondage
   and the hope, the promise, wanes,
   then the rock shall yield its water
   and the manna fall by night,
   and with visions of a future
   shall we march toward the light.

4 In the maelstrom of the nations,
   in the journeying into space,
   in the clash of generations,
   in the hungering for grace,
   in man's agony and glory,
   we are called to newer ways
   by the Lord of our tomorrows
   and the God of earth's todays.

T Herbert O'Driscoll 1928-

171

SOLDIERS OF CHRIST

FROM STRENGTH TO STRENGTH 6 6 8 6 D   FIRST TUNE   E W Naylor 1867-1934

1 Sol-diers of Christ! a - rise, and put your ar - mour on,
strong in the strength which God sup-plies through his e - ter - nal Son;
strong in the Lord of hosts, and in his migh - ty power;
who in the strength of Je - sus trusts is more than con - quer - or.

2 Stand, then, in his great might,
   with all his strength endued;
   and take, to arm you for the fight,
   the panoply of God.
   To keep your armour bright
   attend with constant care,
   still walking in your Captain's sight
   and watching unto prayer.

3 From strength to strength go on;
   wrestle, and fight, and pray;
   tread all the powers of darkness down,
   and win the well-fought day,
   that, having all things done,
   and all your conflicts passed,
   ye may o'ercome through Christ alone,
   and stand complete at last.

Charles Wesley 1707-1788
based on Ephasians 6:10-17

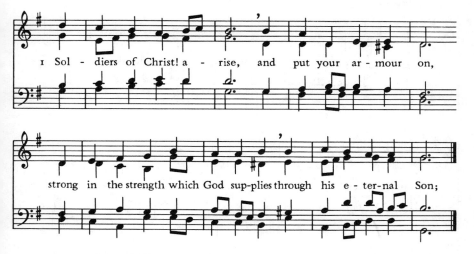

1 Sol - diers of Christ! a - rise, and put your ar - mour on, strong in the strength which God sup-plies through his e - ter-nal Son;

2 strong in the Lord of hosts,
  and in his mighty power;
  who in the strength of Jesus trusts
  is more than conqueror.

3 Stand, then, in his great might,
  with all his strength endued;
  and take, to arm you for the fight,
  the panoply of God.

4 To keep your armour bright
  attend with constant care,
  still walking in your Captain's sight
  and watching unto prayer.

5 From strength to strength go on;
  wrestle, and fight, and pray;
  tread all the powers of darkness down,
  and win the well-fought day,

6 that, having all things done,
  and all your conflicts passed,
  ye may o'ercome through Christ alone,
  and stand complete at last.

Charles Wesley 1707-1788
based on Ephasians 6:10-17

172

RISE UP, O MEN OF GOD

ST MICHAEL 6 6 8 6

adapted from the Genevan Psalter 1551
by William Crotch 1775-1847

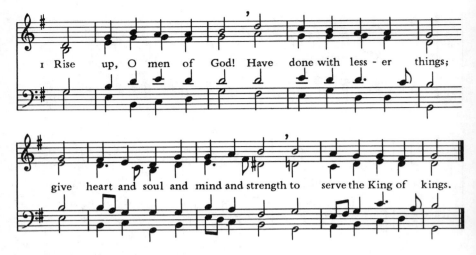

1 Rise up, O men of God! Have done with less-er things;
give heart and soul and mind and strength to serve the King of kings.

2 Rise up, O men of God!
His kingdom tarries long;
bring in the day of brotherhood
and end the night of wrong.

3 Rise up, O men of God!
The church for you doth wait,
her strength unequal to her task;
rise up and make her great.

4 Lift high the cross of Christ!
Tread where his feet have trod;
as brothers of the Son of Man
rise up, O men of God!

William Pierson Merrill 1867-1954

173

LEAD ON, O KING ETERNAL

LANCASHIRE 7 6 7 6 D

Henry Thomas Smart 1813-1879

1 Lead on, O King e - ter - nal: the day of march has come.

Hence - forth in fields of con - quest thy tents shall be our home.

Through days of pre - pa - ra - tion thy grace has made us strong,

and now, O King e - ter - nal, we lift our bat - tle - song.

2 Lead on, O King eternal,
  till sin's fierce war shall cease,
  and holiness shall whisper
  the sweet Amen of peace;
  for not with swords loud clashing,
  nor roll of stirring drums,
  but deeds of love and mercy,
  the heavenly kingdom comes.

3 Lead on, O King eternal!
  We follow, not with fears;
  for gladness breaks like morning
  where'er thy face appears.
  Thy cross is lifted o'er us;
  we journey in its light;
  the crown awaits the conquest:
  lead on, O God of might.

Ernest Warburton Shurtleff 1862-1917

174

STAND UP! STAND UP FOR JESUS

MORNING LIGHT 7 6 7 6 D

George James Webb 1803-1887

1 Stand up! stand up for Je - sus, ye sol - diers of the cross!
De - bout, sain - te co - hor - te, sol - dats du Roi des rois!

Lift high his roy - al ban - ner; it must not suf - fer loss.
Te - nez d'u - ne main for - te l'é - ten - dard de la croix.

From vic - tory un - to vic - tory his ar - my he shall lead,
Au sen - tier de la gloi - re Jé - sus-Christ nous con - duit;

till ev - ery foe is van - quished, and Christ is Lord in - deed.
de vic - toire en vic - toi - re il mè - ne qui le suit.

2   Stand up! stand up for Jesus!
    The trumpet-call obey:
    forth to the mighty conflict
    in this his glorious day!
    Ye that are men, now serve him
    against unnumbered foes;
    your courage rise with danger,
    and strength to strength oppose.

3   Stand up! stand up for Jesus!
    Stand in his strength alone;
    the arm of flesh will fail you;
    ye dare not trust your own.
    Put on the gospel armour,
    each piece put on with prayer;
    where duty calls, or danger,
    be never wanting there.

4   Stand up! stand up for Jesus!
    The strife will not be long;
    this day the noise of battle,
    the next the victor's song:
    to him that overcometh
    a crown of life shall be;
    he with the King of glory
    shall reign eternally.

George Duffield 1818-1888

2   La trompette résonne:
    debout, vaillants soldats!
    L'immortelle couronne
    est le prix des combats.
    Si l'ennemi fait rage,
    soyez fermes et forts;
    redoublez de courage
    s'il redouble d'efforts.

3   Debout pour la bataille,
    point de trêve aux vaincus!
    Si votre bras défaille
    regardez à Jésus!
    De l'armure invincible
    soldats, revêtez-vous;
    le triomphe est possible
    pour qui lutte à genoux.

4   Debout, debout encore!
    Luttez, jusqu'au matin;
    déjà brille l'aurore,
    à l'horizon lointain.
    Bientôt jetant nos armes
    aux pieds du Roi des rois,
    les chants après les larmes,
    le trône après la croix.

traducteur inconnu

175

FIGHT THE GOOD FIGHT

GRACE CHURCH, GANANOQUE 8 8 8 8   FIRST TUNE   Graham George 1912-

1 Fight the good fight with all thy might, Christ is thy strength and Christ thy right;
lay hold on life and it shall be thy joy and crown e-ter-nal-ly.

2 Run the straight race through God's good grace;
   lift up thine eyes, and seek his face.
   Life with its path before us lies;
   Christ is the way, and Christ the prize.

3 Cast care aside, lean on thy guide;
   his boundless mercy will provide;
   trust, and the trusting soul shall prove
   Christ is its life, and Christ its love.

4 Faint not, nor fear, his arms are near;
   he changeth not and thou art dear.
   Only believe, and thou shalt see   John Samuel Bewley Monsell 1811-1875
   that Christ is all in all to thee.   based on 1 Timothy 6:12

William Boyd 1847-1928
harmonized by Frederick R C Clarke 1931-

1 Fight the good fight with all thy might,
Christ is thy strength and Christ thy right;
lay hold on life, and it shall be
thy joy and crown e - ter - nal - ly.

2 Run the straight race through God's good grace;
lift up thine eyes, and seek his face.
Life with its path before us lies;
Christ is the way, and Christ the prize.

3 Cast care aside, lean on thy guide;
his boundless mercy will provide;
trust, and the trusting soul shall prove
Christ is its life, and Christ its love.

4 Faint not, nor fear, his arms are near;
he changeth not and thou art dear.
Only believe, and thou shalt see
that Christ is all in all to thee.

John Samuel Bewley Monsell 1811-1875
based on 1 Timothy 6:12

176

TAKE UP YOUR CROSS

BRESLAU 8 8 8 8

from 'As Hymnodus sacer', Leipzig, 1625

1 Take up your cross, the Sav-iour said, if you would my dis - ci - ple be;
de - ny your-self, the world for-sake, and hum-bly fol-low af - ter me.

2 Take up your cross; let not its weight
   fill your weak soul with vain alarm;
   his strength shall bear your spirit up,
   and brace your heart, and nerve your arm.

3 Take up your cross, nor heed the shame,
   and let your foolish pride be still;
   your Lord for you endured to die
   upon a cross, on Calvary's hill.

4 Take up your cross, then, in his strength,
   and calmly every danger brave:
   'twill guide you to a better home
   and lead to victory o'er the grave.

5 Take up your cross, and follow Christ,
   nor think till death to lay it down;
   for only he who bears the cross
   may hope to wear the glorious crown.

Charles William Everest 1814-1877

177

SING WE A SONG OF HIGH REVOLT

EIN NEUES GLAUBENLIED 8 8 8 8   from 'Evangelisches Kirchengesangbuch', Sachsens
harmonized by Stanley L Osborne 1907-

1 Sing we a song of high re-volt; make great the Lord, his name ex-alt!

Sing we the song that Ma-ry sang, of God at war with hu-man wrong.

2 Sing we of him who deeply cares
and still with us our burden bears;
he, who with strength the proud disowns,
brings down the mighty from their thrones.

3 By him the poor are lifted up;
he satisfies with bread and cup
the hungry men of many lands;
the rich must go with empty hands.

4 He calls us to revolt and fight
with him for what is just and right,
to sing and live Magnificat
in crowded street and walkup flat.

Frederik Herman Kaan 1929-
based on Luke 1 :47-55

178
ONWARD! CHRISTIAN SOLDIERS

ST GERTRUDE 6 5 6 5 D and refrain

Arthur Seymour Sullivan 1842-1900

1 On-ward! Christ-ian sol - diers, march-ing as to war,

with the cross of Je - sus go - ing on be - fore.

Christ the roy - al Mas - ter leads a - gainst the foe;

for - ward in - to bat - tle see his ban-ners go.

Refrain

On-ward! Christ-ian sol - diers, march-ing as to war, with the

with the cross of Je - sus go - ing on be - fore.
cross of Je - sus

2   At the sign of triumph
    Satan's legions flee;
    on then, Christian soldiers,
    on to victory!
    Hell's foundations quiver
    at the shout of praise;
    brothers, lift your voices,
    loud your anthems raise.

3   Like a mighty army
    moves the church of God;
    brothers, we are treading
    where the saints have trod.
    We are not divided,
    all one body we,
    one in hope and doctrine,
    one in charity.

4   Crowns and thrones may perish,
    kingdoms rise and wane,
    but the church of Jesus
    constant will remain,
    Gates of hell can never
    'gainst that church prevail:
    we have Christ's own promise,
    and that cannot fail.

5   Onward, then, ye people!
    Join our happy throng;
    blend with ours your voices
    in the triumph song:
    'glory, laud, and honour
    unto Christ the King!'
    this through countless ages
    men and angels sing.

Sabine Baring-Gould 1834-1924

AND THE FOLLOWING

179

JESUS LIVES

CHRIST IST ERSTANDEN 7 8 7 8 4   FIRST TUNE   from a 12th century German melody

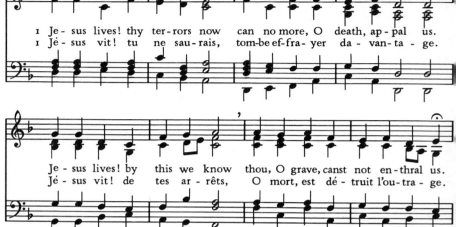

1 Je - sus lives! thy ter - rors now can no more, O death, ap - pal us.
1 Jé - sus vit! tu ne sau - rais, tom-be ef-fra- yer da - van - ta - ge.

Je - sus lives! by this we know thou, O grave, canst not en - thral us.
Jé - sus vit! de tes ar - rêts, O mort, est dé - truit l'ou - tra - ge.

Al - le - lu - ia!
Al - lé - lu - ia!

2 Jesus lives! henceforth is death
but the gate of life immortal;
this shall calm our trembling breath
when we pass its gloomy portal.
Alleluia!

2 Jésus vit! et désormais
la mort du ciel est l'entrée;
au lieu du trouble, la paix
remplit mon âme assurée.
Alléluia!

3 Jesus lives! for us he died;
then, alone to Jesus living,
pure in heart may we abide,
glory to our Saviour giving.
Alleluia!

3 Jésus vit! sur une croix
pour nous il donna sa vie;
vivre avec lui, c'est mon choix,
mon doux espoir, mon envie.
Alléluia!

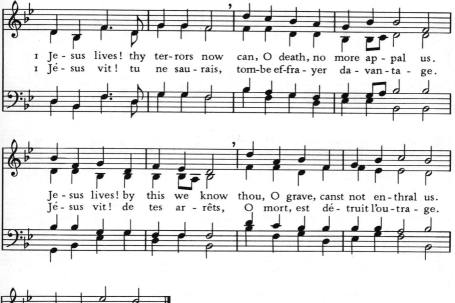

1 Je - sus lives! thy ter-rors now can, O death, no more ap - pal us.
1 Jé - sus vit! tu ne sau - rais, tom-be ef-fra - yer da - van-ta - ge.

Je - sus lives! by this we know thou, O grave, canst not en-thral us.
Jé - sus vit! de tes ar - rêts, O mort, est dé - truit l'ou-tra - ge.

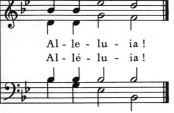

Al - le - lu - ia !
Al - lé - lu - ia !

4 Jesus lives! our hearts know well
   nought from us his love shall sever;
   life, nor death, nor powers of hell
   tear us from his keeping ever.
   Alleluia!

4 Jésus vit! tu ne pourras
   nous ravir à sa tendresse;
   fuis, Satan; car dans ses bras
   c'est son amour qui nous presse.
   Alléluia!

Christian Fürchtegott Gellert 1715-1769   traducteur inconnu
tr. Frances Elizabeth Cox 1812-1897

180

ABIDE WITH ME

EVENTIDE 10 10 10 10

William Henry Monk 1823-1889

1 A - bide with me; fast falls the ev - en - tide;
the dark-ness deep - ens; Lord, with me a - bide;
when o - ther help - ers fail, and com - forts flee,
help of the help - less, O a - bide with me.

2 Swift to its close ebbs out life's little day;
earth's joys grow dim, its glories pass away;
change and decay in all around I see;
O thou who changest not, abide with me.

3 I need thy presence every passing hour;
what but thy grace can foil the tempter's power?
who like thyself my guide and stay can be?
Through cloud and sunshine, Lord, abide with me.

4 I fear no foe with thee at hand to bless;
ills have no weight, and tears no bitterness.
Where is death's sting? Where, grave, thy victory?
I triumph still, if thou abide with me.

5   Hold thou thy cross before my closing eyes;
     shine through the gloom, and point me to the skies;
     heaven's morning breaks, and earth's vain shadows flee:
     in life, in death, O Lord, abide with me.

Henry Francis Lyte 1793-1847

181

MY SOUL, THERE IS A COUNTRY   Melchior Vulpius c1560-1616

CHRISTUS, DER IST MEIN LEBEN 7 6 7 6   arranged by Johann Sebastian Bach 1685-1750

1 My soul, there is a coun - try far be-yond the stars,

where stands a wing-ed sen - try all skil-ful in the wars:

2 there, above noise and danger,
   sweet Peace sits crowned with smiles,
   and One born in a manger
   commands the beauteous files.

3 He is thy gracious friend,
   and – O my soul awake! –
   did in pure love descend,
   to die here for thy sake.

4 If thou canst get but thither,
   there grows the flower of peace,
   the rose that cannot wither,
   thy fortress and thy ease.

5 Leave then thy foolish ranges,
   for none can thee secure
   but One, who never changes,
   thy God, thy life, thy cure.

Henry Vaughan 1622-1695

182

BLEST BE THE EVERLASTING GOD

ABRIDGE 8 6 8 6

Isaac Smith c1730–c1800

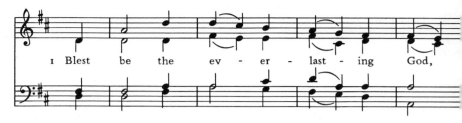

1 Blest be the ev - er - last - ing God,

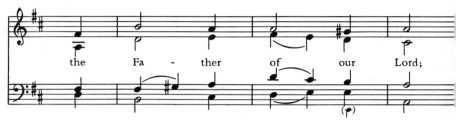

the Fa - ther of our Lord;

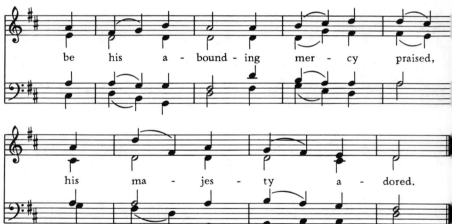

be his a - bound - ing mer - cy praised,

his ma - jes - ty a - dored.

2 When from the dead he raised his Son
to dwell with him on high,
he gave our souls a lively hope
that they should never die.

3 To an inheritance divine
he taught our hearts to rise:
'tis uncorrupted, undefiled,
unfading in the skies.

4 Saints by the power of God are kept
till the salvation come;
we walk by faith as strangers here,
but Christ shall call us home.

Isaac Watts 1674–1748
based on 1 Peter 1:3 5

183

O LORD OF LIFE

VULPIUS 8 8 8 and alleluias

Melchior Vulpius c1560–1616
harmonized by Ernest Campbell MacMillan 1893–

1 O Lord of life, wher-e'er they be,
safe in thine own e-ter-ni-ty,
our dead are liv-ing un-to thee.
Al-le-lu-ia, al-le-lu-ia, al-le-lu-ia!

2 All souls are thine, and here or there
they rest within thy sheltering care;
one providence alike they share.
Alleluia!

3 Thy word is true, thy ways are just;
above the requiem, 'Dust to dust',
shall rise our psalm of grateful trust:
alleluia!

4 O happy they in God who rest,
no more by fear and doubt oppressed;
living or dying, they are blest.
Alleluia!

Frederick Lucian Hosmer 1840–1929

184
JERUSALEM THE GOLDEN
EWING 7676D

Alexander C Ewing 1830-1895

1 Jerusalem the golden, with milk and honey blest,
beneath thy contemplation sink heart and voice oppressed.
I know not, O I know not what joys await us there,
what radiancy of glory, what bliss beyond compare.

2 They stand, those halls of Sion,
conjublilant with song,
and bright with many an angel
and all the martyr throng;
the Prince is ever in them,
the daylight is serene,
the pastures of the blessed
are decked in glorious sheen.

3 There is the throne of David,
and there, from care released,
the shout of them that triumph,
the song of them that feast;
and they who with their Leader
have conquered in the fight,
for ever and for ever
are clad in robes of white.

4 O sweet and blessed country,
   the home of God's elect;
   O dear and future vision,
   that eager hearts expect:
   even now by faith we see thee,
   even here thy walls discern;
   to thee our thoughts are kindled,   Bernard of Cluny 12th century
   for thee our spirits yearn.   tr. John Mason Neale 1818-1866

185

LET SAINTS ON EARTH IN CONCERT SING
SALISBURY 8 6 8 6   Ravenscroft's Psalter 1621

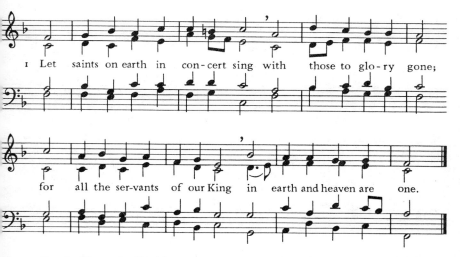

1 Let saints on earth in con-cert sing with those to glo-ry gone;

for all the ser-vants of our King in earth and heaven are one.

2 One family we dwell in him,   4 Even now by faith we join our hands
   one church, above, beneath,   with those that went before,
   though now divided by the stream,   and greet our captain's ransomed bands
   the narrow stream of death.   on the eternal shore.

3 One army of the living God,
   to his command we bow;
   part of his host have crossed the flood,
   and part are crossing now.   Charles Wesley 1707-1788
                                           This may be sung to Dundee 128

186

O WHAT THEIR JOY AND THEIR GLORY MUST BE

O QUANTA QUALIA 10 10 10 10

from the 'Paris Antiphoner' 16?

1 O what their joy and their glory must be,

those end-less sab-baths the bless-ed ones see:

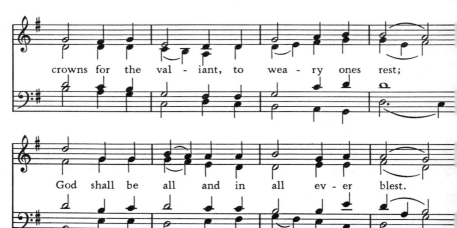

crowns for the val - iant, to wea - ry ones rest;

God shall be all and in all ev - er blest.

2 What are the Monarch, his court, and his throne?
   What are the peace and the joy that they own?
   O that the blest ones, who in it have share,
   all that they feel could as fully declare!

3 Truly Jerusalem name we that shore,
   vision of peace, that brings joy evermore;
   wish and fulfilment can severed be ne'er,
   nor the thing prayed for come short of the prayer.

4 There, where no troubles distraction can bring,
   we the sweet anthems of Sion shall sing,
   while for thy grace, Lord, their voices of praise
   thy blessed people eternally raise.

5 Now in the meantime, with hearts raised on high,
 we for that country must yearn and must sigh,
 seeking Jerusalem, dear native land,
 through our long exile on Babylon's strand.

6 Low before him with our praises we fall,
 of whom, and in whom, and through whom are all:
 praise to the Father, and praise to the Son,
 praise to the Spirit, with them ever one.

Pierre Abelard 1079-1142
tr. John Mason Neale 1818-1866

AND THE FOLLOWING

187

FAITH OF OUR FATHERS

RYBURN 888888 FIRST TUNE

Norman Cocker 1889-

1 Faith of our fa - thers! liv - ing still   in spite of dun-geon, fire, and sword;

O how our hearts beat high with joy   when-e'er we hear that glo - rious word!

Faith of our fa - thers, ho - ly faith, we will be true to thee till death.

2 Faith of our fathers! God's great power
shall soon all nations win for thee;
and through the truth that comes from God
mankind shall then be truly free.
Faith of our fathers, holy faith,
we will be true to thee till death.

3 Faith of our fathers! we will love
both friend and foe in all our strife,
and preach thee too, as love knows how,
by kindly words and virtuous life.
Faith of our fathers, holy faith,
we will be true to thee till death.

Frederick William Faber 1814-1863

1 Faith of our fa-thers! liv-ing still in spite of dun-geon, fire, and sword;

O how our hearts beat high with joy when-e'er we hear that glo-rious word!

Faith of our fa-thers, ho-ly faith, we will be true to thee till death.

2 Faith of our fathers! God's great power
    shall soon all nations win for thee;
    and through the truth that comes from God
    mankind shall then be truly free.
    Faith of our fathers, holy faith,
    we will be true to thee till death.

3 Faith of our fathers! we will love
    both friend and foe in all our strife,
    and preach thee too, as love knows how,
    by kindly words and virtuous life.
    Faith of our fathers, holy faith,
    we will be true to thee till death.

Frederick William Faber 1814-1863

188

I'M NOT ASHAMED TO OWN MY LORD

ST ANDREW 8 6 8 6

Tans'ur's 'New Harmony of Zion' 1764
harmonized by Stanley L Osborne 1907-

2 Jesus, my Lord! I know his name:
his name is all my boast;
nor will he put my soul to shame,
nor let my hope be lost.

3 I know that safe with him remains,
protected by his power,
what I've committed to his trust
till the decisive hour.

4 Then will he own his servant's name
before his Father's face,
and in the new Jerusalem
appoint my soul a place.

Isaac Watts 1674-1748
based on 2 Timothy 1:12
This may be sung to Arlington 255

189

O CHRIST, IN THEE MY SOUL HATH FOUND

NONE BUT CHRIST 8 6 8 6 and refrain   melody by James McGranahan 1840-1907

1 O Christ, in thee my soul hath found, and found in thee alone,
the peace, the joy, I sought so long, the bliss till now unknown.
Now none but Christ can satisfy, none other name for me!
There's love, and life, and lasting joy, Lord Jesus, found in thee.

2 I sighed for rest and happiness,
  I yearned for them, not thee;
  but, while I passed my Saviour by,
  his love laid hold on me.
  Now none but Christ...

3 I tried the broken cisterns, Lord,
  but, ah, the waters failed;
  even as I stooped to drink they fled,
  and mocked me as I wailed.
  Now none but Christ...

4 The pleasures lost I sadly mourned,
  but never wept for thee,
  till grace the sightless eyes received,
  thy loveliness to see.
  Now none but Christ...

author unknown

190

LORD, IT BELONGS NOT TO MY CARE

EVAN 8 6 8 6

William Henry Havergal 1793-1870
harmonized by Stanley L Osborne 1907-

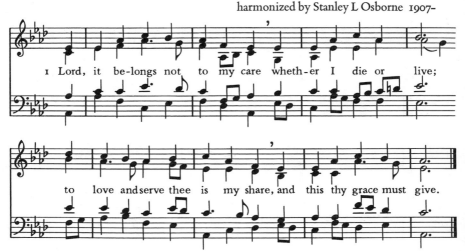

1 Lord, it be-longs not to my care wheth-er I die or live;
to love and serve thee is my share, and this thy grace must give.

2 If life be long, I will be glad,
   that I may long obey;
if short, yet why should I be sad
   to welcome endless day?

3 Christ leads me through no darker rooms
   than he went through before;
he that unto God's kingdom comes
   must enter by this door.

4 Come, Lord, when grace hath made me meet
   thy blessed face to see;
for if thy work on earth be sweet,
   what will thy glory be!

5 My knowledge of that life is small,
   the eye of faith is dim;
but it's enough that Christ knows all,
   and I shall be with him.

Richard Baxter 1615-1691

191

WILL YOUR ANCHOR HOLD

WILL YOUR ANCHOR HOLD 10 10 10 10 and refrain, irregular

melody by William James Kirkpatrick 1838-1921

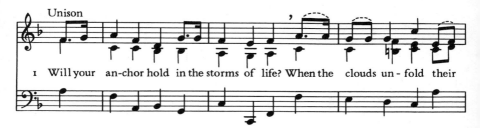

Unison

1 Will your an-chor hold in the storms of life? When the clouds un-fold their

wings of strife, when the strong tides lift and the ca-bles strain, will your an-chor drift or firm re-main? We have an an-chor that keeps the soul stead-fast and sure while the bil-lows roll, fastened to the rock which can-not move, ground-ed firm and deep in the Sa-viour's love.

2 It will surely hold in the straits of fear,
when the breakers tell that the reef is near;
though the tempest rave and the wild winds blow,
not an angry wave shall our bark o'erflow.

3 It will surely hold in the floods of death,
when the waters cold chill our latest breath;
on the rising tide it can never fail
while our hopes abide within the veil.

4 When our eyes behold, through the gathering night,
the city of gold, our harbour bright,
we shall anchor fast by the heavenly shore,
with the storms all past for evermore.

Priscilla Jane Owens 1829-1899

192

O LOVE THAT WILT NOT LET ME GO

ES IST GEWISSLICH 8 8 8 8 6

Klug's Gesangbuch

harmonized by Johann Sebastian Bach 1685-1750

1 O Love that wilt not let me go, I rest my weary soul in thee;
I give thee back the life I owe, that in thine ocean depths its flow
may rich - er, full - er be.

2 O Light that followest all my way,
I yield my flickering torch to thee;
my heart restores its borrowed ray,
that in thy sunshine-blaze its day
may brighter, fairer be.

3 O Joy that seekest me through pain,
I cannot close my heart to thee;
I trace the rainbow through the rain,
and feel the promise is not vain
that morn shall tearless be.

4 O Cross that liftest up my head,
I dare not ask to fly from thee;
I lay in dust life's glory dead,
and from the ground there blossoms red
life that shall endless be.

George Matheson 1842-1906

last line for v. 4

life that shall end - less be.

193

ALONE WITH NONE BUT THEE

SOWBY 868688

Godfrey Ridout 1918–

1 A-lone with none but thee, my God, I jour-ney on my way.

What need I fear when thou art near, O King of night and day?

More safe am I with-in thy hand than if a host should round me stand.

2 My destined time is known to thee,
and death will keep his hour;
did warriors strong around me throng,
they could not stay his power:
no walls of stone can man defend
when thou thy messenger dost send.

3 My life I yield to thy decree,
and bow to thy control
in peaceful calm, for from thine arm
no power can wrest my soul.
Could earthly omens e'er appal
a man that heeds the heavenly call?

4 The child of God can fear no ill,
his chosen dread no foe;
we leave our fate with thee, and wait
thy bidding when to go.
'Tis not from chance our comfort springs,
thou art our trust, O King of kings.

attributed to St. Columba 521-597
translator unknown

194
AUTHOR OF FAITH

CANNOCK 8 8 8 8

Walter Kendall Stanton 1891-

1 Au - thor of faith, e - ter - nal word,

whose Spir - it breathes the ac - tive flame;

faith, like its fin - ish - er and Lord,

to - day as yes - ter - day the same:

2   to thee our humble hearts aspire
     and ask the gift unspeakable –
     increase in us the kindled fire,
     in us the work of faith fulfil.

3   By faith we know thee strong to save:
     save us, a present Saviour thou!
     Whate'er we hope, by faith we have,
     future and past subsisting now.

4   To him that in thy name believes
     eternal life with thee is given;
     into himself he all receives,
     pardon, and holiness, and heaven.

5   The things unknown to feeble sense,
     unseen by reason's glimmering ray,
     with strong, commanding evidence
     their heavenly origin display.

6   Faith lends its realizing light,
     the clouds disperse, the shadows fly:
     the invisible appears in sight,
     and God is seen by mortal eye.   Charles Wesley 1707-1788

195

KING OF GLORY

JESU, MEINES HERZENS FREUD' 7 4 7 4 D 4

adapted from
Johann Rodolph Ahle 1625-1673
by Hugh J McLean 1930-

1 King of glo-ry, King of peace, I will love thee;

and that love may ne - ver cease I will move thee.

Thou hast grant-ed my re-quest, thou hast heard me;

thou didst note my work-ing breast, thou hast spared me,

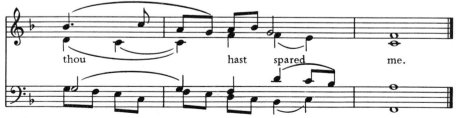

thou hast spared me.

2   Wherefore with my utmost art
      I will sing thee,
    and the cream of all my heart
      I will bring thee.
    Though my sins against me cried,
      thou didst clear me;
    and alone, when they replied,
      thou didst hear me.

3   Seven whole days, not one in seven,
      I will praise thee;
    in my heart, though not in heaven,
      I can raise thee.
    Small it is, in this poor sort
      to enrol thee;
    e'en eternity's too short
      to extol thee.

George Herbert 1593–1633
This may be sung to Gwalchmai 11

AND THE FOLLOWING

196

TO RENDER THANKS UNTO THE LORD

BISHOPTHORPE 8 6 8 6

Jeremiah Clark 1670–1707

1 To ren - der thanks un - to the Lord
it is a come - ly thing,
and to thy name, O thou most high,
due praise a - loud to sing.

2 Thy loving-kindness to show forth
when shines the morning light;
and to declare thy faithfulness
with pleasure every night,

3 on a ten-stringed instrument,
upon the psaltery,
and on the harp with solemn sound,
and grave sweet melody.

4 For thou, Lord, by thy mighty works,
hast made my heart right glad;
and I will triumph in the works
which by thine hands were made.

Scottish Psalter 1650
based on Psalm 92
for a lower setting see 162

197

NOW THANK WE ALL OUR GOD

NUN DANKET 6767 6666

Johann Crüger 1598–1662

1 Now thank we all our God, with heart, and hands, and voic - es,

who won-drous things hath done, in whom his world re - joic - es;

who from our mo-ther's arms hath blessed us on our way

with count-less gifts of love, and still is ours to - day.

2 O may this bounteous God
through all our life be near us,
with ever joyful hearts
and blessed peace to cheer us,
and keep us in his grace,
and guide us when perplexed,
and free us from all ills
in this world and the next.

3 All praise and thanks to God
the Father now be given,
the Son, and him who reigns
with them in highest heaven,
the one eternal God,
whom heaven and earth adore;
for thus it was, is now,
and shall be evermore.

Martin Rinckart 1586–1649
tr. Catherine Winkworth 1829–1878
based on Ecclesiastes 50:22–24

198

SING TO THE LORD A JOYFUL SONG

SOLEMNIS HAEC FESTIVITAS 8 8 8 8   Angers melody, 16th or 17th century

1 Sing to the Lord a joyful song,
lift up your hearts, your voices raise;
to us his gracious gifts belong,
to him our songs of love and praise.

2 For life and love, for home and food,
for daily help and nightly rest,
sing to the Lord, for he is good,
and praise his name, for it is blest.

3 For strength to those who on him wait
his truth to prove, his will to do,
praise ye our God, for he is great;
trust in his name, for it is true.

4 For joys untold, that from above
cheer those who love his high employ,
sing to our God, for he is love;
exalt his name, for it is joy.

John Samuel Bewley Monsell 1811-1875

199

FOR THE BEAUTY OF THE EARTH

ENGLAND'S LANE 7 7 7 7 7 7

from an English melody

harmonized by Geoffrey Turton Shaw 1879-1943

1 For the beau-ty of the earth, for the glo-ry of the skies, for the love which from our birth o-ver and a-round us lies, Lord of all, to thee we raise this our sac-ri-fice of praise.

2 For the beauty of each hour
of the day and of the night,
hill and vale, and tree and flower,
sun and moon and stars of light,
Lord of all, to thee we raise
this our sacrifice of praise.

3 For the joy of human love,
brother, sister, parent, child,
friends on earth, and friends above,
for all gentle thoughts and mild,
Lord of all, to thee we raise
this our sacrifice of praise.

4 For each perfect gift of thine
to our race so freely given,
graces human and divine,
flowers of earth and buds of heaven,
Lord of all, to thee we raise
this our sacrifice of praise.

Folliott Sandford Pierpoint 1835-1917

200

PRAISE TO GOD FOR THINGS WE SEE

PRAISE TO GOD 7 8 8 8 6   Kenneth George Finlay 1882–

1 Praise to God for things we see, the grow-ing flower, the wav-ing tree, our mo-ther's face, the bright blue sky where birds and clouds go float-ing by; praise to God for see - ing.

2 Praise to God for things we hear,
   for sounds of friends who laugh and cheer,
   the merry bells, the song of birds,
   for stories, tunes, and kindly words;
   praise to God for hearing.

Maria Matilda Penstone 1859–1910

201

ETERNAL FATHER, LORD OF SPACE AND TIME

SONG 24 10 10 10 10   Orlando Gibbons 1583-1625

1 Eternal Father, Lord of space and time,
the source of truth and righteousness and grace,
we thank thee that thy majesty sublime
thou dost reveal in every human face.

2 We thank thee, Lord, for love's deep fount of joy,
for inward peace that never can be told,
for comradeship no changes can destroy,
for faith and hope that all our days enfold.

3 For love uniquely makes us one with thee,
remoulding us according to thy will,
enabling us in true humanity
the purpose of thy kingdom to fulfil.

4 Fixed deeper than the sources of man's strife,
may we in love a steadfast anchor find;
do thou, unchanging through the stress of life,
to thine own love our hearts for ever bind.

Robert Dobbie 1901-

202

NOW THANK WE ALL FOR BODIES STRONG

KINGSFOLD 8 6 8 6 D
traditional melody of England and Ireland

1 Now thank we God for bo-dies strong, vi-ta-li-ty and zest, for strength to meet the day's de-mands, the urge to give our best, for all our bo-dy's ap-pe-tites which can ful-fil-ment find, and for the sac-ra-ment of sex that re-cre-ates our kind.

2   We thank him too that he has given
the gift of human minds,
and for the thrill of piecing out
the pattern that one finds –
to see in science and in art,
in lore of every kind,
that we, in searching out life's ways
do but discern his mind.

3   And most of all we thank him for
the highest gift of all:
that body, mind and all our powers
respond to Spirit's call.
Though kin to beasts and born of flesh,
in mortal bodies dressed,
yet God has linked our souls to his:
they nowhere else can rest.

Derwyn Dixon Jones 1925-
for a lower setting see 115

203

WE THANK YOU, GOD

EMERY 8 4 8 4   Gerald Wheeler 1929–

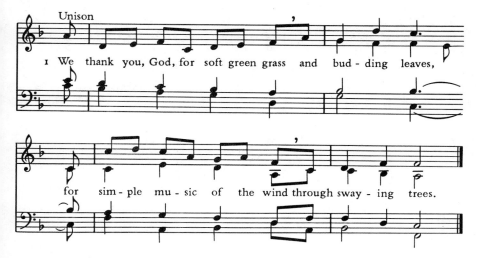

1 We thank you, God, for soft green grass and bud - ding leaves,

for sim - ple mu - sic of the wind through sway - ing trees.

2 We thank you, God, for ocean tides,
   and clear, salt air,
   for ships that sail across the waves
   with cargoes rare.

3 We thank you, God, for quiet nights,
   and stars that shine,
   for order in this universe
   of your design.

4 We thank you, God, for thoughts of men,
   and deeds of worth,
   for those whose lives and love reveal
   your will on earth.   Frances Hill West c1930–

204

WE PRAISE YOU FOR THE SUN

MOUNT 6686

Gifford Jerome Mitchell 1913–

1 We praise you for the sun, the gold - en shin - ing sun,

that gives us heal - ing, strength and joy; we praise you for the sun.

2 We praise you for the rain,
the softly falling rain,
that gives us healing, strength and joy;
we praise you for the rain.

3 We praise you for your love,
our friend and Father God,
who gives us healing, strength and joy;
we praise you for your love.

Alice Muriel Pullen c1900–

205

THANK YOU, O LORD, FOR THE TIME THAT IS NOW

TRADITION 10 10 10 10

Frederick R C Clarke 1931–

1 Thank you, O Lord, for the time that is now,

for all the new - ness your min - utes al - low:

make us a - lert with your pre - sence of mind,
keep us a - live to the claims of man - kind.

2 Thank you, O Lord, for the time that is past,
   for all the values and thoughts that will last:
   may we all stagnant tradition ignore,
   leaving behind things that matter no more.

3 Thank you for hopes of the day that will come,
   for all the change that will happen in time:
   Lord, for the future our spirits prepare,
   hallow our doubts and redeem us from fear.

4 Make us afraid of the thoughts that delay,
   faithful in all the affairs of today;
   keep us, our Father, from playing it safe;
   thank you that now is the time of our life!   Frederik Herman Kaan 1929-

The bass to this tune has been set for the organ;
the smaller, alternative notes are provided for
piano accompaniment.

206

O LORD OF HEAVEN AND EARTH

ES IST KEIN TAG 8 8 8 4   Johann Meyer's 'Geistliche Seelen-Freud' Ulm 1692

1 O Lord of heaven and earth and sea,

to thee all praise and glo - ry be;

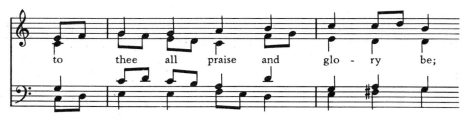

how shall we show our love to thee,

who giv - est all?

2 For peaceful homes and healthful days,
for all the blessings earth displays,
we owe thee thankfulness and praise,
who givest all.

3 Thou didst not spare thine only Son,
but gav'st him for a world undone,
and freely with that blessed One
thou givest all.

4 Thou giv'st the Spirit's blessed dower,
Spirit of life and love and power,
and dost his sevenfold graces shower
upon us all.

5 For souls redeemed, for sins forgiven,
for means of grace and hopes of heaven,
Father, what can to thee be given,
who givest all,–

6 to thee, from whom we all derive
our life, our gifts, our power to give?
O may we ever with thee live,
who givest all.

Christopher Wordsworth 1807-1885

207

WHEN ALL THY MERCIES, O MY GOD
ST STEPHEN 8 6 8 6

William Jones 1726-1800

1 When all thy mer-cies, O my God, my ris - ing soul sur - veys,

trans-port-ed with the view I'm lost in won - der, love and praise.

2   Ten thousand thousand precious gifts
my daily thanks employ;
nor is the least a cheerful heart
that tastes those gifts with joy.

3   Through every period of my life
thy goodness I'll pursue;
and after death, in distant worlds
the glorious theme renew.

4   Through all eternity to thee
a joyful song I'll raise;
but oh! eternity's too short
to utter all thy praise.

Joseph Addison 1672-1719
for another arrangement see 151

208

LORD, SAVE THY WORLD

LANSDOWNE 8 8 8 8

E Norman Greenwood 1902–1962

Unison

1 Lord, save thy world: in bit-ter need thy child-ren lift their cry to thee; we wait thy lib-er-at-ing deed to sig-nal hope and set us free.

2 Lord, save thy world: our souls are bound
in iron chains of fear and pride;
high walls of ignorance around
our faces from each other hide.

3 Lord, save thy world: we strive in vain
to save ourselves without thine aid;
what skill and science slowly gain
is soon to evil ends betrayed.

4 Lord, save thy world: but thou hast sent
the Saviour whom we sorely need;
for us his tears and blood were spent,
that from our bonds we might be freed.

5 Then save us now, by Jesus' power,
   and use the lives thy love sets free
   to bring at last the glorious hour
   when all men find thy liberty.

Albert Frederick Bayly 1901-
This may be sung to Eisenach 265

209

O GOD OF TRUTH

MARTYRS 8 6 8 6

Scottish Psalter 1615
harmonized by Frederick R C Clarke 1931-

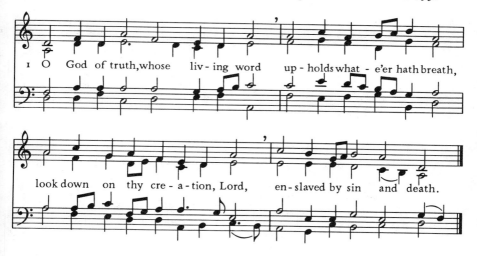

1 O God of truth, whose liv-ing word up-holds what-e'er hath breath,

look down on thy cre-a-tion, Lord, en-slaved by sin and death.

2 Set up thy standard, Lord, that we,
   who claim a heavenly birth,
   may march with thee to smite the lies
   that vex thy groaning earth.

3 We fight for truth, we fight for God, –
   poor slaves of lies and sin!
   He who would fight for thee on earth
   must first be true within.

4 Then, God of truth, for whom we long,
   thou who wilt hear our prayer,
   do thine own battle in our hearts,
   and slay the falsehood there.

5 Still smite, still burn, till naught is left
   but God's own truth and love;
   then, Lord, as morning dew come down,
   rest on us from above.

6 Yea, come! then, tried as in the fire,
   from every lie set free,
   thy perfect truth shall dwell in us,
   and we shall live in thee.

Thomas Hughes 1823-1896
This may be sung to Martyrdom 263

210

FOR THE HEALING OF THE NATIONS

WOLVESEY 878787   Edward Thomas Sweeting 1863–1930

1 For the heal-ing of the na-tions, Lord, we pray with one ac - cord;

for a just and e - qual shar-ing of the things that earth af - fords.

To a life of love in ac-tion help us rise and pledge our word.

2 Lead us, Father, into freedom,
from despair your world release;
that redeemed from war and hatred,
men may come and go in peace.
Show us how through care and goodness
fear will die and hope increase.

3 All that kills abundant living,
let it from the earth be banned:
pride of status, race or schooling,
dogmas keeping man from man.
In our common quest for justice
may we hallow life's brief span.

4 You, creator-God, have written
your great name on all mankind:
for our growing in your likeness
bring the life of Christ to mind,
that, by our response and service,
earth its destiny may find.

Frederick Herman Kaan 1929–

211

GOD OF THE FARMLANDS

TREVENSON 8 6 8 6   Derek Holman 1931–

1 God of the farm-lands, hear our prayer, Lord of the grow-ing seed, bless thou the fields, for to thy care we look in all our need.

2 God of the rivers in their course,
Lord of the swelling sea,
where man must strive with nature's force,
do thou his guardian be.

3 God of the dark and sombre mine,
Lord of its hard-won store,
in toil and peril all be thine;
thy help and strength are sure.

4 God of the city's throbbing heart,
Lord of its industry,
bid greed and base deceit depart,
give true prosperity.

5 Source of authority and right,
God of all earthly power,
to those who govern grant thy light,
thy wisdom be their dower.

6 God of the nations, King of men,
Lord of each humble soul,
we seek thy gracious aid again:
O come and make us whole.

Thomas Charles Hunter Clare 1910–

212

THY LOVE, O GOD, HAS ALL MANKIND CREATED

NORTHBROOK 11 10 11 10   Reginald Sparshatt Thatcher 1888-1957

1 Thy love, O God, has all man-kind cre - a - ted, and led thy peo - ple to this pre - sent hour; in Christ we see life's glo - ry con - sum - ma - ted; thy Spir - it man - i - fests his liv - ing power.

2 We bring thee, Lord, in fervent intercession
the children of thy world-wide family:
with contrite hearts we offer our confession,
for we have sinned against thy charity.

3 From out the darkness of our hope's frustration,
from all the broken idols of our pride,
we turn to seek thy truth's illumination,
and find thy mercy waiting at our side.

4 In pity look upon thy children's striving
for life and freedom, peace and brotherhood,
till at the fullness of thy truth arriving,
we find in Christ the crown of every good.

5 Inspire thy church, mid earth's discordant voices,
to preach the gospel of her Lord above,
until the day this warring world rejoices
to hear the mighty harmonies of love.

Albert Frederick Bayly 1901-

AND THE FOLLOWING

213

JUDGE ETERNAL, THRONED IN SPLENDOUR

LINGWOOD 8 7 8 7 8 7

Cecil Armstrong Gibbs 1889-1960

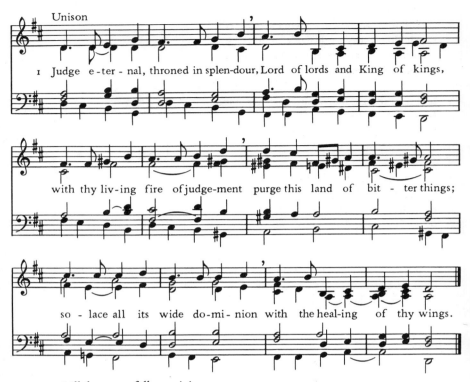

1 Judge e-ter-nal, throned in splen-dour, Lord of lords and King of kings,
with thy liv-ing fire of judge-ment purge this land of bit - ter things;
so - lace all its wide do-mi- nion with the heal-ing of thy wings.

2   Still the weary folk are pining
for the hour that brings release;
and the city's crowded clangour
cries aloud for sin to cease;
and the homestead and the woodland
plead in silence for their peace.

3   Crown, O God, thine own endeavour;
cleave our darkness with thy sword;
feed the faint and hungry peoples
with the richness of thy word;
cleanse the body of this nation
through the glory of the Lord.

Henry Scott Holland 1847-1918
This may be sung to
Alleluia, dulce carmen 308
or Picardy 332

214
O GOD OF EARTH AND ALTAR
GILLING 7 6 7 6 D

Godfrey Ridout 1918–

1 O God of earth and al - tar, bow down and hear our cry.
Our earth-ly ru - lers fal - ter; our peo-ple drift and die.
The walls of gold en - tomb us; the swords of scorn di - vide:
take not thy thun-der from us, but take a - way our pride.

2 From all that terror teaches,
from lies of tongue and pen,
from all the easy speeches
that comfort cruel men,
from sale and profanation
of honour and the sword,
from sleep and from damnation:
deliver us, good Lord.

3 Tie in a living tether
the prince and priest and thrall;
bind all our lives together;
smite us and save us all;
in ire and exultation
aflame with faith, and free,
lift up a living nation,
a single sword to thee.

Gilbert Keith Chesterton 1874–1936
This may be sung to Munich 385

215

O GOD OF ALL THE MANY LANDS

VALIANT 8 6 8 6 D

Keith Warren Bissell 1912–

1 O God of all the ma-ny lands, we lift our hearts to thee,

for this fair land our Ca-na-da, a coun-try wide and free;

for moun-tain heights and nor-thern lights, for prai-rie, lake and sea,

for lav-ish-ness in all the gifts that find their source in thee.

2   We thank thee for the sacrifice
of daring men of old,
for faith to cross uncharted seas,
for dreams to make men bold;
for valiant souls and pioneers,
for all who served their age,
and left for us who follow on
a sacred heritage.

3   We thank thee that from many a land
with varied gifts they came,
to pledge their love and loyalty
where scarlet maples flame.
May justice here belong to all,
and may our nation play
her rightful role in ushering in
the peace for which we pray.

4   May we be worthy of our land
and seek her highest good,
shaping a noble destiny
of truest brotherhood.
May this fair land, our Canada,
thy own dominion be;
thy people bless abundantly
from seas to Arctic sea.

Mary Susanne Edgar 1889–

216

FROM OCEAN UNTO OCEAN

STOKESAY CASTLE 7 6 7 6 D FIRST TUNE

Eric Harding Thiman 1900–

1 From ocean unto ocean our land shall own thee Lord, and, filled with true devotion, obey thy sovereign word. Our prairies and our mountains, forest and fertile field, our rivers, lakes, and fountains, to thee shall tribute yield.

2 O Christ, for thine own glory,
and for our country's weal,
we humbly plead before thee,
thyself in us reveal;
and may we know, Lord Jesus,
the touch of thy dear hand,
and healed of our diseases,
the tempter's power withstand.

3 Where error smites with blindness,
enslaves and leads astray,
do thou in loving-kindness
proclaim thy gospel day,
till all the tribes and races
that dwell in this fair land,
adorned with Christian graces
within thy courts shall stand.

1 From o - cean un - to o - cean our land shall own thee Lord,
and, filled with true de - vo - tion, o - bey thy sov-ereign word.
Our prai - ries and our moun - tains, for - est and fer - tile field,
our riv - ers, lakes, and foun - tains, to thee shall tri - bute yield.

4 Our Saviour King, defend us,
 and guide where we should go.
 Forth with thy message send us,
 thy love and light to show.
 till, fired with true devotion
 enkindled by thy word,
 from ocean unto ocean
 our land shall own thee Lord.

Robert Murray 1832-1909

217

O CANADA 10 10 8 6 8 6 10 10

melody by Calixa Lavallee 1842-1891
harmonized by Godfrey Ridout 1918-

1 O Ca - na - da! Our home and na - tive land!
O Ca - na - da! Ter - re de nos aï - eux,

True pa - triot love in all thy sons com - mand.
ton front est ceint de fleu - rons glo - ri - eux!

With glow - ing hearts we see thee rise the True North, strong and free;
Car ton bras sait por - ter l'é - pé - e, il sait por - ter la croix!

And stand on guard, O Can - a - da, we stand on guard for thee.
Ton his - toire est une é - po - pé - e des plus bril - lants ex - ploits.

O Can - a - da! Glo - rious and free!
Et ta va - leur, de foi trem - pé - e,

We stand on guard, we stand on guard for thee,
pro - té - ge - ra nos foy - ers et nos droits,

O Can - a - da! We stand on guard for thee.
pro - té - ge - ra nos foy - ers et nos droits.

Robert Stanley Weir 1856-1926

2I8

GOD SAVE OUR GRACIOUS QUEEN

GOD SAVE THE QUEEN 664 6664   Melody from 'Thesaurus Musicus' London 1745
harmonized by Ernest Campbell MacMillan 1893–

1 God save our gra - cious Queen, long live our no - ble Queen:
1 Dieu pro - tè - ge la Reine de sa main sou - ve - raine!

God save the Queen. Send her vic - tor - i - ous,
Vi - ve la Reine! Qu'un rè - gne glo - ri - eux

hap - py and glo - ri - ous, long to reign o - ver us:
long et vic - to - ri - eux ren - de son peu - ple heu - reux!

God save the Queen.
Vi - ve la Reine!

2 Thy choicest gifts in store
on her be pleased to pour;
long may she reign.
May she defend our laws,
and ever give us cause
to sing with heart and voice,
God save the Queen.

3 Our loved dominion bless
with peace and happiness
from shore to shore;
and let our nation be
loyal, united, free,
true to herself and thee
for evermore.

st. 1 & 2, author unknown
st. 3, Robert Murray 1832-1909

AND THE FOLLOWING

35 Ye servants of God
73 Turn back, O man
208 Lord, save thy world
210 For the healing of the nations

219

OUR FATHER, BY WHOSE NAME

RHOSYMEDRE 6666 888   John David Edwards' 'Original Sacred Music' c1840

1 Our Father, by whose name all fa-ther-hood is known, who dost in love pro-claim each fa-mi-ly thine own: bless thou all par-ents, keep-ing well, with con-stant love as sen-ti-nel, the homes in which thy peo-ple dwell.

2 O Christ, who cam'st to know
like us an earthly home,
in favour thou didst grow,
and so to manhood come:
our children bless, in every place,
that they may all behold thy face,
and knowing thee may grow in grace.

3 O Spirit, who dost bind
our hearts in unity,
who teachest us to find
the love from self set free:
in all our hearts such love increase,
that every home, by this release,
may be the dwelling place of peace.

Francis Bland Tucker 1895-

220

O GOD IN HEAVEN
WYCH CROSS 888888

Erik Routley 1917–

1 O God in heaven, whose lov-ing plan or-dained for us our par-ents' care, and gave us when our life be - gan the shel-ter of a home to share: our Fa-ther, on the homes we love send down thy bless-ing from a - bove.

2 May young and old together find
 in Christ the Lord of every day,
 that fellowship our homes may bind
 in joy and sorrow, work and play.
 Our Father, on the homes we love
 send down thy blessing from above.

3 The sins that mar our homes forgive;
 from all self-seeking set us free;
 parents and children, may we live
 in glad obedience to thee.
 Our Father, on the homes we love
 send down thy blessing from above.

4 O Father, in our homes preside,
 their duties shared as in thy sight;
 in kindly ways be thou our guide;
 on mirth and trouble shed thy light.
 Our Father, bless the homes we love
 and make them like thy home above.

Hugh Martin 1890–1964

AND THE FOLLOWING

221

ETERNAL FATHER, STRONG TO SAVE

MELITA 8 8 8 8 8 8

John Bacchus Dykes 1823-1876

1 E - ter - nal Fa - ther, strong to save, whose arm hath bound the rest-less wave,
who bidd'st the migh - ty o - cean deep its own ap - point - ed lim - its keep:
O hear us when we cry to thee for those in per - il on the sea.

2 O Christ, whose voice the waters heard,
and hushed their raging at thy word,
who walkedst on the foaming deep,
and calm amid the storm didst sleep:
O hear us when we cry to thee
for those in peril on the sea.

3 O Holy Spirit, who didst brood
upon the chaos dark and rude,
and bid the angry tumult cease,
and give for wild confusion peace:
O hear us when we cry to thee
for those in peril on the sea.

4 O trinity of love and power,
our brethren shield in danger's hour.
From rock and tempest, fire and foe,
protect them wheresoe'er they go:
thus evermore shall rise to thee
glad hymns of praise from land and sea.

William Whiting 1825-1878

222

MAN IS NOW A RACE OF TRAVELLERS

MARCHING 8 7 8 7

Martin Fallas Shaw 1875-1958

1 Man is now a race of tra-vellers, rang-ing wide o'er earth's whole face;

ev- ery state is now our vil- lage, ev- ery town our mar-ket-place.

2 Not on earth alone we travel,
but invade the farthest skies;
circling earth and tracking planets
through the brightest heaven man flies.

3 Yet where'er the quest shall take us
we are ever in God's sight,
for he loves the very sparrow
and the astronaut in flight.

4 Grant, O Lord, that all our journeys
make us offer praise that's due;
for we would not dare to travel
were the world not made by you.

Derwyn Dixon Jones 1925-

AND THE FOLLOWING

128 I to the hills will lift mine eyes
129 Unto the hills around do I lift up
498 We bless the God and Father   st. 3

223

GOD OF GRACE AND GOD OF GLORY   Welsh traditional melody

RHUDDLAN 8 7 8 7 8 7   harmonized by Frederick R C Clarke 1931-

1 God of grace and God of glo-ry, on thy peo-ple pour thy power;

now ful-fil thy church's sto-ry; bring her bud to glo-rious flower.

Grant us wis-dom, grant us cour-age, for the fac-ing of this hour.

2 Lo, the hosts of evil round us
scorn thy Christ, assail his ways;
fears and doubts too long have bound us,
free our hearts to work and praise.
Grant us wisdom, grant us courage,
for the living of these days.

3 Cure thy children's warring madness,
bend our pride to thy control;
shame our wanton selfish gladness,
rich in goods and poor in soul.
Grant us wisdom, grant us courage,
lest we miss thy kingdom's goal.

4 Set our feet on lofty places,
gird our lives that they may be
armoured with all Christ-like graces
in the fight to set men free.
Grant us wisdom, grant us courage,
that we fail not man nor thee.

Harry Emerson Fosdick 1878-1969

224

JESUS, SHEPHERD OF OUR SOULS

VARNDEAN 7 6 7 6 7 7

Erik Routley 1917-

1 Je - sus, shep-herd of our souls, self - less in your car - ing, lead us out to days of peace and of thought - ful shar - ing. Free our life from ill and war; what is good in man re-store.

2 Jesus, be our shepherd still,
though the settings alter;
grant us for our changing days
faith that will not falter.
Bless us in our modern scene
of computer and machine.

3 Living Lord, renew the charge
at your rising given:
that the church in love should bring
to this earth your heaven.
Give us insight, show us how
life is here, the task is now.

4 May we with a shepherd's heart
love the people round us,
still recalling how your love
in our straying found us.
Keep us, Lord, in humble ways;
lead us clearly all our days.

Frederik Herman Kaan 1929-

225

FATHER, WE THANK THEE WHO HAST PLANTED

LES COMMANDEMENS 9 8 9 8

Genevan Psalter 1549
harmonized by Stanley L Osborne 1907-

Fa - ther, we thank thee who hast plant - ed

thy ho - ly name with - in our hearts.

Know - ledge and faith and life im - mor - tal

Je - sus thy Son to us im - parts.

2 Thou, Lord, didst make all for thy pleasure,
   didst give man food for all his days,
   giving in Christ the bread eternal:
   thine is the power, be thine the praise.

3 Watch o'er thy church, O Lord, in mercy,
   save it from evil, guard it still,
   perfect it in thy love, unite it,
   cleansed and conformed unto thy will.

4 As grain, once scattered on the hillsides,
   was in the broken bread made one,
   so may thy world-wide church be gathered
   into the kingdom of thy Son.

from the Didache, 2nd century
versified by
Francis Bland Tucker 1895-

226

FILLED WITH THE SPIRIT'S POWER

SHELDONIAN 10 10 10 10   Cyril Vincent Taylor 1907–

1 Filled with the Spir-it's power, with one ac-cord
the in-fant church con-fessed its ris-en Lord.
O Ho-ly Spir-it, in the church to-day
no less your power of fel-low-ship dis-play.

2 Now with the mind of Christ set us on fire,
that unity may be our great desire.
Give joy and peace; give faith to hear your call,
and readiness in each to work for all.

3 Widen our love, good Spirit, to embrace
in your strong care the men of every race.
Like wind and fire with life among us move,
till we are known as Christ's, and Christians prove.

John Raphael Peacey 1896–

227

SUN OF RIGHTEOUSNESS

SONNE DER GERECHTIGKEIT 7 7 7 7 4

from the 'Geistlich Böhmische Brüder' 1566
harmonized by Stanley L Osborne 1907–

1 Sun of right-eous - ness, shine forth;
dawn up - on this age of earth;
in thy church let light ap-pear, till the world shall see it clear.
Have mer - cy, Lord.

2 Wake dead Christendom from sleep,
lapped in comfort, drowsing deep;
tell thy name and acts abroad;
show this land thou art our God.
Have mercy, Lord.

3 See our sad divisions, Lord;
heal by thy unbroken word;
gather, shepherd of mankind,
all the lost, the hurt, the blind.
Have mercy, Lord.

4 Help us to behold afar
in this age thy glory's star,
that, in what small strength we own,
knightly virtue may be shown.
Have mercy, Lord.

Christian David 1690-1751
Christian Gottlob Barth 1799-1862
Johann Christian Nehring 1671-1736
tr. J Macpherson 1931-

228

BEHOLD THY PEOPLE, LORD

SONG 20 6686

Orlando Gibbons 1583-1625

1 Behold thy people, Lord, gathered before thy throne;
our sad divisions we confess, and pray we may be one.

2 One God, one Lord, one faith,
one heavenly food we share,
one call to serve and follow Christ
whose blessed name we bear.

3 Baptized into one church
by water and the word,
our schisms cripple and disgrace
the Body of the Lord.

4 Forgive our many sins,
our lack of mutual love,
and make us to be truly one,
as thou art one above.

5 Unto the triune God,
one God through persons three,
from men and from the heavenly host
eternal glory be.

Ronald W Bryan c1910-

AND THE FOLLOWING

229

O CHRIST, THE HEALER

MELCOMBE 8 8 8 8   Samuel Webbe 1740-1816

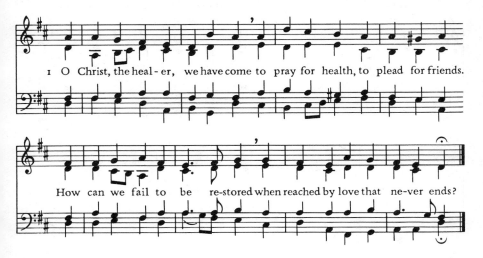

1 O Christ, the heal - er, we have come to pray for health, to plead for friends.
How can we fail to be re-stored when reached by love that ne-ver ends?

2 From every ailment flesh endures
our bodies clamour to be freed;
yet in our hearts we would confess
that wholeness is our deepest need.

3 How strong, O Lord, are our desires,
how weak our knowledge of ourselves!
Release in us those healing truths
unconscious pride resists and shelves.

4 In conflicts that destroy our health
we diagnose the world's disease;
our common life declares our ills:
is there no cure, O Christ, for these?

5 Grant that we all, made one in faith,
in your community may find
the wholeness that, enriching us,   Frederick Pratt Green 1903-
shall reach and shall enrich mankind.   for a higher setting see 360

230

FROM YOU ALL SKILL AND SCIENCE FLOW

DER TAG 8 6 8 6

Fritz Werner 1898–
harmonized by Stanley L Osborne 1907–

1 From you all skill and sci - ence flow;
all pi - ty, care, and love,
all calm and cour - age, faith and hope,
oh! pour them from a - bove.

2 Impart them, Lord, to each and all
as each and all shall need,
to rise like incense, each to you
in noble thought and deed.

3 And hasten, Lord, that perfect day
when pain and death shall cease,
and your just rule shall fill the earth
with health and light and peace.

Charles Kingsley 1819-1875

231

FATHER, WHOSE WILL IS LIFE AND GOOD

CRUCIS VICTORIA 8 6 8 6   Myles Birket Foster 1851–1922

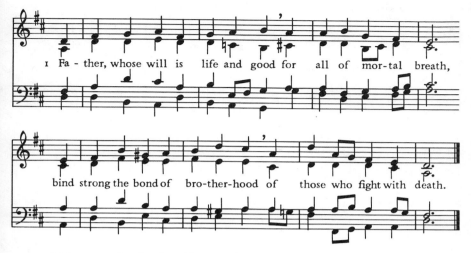

1 Fa - ther, whose will is life and good for all of mor-tal breath,

bind strong the bond of bro-ther-hood of those who fight with death.

2 Make strong their hands and hearts and wills
to drive disease afar,
to battle with the body's ills
and wage your holy war.

3 Where'er they heal the sick and blind,
Christ's love may they proclaim,
make known the good Physician's mind,
and prove the Saviour's name.

Hardwicke Drummond Rawnsley 1851–1920

AND THE FOLLOWING

37 To the name of our salvation
48 O for a thousand tongues to sing
235 Thou whose almighty word
303 Where cross the crowded ways of life
506 Christ the fair glory of the holy angels   st. 1,4,5

232

O THOU WHO MAKEST SOULS TO SHINE Swiss melody

SOLOTHURN 8 8 8 8 harmonized by Stanley L Osborne 1907–

1 O thou who mak - est souls to shine
with light from bright - er worlds a - bove,
and drop - pest glis - tening dews di - vine
on all who seek a Sav - iour's love:

2   do thou thy benediction give
    on all who teach, on all who learn,
    that so thy church may holier live,
    and every lamp more brightly burn.

3   Give all who teach pure hearts and wise,
    faith, hope, and love, all warmed by prayer:
    themselves first training for the skies,
    they best will raise their people there.

4   Give all who learn the open ear,
    the spirit meek, the willing mind;
    such gifts will make the lowliest here
    far better than a kingdom find.   John Armstrong 1813-1856

AND THE FOLLOWING

233
O SPIRIT OF THE LIVING GOD

WAREHAM 8 8 8 8   William Knapp 1698–1768

1 O Spir-it of the liv-ing God, in all the full-ness of thy grace, wher-e'er the foot of man hath trod, de-scend on our a-pos-tate race.

2   Give tongues of fire and hearts of love
    to preach the reconciling word;
    give power and unction from above
    where'er the joyful sound is heard.

3   Be darkness at thy coming, light;
    confusion, order in thy path;
    souls without strength inspire with might;
    bid mercy triumph over wrath.

4   O Spirit of the Lord, prepare
    all the round earth her God to meet;
    breathe thou abroad like morning air, ·
    till hearts of stone begin to beat.

5   Baptize the nations; far and nigh
    the triumphs of the cross record;
    the name of Jesus glorify,
    till every kindred call him Lord.

James Montgomery 1771-1854
for a higher setting see 161

234
GOD OF MERCY
HEATHLANDS 7 7 7 7 7 7

Henry Thomas Smart 1813–1879

1 God of mer-cy, God of grace, show the bright-ness of thy face;
shine up-on us, Sav-iour, shine, fill thy church with light di-vine;
and thy sav-ing health ex-tend un-to earth's re-mot-est end.

2 Let the people praise thee, Lord;
   be by all that live adored;
   let the nations shout and sing
   glory to their Saviour King;
   at thy feet their tribute pay,
   and thy holy will obey.

3 Let the people praise thee, Lord;
   earth shall then her fruits afford,
   God to man his blessing give,
   man to God devoted live;
   all below and all above
   one in joy, and light, and love.

Henry Francis Lyte 1793–1847
based on Psalm 67
for a higher setting see 320

235

THOU WHOSE ALMIGHTY WORD

MOSCOW 664 6664   adapted from Felice de Giardini 1716-1796

1 Thou whose al-migh-ty word chaos and dark-ness heard, and took their flight, hear us, we hum-bly pray; and where the gos-pel day sheds not its glo-rious ray, let there be light.

2 Thou who didst come to bring,
on thy redeeming wing,
healing and sight,
health to the sick in mind,
sight to the inly blind,
O now to all mankind
let there be light.

3 Spirit of truth and love,
life-giving, holy dove,
speed forth thy flight;
move on the water's face,
bearing the lamp of grace,
and in earth's darkest place
let there be light.

4 Blessed and holy three,
glorious trinity,
wisdom, love, might,
boundless as ocean's tide
rolling in fullest pride,
through the world far and wide
let there be light.

John Marriott 1780-1825
based on Genesis 1:3

236

ETERNAL GOD, WHOSE POWER UPHOLDS

SARAH 8 6 8 6 D

Rhys Thomas 1867-1932

1 E - ter-nal God, whose power up-holds both flower and flam-ing star,
to whom there is no here nor there, no time, no near nor far,
no a - lien race, no for - eign shore, no child un-sought, un - known:
O send us forth, thy pro-phets true, to make all lands thine own!

2 O God of truth, whom science seeks
and reverent souls adore,
who lightest every searching mind
of every clime and shore,
dispel the gloom of error's night
of ignorance and fear,
until true wisdom from above
shall make life's pathway clear!

3 O God of righteousness and grace,
seen in the Christ, thy Son,
whose life and death reveal thy face,
by whom thy will was done,
inspire thy heralds of good news
to live thy life divine,
till Christ is formed in all mankind
and every land is thine.

Henry Hallam Tweedy 1868–1953
This may be sung to Forest Green 388 or 421

AND THE FOLLOWING

237

WE TURN TO YOU
ZU MEINEM HERRN 11 10 11 10

Johann Gottfried Schicht 1753-1823
harmonized by David Evans 1874-1948

1 We turn to you, O God of ev - ery na - tion,
giv - er of life and o - ri - gin of good;
your love is at the heart of all cre - a - tion,
your hurt is peo - ple's bro - ken bro - ther - hood.

2 We turn to you, that we may be forgiven
  for crucifying Christ on earth again.
  We know that we have never wholly striven,
  forgetting self, to love the other man.

3 Free every heart from pride and self-reliance,
  our ways of thought inspire with simple grace;
  break down among us barriers of defiance,
  speak to the soul of all the human race.

4 On men who fight on earth for right relations
  we pray the light of love from hour to hour.
  Grant wisdom to the leaders of the nations,
  the gift of carefulness to those in power.

5 Teach us, good Lord, to serve the need of others,
  help us to give and not to count the cost.
  Unite us all, for we are born as brothers:
  defeat our Babel with your Pentecost!

  Frederik Herman Kaan 1929–

238

KING OF LOVE

HERMON 8 7 8 7 D

Charles Venn Pilcher 1879-1961
harmonized by Walter MacNutt 1910-

1 King of love, O Christ, we crown thee Lord of thought and Lord of will,

each de-mand of thy high chal-lenge de-di-ca-ted to ful-fil,

we with thee by grace co-work-ers, till, wher-e'er man's foot hath trod,

peo-ples, kings, do-min-ions, ra-ces, own the em-pire of our God.

2 King of life, who hast created
  wheat in golden harvest spread,
  make thy servants strong to serve thee
  by the gift of daily bread;
  feed us with thy body broken,
  with thy blood outpoured sustain,
  that our souls divinely strengthened
  may the life eternal gain.

3 King of mercy, thou hast saved us
  from the haunting sense of loss,
  nailing in thy vast compassion
  sin's indictment to the cross;
  them who love, by thy sore anguish,
  from the past thou makest free,
  breathing words of absolution
  where thou reignest from the tree.

4 King triumphant, King victorious,
  take thy throne our hearts within,
  lest the might of fierce temptation
  snare us into mortal sin;
  by thy Spirit's rich anointing
  grant us power life's race to run,
  till the lure of sense be vanquished,
  till the prize of God be won.

Charles Venn Pilcher 1879-1961

AND THE FOLLOWING

239

O THOU WHO CAMEST FROM ABOVE

HEREFORD 8 8 8 8   Samuel Sebastian Wesley 1810-1876

1 O thou who cam-est from a-bove,

the pure ce-les-tial fire to im-part,

kin-dle a flame of sac-red love

on the mean al-tar of my heart.

2 There let it for thy glory burn
   with inextinguishable blaze,
   and trembling to its source return
   in humble prayer and fervent praise.

3 Jesus, confirm my heart's desire
   to work and speak and think for thee;
   still let me guard the holy fire,
   and still stir up thy gift in me.

4 Ready for all thy perfect will,
   my acts of faith and love repeat,
   till death thy endless mercies seal   Charles Wesley 1707-1788
   and make the sacrifice complete.   based on Leviticus 6:13
                                               This may be sung to Wareham 161 or 233

240

BREATHE ON ME, BREATH OF GOD

KINGSTON 6686 FIRST TUNE

Frederick R C Clarke 1931-

1 Breathe on me, breath of God, fill me with life a - new,

that I may love what thou dost love, and do what thou wouldst do.

2 Breathe on me, breath of God,
until my heart is pure,
until my will is one with thine
to do and to endure.

3 Breathe on me, breath of God,
till I am wholly thine,
until this earthly part of me
glows with thy fire divine.

4 Breathe on me, breath of God:
so shall I never die,
but live with thee the perfect life
of thine eternity.

Edwin Hatch 1835-1889

TRENTHAM 6686 SECOND TUNE

melody by Robert Jackson 1840-1914
reharmonized by Frederick R C Clarke 1931-

1 Breathe on me, breath of God, fill me with life a - new,

that I may love what thou dost love, and do what thou wouldst do.

241

LOVE DIVINE

HYFRYDOL 8 7 8 7 D

melody by Rowland Hugh Pritchard 1811-188

harmonized by Hugh J McLean 1930–

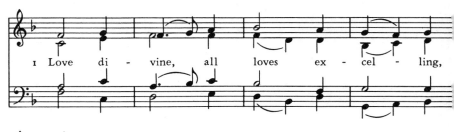

1 Love di - vine, all loves ex - cel - ling,

joy of heaven to earth come down,

fix in us thy hum - ble dwell - ing,

all thy faith - ful mer - cies crown.

Je - sus, thou art all com - pas - sion,

pure, un - bound - ed love thou art;

vis - it us with thy sal - va - tion,

en - ter ev - ery trem - bling heart.

2   Come, almighty to deliver;
    let us all thy grace receive;
    suddenly return, and never,
    never more thy temples leave.
    Thee we would be always blessing,
    serve thee as thy hosts above,
    pray, and praise thee, without ceasing,
    glory in thy perfect love.

3   Finish, then, thy new creation;
    pure and spotless let us be;
    let us see thy great salvation
    perfectly restored in thee,
    changed from glory into glory,
    till in heaven we take our place,
    till we cast our crowns before thee,
    lost in wonder, love, and praise.   Charles Wesley 1707-1788

242

MAKE ME A CAPTIVE, LORD

CORONA 6 6 8 6 D

Charles Hylton Stewart 1884-1932

1 Make me a cap-tive, Lord, and then I shall be free;
force me to ren-der up my sword, and I shall con-queror be.
I sink in life's a - larms when by my - self I stand;
im - pri - son me with - in thine arms, and strong shall be my hand.

2 My heart is weak and poor
     until it master find;
     it has no spring of action sure;
     it varies with the wind:
     it cannot freely move
     till thou hast wrought its chain.
     Enslave it with thy matchless love,
     and deathless it shall reign.

3 My power is faint and low
     till I have learned to serve;
     it wants the needed fire to glow;
     it wants the breeze to nerve;
     it cannot drive the world
     until itself be driven:
     its flag can only be unfurled
     when thou shalt breathe from heaven.

4 My will is not my own
     till thou hast made it thine;
     if it would reach a monarch's throne,
     it must its crown resign;
     it only stands unbent
     amid the clashing strife,
     when on thy bosom it has leant
     and found in thee its life.

George Matheson 1842-1906

243

GOD WHO TOUCHEST EARTH WITH BEAUTY

SPIRITUS CHRISTI 8 5 8 5

Henry Walford Davies 1869-1941

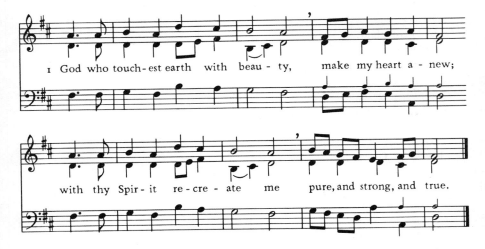

1 God who touch-est earth with beau-ty, make my heart a-new;
with thy Spir-it re-cre-ate me pure, and strong, and true.

2 Like thy springs and running waters,
make me crystal pure;
like thy rocks of towering grandeur,
make me strong and sure.

3 Like thy dancing waves in sunlight,
make me glad and free;
like the straightness of the pine trees
let me upright be.

4 Like the arching of the heavens
lift my thoughts above;
turn my dreams to noble action,
ministries of love.

5 Like the birds that soar while singing,
give my heart a song;
may the music of thanksgiving
echo clear and strong.

6 God who touchest earth with beauty,
make my heart anew;
keep me ever by thy Spirit
pure, and strong, and true.

Mary Susanne Edgar 1889-

244

COME, HOLY SPIRIT, HEAVENLY DOVE

HARESFIELD 8 6 8 6

John Dykes Bower 1905-

1 Come, Ho-ly Spir - it, heaven - ly dove, with all thy quick-ening powers, kin - dle a flame of sac-red love in these cold hearts of ours.

2 In vain we turn our formal songs,
in vain we strive to rise:
hosannas languish on our tongues,
and our devotion dies.

3 Dear Lord! and shall we ever live
at this poor dying rate?
Our love so faint, so cold to thee,
and thine to us so great!

4 Come, Holy Spirit, heavenly dove,
with all thy quickening powers:
come, shed abroad a Saviour's love,
and that shall kindle ours.

Isaac Watts 1674-1748
This may be sung to Abridge 182

AND THE FOLLOWING

245

COME, HOLY GHOST

VENI CREATOR 8 8 8 8 and coda

plainsong melody, Mechlin
arranged by Healey Willan 1880–1968

1 Come, Ho - ly Ghost, our souls in - spire

and light - en with ce - les - tial fire;

thou the a - noint - ing Spir - it art,

who dost thy seven - fold gifts im - part.

praise to thy e - ter - nal merit,

Fa - ther, Son, and Ho - ly Spir - it. A - men.

2   Thy blessed unction from above
is comfort, life, and fire of love;
enable with perpetual light
the dullness of our blinded sight;

3   anoint and cheer our soiled face
with the abundance of thy grace;
keep far our foes; give peace at home:
where thou art guide no ill can come.

4   Teach us to know the Father, Son,
and thee of both to be but one,
that through the ages all along
this may be our endless song:
praise to thy eternal merit,
Father, Son, and Holy Spirit.

from the Latin, 9th century
tr. John Cosin 1594-1672

246

O HOLY SPIRIT, BY WHOSE BREATH
Tune: Veni Creator 245

1   O Holy Spirit, by whose breath
life rises vibrant out of death:
come to create, renew, inspire;
come, kindle in our hearts your fire.

2   You are the seeker's sure resource,
of burning love the living source,
protector in the midst of strife,
the giver and the Lord of life.

3   In you God's energy is shown,
to us your varied gifts made known.
Teach us to speak; teach us to hear;
yours is the tongue and yours the ear.

4   Flood our dull senses with your light;
in mutual love our hearts unite.
Your power the whole creation fills;
confirm our weak, uncertain wills.

5   From inner strife grant us release;
turn nations to the ways of peace.
To fuller life your people bring
that as one body we may sing:
praise to the Father, Christ his Word,
and to the Spirit: God the Lord.

from the Latin, 9th century
tr. John Webster Grant 1919-

247

FIRE OF GOD

NUN KOMM 7 7 7 7

melody from Johann Walther's 'Gesangbüchlein' 1524
harmonized by Johann Sebastian Bach 1685-1750

1 Fire of God, thou sac - red flame,
Spir - it who in splen - dour came,
let thy heat my soul re - fine,
till it glows with love di - vine.

2 Breath of God, that swept in power
in the pentecostal hour,
holy breath, be thou in me
source of vital energy.

3 Strength of God, thy might within
conquers sorrow, pain and sin:
fortify from evil's art
all the gateways of my heart.

4 Truth of God, thy piercing rays
penetrate my secret ways.
May the light that shames my sin
guide me holier paths to win.

5 Love of God, thy grace profound
knoweth neither age nor bound:
come, my heart's own guest to be,
dwell for evermore in me.

Albert Frederick Bayly 1901-

248

HOLY SPIRIT, FONT OF LIGHT

VENI SANCTE SPIRITUS 777D

Samuel Webbe 1740-1816

1 Holy Spirit, font of light, focus of God's glory bright, shed on us a shining ray. Father of the fatherless, giver of gifts limitless, come and touch our hearts today.

2 Source of strength and sure relief,
comforter in time of grief,
enter in and be our guest.
On our journey grant us aid,
freshening breeze and cooling shade,
in our labour inward rest.

3 Enter each aspiring heart,
occupy its inmost part
with your dazzling purity.
All that gives to man his worth,
all that benefits the earth,
you bring to maturity.

4 With your soft, refreshing rains
break our drought, remove our stains;
bind up all our injuries.
Shake with rushing wind our will;
melt with fire our icy chill;
bring to light our perjuries.

5 As your promise we believe
make us ready to receive
gifts from your unbounded store.
Grant enabling energy,
courage in adversity,
joys that last for evermore.

from the Latin, 13th century
tr. John Webster Grant 1919-

AND THE FOLLOWING

60 Spirit divine, attend our prayers
67 Come down, O love divine
71 O Holy Spirit, Lord of grace
239 O thou who camest from above

244 Come, Holy Spirit, heavenly dove
482 Lord God, the Holy Ghost
485 Spirit of mercy
486 Rejoice! the year upon its way

249

DEAR LORD AND FATHER

REPTON 8 6 8 8 6 FIRST TUNE

Charles Hubert Hastings Parry 1848-1918
arranged by Stanley L Osborne 1907-

Unison

1 Dear Lord and Fa-ther of man-kind, for-give our fool-ish ways;

re-clothe us in our right-ful mind; in pur-er lives thy ser-vice find,

in deep-er rev-erence, praise, in deep-er rev-erence, praise.

2 In simple trust like theirs who heard,
   beside the Syrian sea,
   the gracious calling of the Lord,
   let us, like them, without a word
   rise up, and follow thee.

3 O sabbath rest by Galilee!
   O calm of hills above,
   where Jesus knelt to share with thee
   the silence of eternity,
   interpreted by love!

Frederick Charles Maker 1844-1927

1 Dear Lord and Fa-ther of man-kind, for-give our fool-ish ways;
re-clothe us in our right-ful mind; in pur-er lives thy ser-vice find,
in deep-er rev-erence, praise.

4 Drop thy still dews of quietness,
till all our strivings cease;
take from our souls the strain and stress,
and let our ordered lives confess
the beauty of thy peace.

5 Breathe through the heats of our desire
thy coolness and thy balm;
let sense be dumb, let flesh retire:
speak through the earthquake, wind, and fire,
O still small voice of calm!

John Greenleaf Whittier 1807-1892

250

FATHER IN HEAVEN
LLEDROD 8 8 8 8

Welsh hymn melody

1 Father in heaven, who lovest all,
O help thy children when they call,
that they may build from age to age
an undefiled heritage.

2 Teach us to bear the yoke in youth
with steadfastness and careful truth,
that in our time thy grace may give
the truth whereby the nations live.

3 Teach us to rule ourselves alway,
controlled and cleanly night and day,
that we may bring, if need arise,
no maimed or worthless sacrifice.

4 Teach us to look in all our ends
on thee for judge and not our friends,
that we with thee may walk uncowed
by fear or favour of the crowd.

5 Teach us the strength that cannot seek,
by deed or thought, to hurt the weak,
that under thee we may possess
man's strength to comfort man's distress.

6 Teach us delight in simple things,
and mirth that has no bitter springs,
forgiveness free of evil done,
and love to all men 'neath the sun.

Rudyard Kipling 1865-1936

251

O CHRIST, WHO CAME TO SHARE OUR HUMAN LIFE

CLIFF TOWN 10 10 10 10   Erik Routley 1917-

1 O Christ, who came to share our hu-man life,
God's word made flesh to speak his love for men;
lead us in ser-vice to thy ho-ly cause
till sons of earth are sons of God a-gain.

2 O Christ, who dared to stand on trial alone
before the angry mob and Roman might;
we seek thy courage; make it now our own
that we may stand unflinching for thy right.

3 O Christ, who died with arms outstretched in love
for all who lift their faces to thy cross:
fill thou our lives with charity divine,
till thou and thine are all, and self is loss.

4 O Christ, who rose victorious over death
to loose thy living presence on our earth:
teach us to feel thy greatness till we know,
in life and death, the soul's enduring worth.

Catherine Bonnell Arnott 1927-
F sharp is the key commended
for this tune.

252
ETERNAL RULER OF THE CEASELESS ROUND
SONG I   10 10 10 10 10 10

Orlando Gibbons 1583-1625

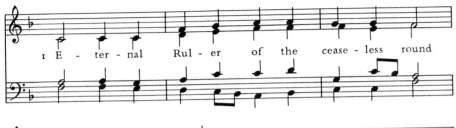

1 E - ter - nal Rul - er of the cease - less round

of cir - cling plan - ets sing - ing on their way,

guide of the na - tions from the night pro - found

in - to the glo - ry of the per - fect day:

rule in our hearts, that we may ev - er be

guid - ed and strength-ened and up - held by thee.

2 We are of thee, the children of thy love,
   the brothers of thy well-beloved Son;
   descend, O Holy Spirit, like a dove,
   into our hearts, that we may be as one:
   as one with thee, to whom we ever tend;
   as one with him, our Brother and our Friend.

3 We would be one in hatred of all wrong,
   one in our love of all things sweet and fair,
   one with the joy that breaketh into song,
   one with the grief that trembles into prayer,
   one in the power that makes thy children free
   to follow truth, and thus to follow thee.

4 O clothe us with thy heavenly armour, Lord,
   thy trusty shield, thy sword of love divine;
   our inspiration be thy constant word;
   we ask no victories that are not thine:
   give or withhold, let pain or pleasure be;
   enough to know that we are serving thee.   John White Chadwick 1840-1904

AND THE FOLLOWING

253

BE THOU MY VISION

SLANE 10 10 10 10

Irish traditional melody
harmonized by Stanley L Osborne 1907-

1 Be thou my vi - sion, O Lord of my heart;
naught be all else to me save that thou art,
thou my best thought, by day or by night,
wak - ing or sleep-ing thy pres - ence my light.

2   Be thou my wisdom, thou my true word;
    I ever with thee, thou with me, Lord;
    thou my great Father, I thy true Son,
    thou in me dwelling, and I with thee one.

3   Be thou my battle-shield, sword for the fight;
    be thou my dignity, thou my delight,
    thou my soul's shelter, thou my high tower;
    raise thou me heavenward, O power of my power.

4   Riches I heed not, nor man's empty praise,
    thou mine inheritance, now and always;
    thou and thou only, first in my heart,
    high King of heaven, my treasure thou art.

5   High King of heaven, after victory won,
    may I reach heaven's joys, O bright heaven's sun!
    Heart of my own heart, whatever befall,
    still be my vision, O ruler of all.

    Irish c8th century
tr. Mary Elizabeth Byrne 1880-1931
    Eleanor H Hull 1860-1935

254

NEARER, MY GOD, TO THEE

WILMINGTON 6 4 6 4 6 6 4 FIRST TUNE

Erik Routley 1917-

1 Near-er, my God, to thee, near-er to thee!
Even though it be a cross that rais-eth me,
still all my song would be 'Near-er, my God, to thee,
near-er to thee!'

2 Though, like the wanderer,
the sun gone down,
darkness be over me,
my rest a stone,
yet in my dreams I'd be
nearer, my God, to thee,
nearer to thee.

3 There let the way appear
steps unto heaven;
all that you send'st to me
in mercy given;
angels to beckon me
nearer, my God, to thee,
nearer to thee.

1 Near - er, my God, to thee, near - er to thee!

Even though it be a cross that rais - eth me,

still all my song would be 'Near - er, my God, to thee,

near - er, my God, to thee, near - er to thee!'

4   Then with my waking thoughts
     bright with thy praise,
     out of my stony griefs
     Bethel I'll raise,
     so by my woes to be
     nearer, my God, to thee,
     nearer to thee.

5   Or if on joyful wing
     cleaving the sky,
     sun, moon, and stars forgot,
     upwards I fly,
     still all my song shall be
     'Nearer, my God, to thee,
     nearer to thee!'

Sarah Flower Adams 1805-1848
based on Genesis 28:10-22

255

JESUS, UNITED BY THY GRACE

CREDITION 8686 FIRST TUNE

melody by Thomas Clark 1775-1859
harmonized by Robert H Bell 1932-

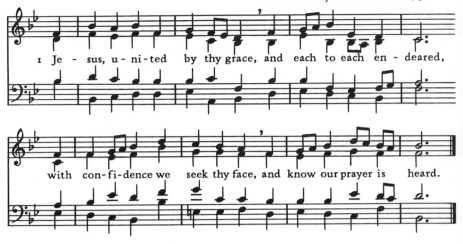

1 Je - sus, u - ni - ted by thy grace, and each to each en - deared,

with con - fi - dence we seek thy face, and know our prayer is heard.

2 Help us to help each other, Lord,
each other's cross to bear
let each his friendly aid afford,
and feel his brother's care.

3 Up unto thee, our living head,
let us in all things grow,
till thou hast made us free indeed
and spotless here below.

4 Touched by the loadstone of thy love,
let all our hearts agree;
and ever toward each other move,
and ever move toward thee.

Charles Wesley 1707-1788

ARLINGTON 8686 SECOND TUNE

Thomas Augustine Arne 1710-1778

1 Je - sus, u - ni - ted by thy grace, and each to each en - deared,

with con - fi - dence we seek thy face, and know our prayer is heard.

(P.)

256

GRACIOUS SPIRIT, HOLY GHOST

CAPETOWN 7775

Friedrich Filitz 1804-1876

adapted by Peter Maurice 1803-1878

1 Gra-cious Spir-it, Ho-ly Ghost, taught by thee, we co-vet most of thy gifts at pen-te-cost, ho-ly, heaven-ly love.

2 Love is kind, and suffers long;
love is meek and thinks no wrong;
love than death itself more strong;
therefore give us love.

3 Prophecy will fade away,
melting in the light of day;
love will ever with us stay;
therefore give us love.

4 Faith will vanish into sight;
hope be emptied in delight;
love in heaven will shine more bright;
therefore give us love.

5 Faith and hope and love we see
joining hand in hand agree;
but the greatest of the three,
and the best, is love.

Christopher Wordsworth 1807-1885

257

JESUS, THY BOUNDLESS LOVE TO ME

SURREY 888888

Henry Carey c1687-1743

1 Je - sus, thy bound - less love to me
O knit my thank - ful heart to thee,

no thought can reach, no tongue de - clare;
and reign with - out a ri - val there;

thine whol - ly, thine a - lone I am;

be thou a - lone my con - stant flame.

2   O grant that nothing in my soul
     may dwell, but thy pure love alone;
     O may thy love possess me whole,
     my joy, my treasure, and my crown;
     strange fires far from my soul remove;
     may every act, word, thought, be love.

3   O love, how cheering is thy ray;
     all pain before thy presence flies;
     care, anguish, sorrow, melt away
     where'er thy healing beams arise;
     O Jesus, nothing may I see,
     nothing desire or seek, but thee.

4   In suffering, be thy love my peace;
     in weakness, be thy love my power;
     and when the storms of life shall cease,
     Jesus, in that important hour,
     in death as life be thou my guide,
     and save me, who for me hast died.

Paul Gerhardt 1607-1676
tr. John Wesley 1703-1791

258

COME, MY WAY, MY TRUTH

THE CALL 7 7 7 7

Ralph Vaughan Williams 1872-1958
adapted by E Harold Geer c1915-

1 Come, my Way, my Truth, my Life:
such a way as gives us breath,
such a truth as ends all strife,
such a life as killeth death.

2 Come, my Light, my Feast, my Strength:
such a light as shows a feast,
such a feast as mends in length,
such a strength as makes his guest.

3 Come, my Joy, my Love, my Heart:
such a joy as none can move,
such a love as none can part,
such a heart as joys in love.

George Herbert 1593-1632

259

THOU ART THE WAY

ST JAMES 8 6 8 6

Raphael Courteville c1680–1772

1 Thou art the way: to thee a-lone from sin and death we flee;
and he who would the Fa-ther seek must seek him, Lord, by thee.

2 Thou art the truth: thy word alone
true wisdom can impart;
thou only canst inform the mind,
and purify the heart.

3 Thou art the life: the rending tomb
proclaims thy conquering arm;
and those who put their trust in thee
nor death nor hell shall harm.

4 Thou art the way, the truth, the life:
grant us that way to know,
that truth to keep, that life to win,
whose joys eternal flow.

George Washington Doane 1799–1859
based on John 14:6

260

FATHER, HEAR THE PRAYER   adapted by Charles Steggal 1826-1905
GOTT DES HIMMELS 8 7 8 7   from a melody by Heinrich Albert 1604-1651

1 Fa-ther, hear the prayer we of-fer: not for ease that prayer shall be,

but for strength that we may ev-er live our lives cour-age-ous-ly.

2 Not for ever in green pastures
    do we ask our way to be;
    but the steep and rugged pathway
    may we tread rejoicingly.

3 Not for ever by still waters
    would we idly rest and stay;
    but would smite the living fountains
    from the rocks along our way.

4 Be our strength in hours of weakness,
    in our wanderings be our guide;
    through endeavour, failure, danger,   Love Maria Willis 1824-1908
    Saviour, be thou at our side.   and others

261

TEACH ME, MY GOD AND KING

BELLA 6 6 8 6   melody from 'New and Easie Method' 1686

1 Teach me, my God and King, in all things thee to see,
and what I do in an-y-thing to do it as for thee.

2   All may of thee partake;
nothing can be so mean,
which with this tincture, 'For thy sake',
will not grow bright and clean.

3   A servant with this clause
makes drudgery divine;
who sweeps a room as for thy laws
makes that an action fine.

4   This is the famous stone
that turneth all to gold;
for that which God doth touch and own
cannot for less be told.   George Herbert 1593-1632

262

LORD OF ALL HOPEFULNESS

AVONLEA 10 11 11 12

Stanley L Osborne 1907-

1 Lord of all hope - ful-ness, Lord of all joy,
whose trust ev - er child - like no cares could de - stroy:
be there at our wak - ing, and give us, we pray,
your bliss in our hearts, Lord, at the break of the day.

2 Lord of all eagerness, Lord of all faith,
   whose strong hands were skilled at the plane and the lathe:
   be there at our labours, and give us, we pray,
   your strength in our hearts, Lord, at the noon of the day.

3 Lord of all kindliness, Lord of all grace,
   your hands swift to welcome, your arms to embrace:
   be there at our homing, and give us, we pray,
   your love in our hearts, Lord, at the eve of the day.

4 Lord of all gentleness, Lord of all calm,
   whose voice is contentment, whose presence is balm:
   be there at our sleeping, and give us, we pray,
   your peace in our hearts, Lord, at the end of the day.

Jan Struther 1901-1953

With two modifications of the melody, the tune Slane 253
may be sung to this hymn. The notes of the melody at the
ends of lines 1 and 2 are to be repeated for the opening words
of lines 2 and 3 in each stanza.

AND THE FOLLOWING

263

O GOD OF BETHEL

MARTYRDOM 8 6 8 6 FIRST TUNE

Hugh Wilson 1766-1824
adapted by R A Smith 1780-1829

1 O God of Bethel, by whose hand
thy people still are fed,
who through this weary pilgrimage
hast all our fathers led:

2 our vows, our prayers, we now present
before thy throne of grace.
God of our fathers, be the God
of their succeeding race.

3 Through each perplexing path of life
our wandering footsteps guide;
give us each day our daily bread,
and raiment fit provide.

4 O spread thy covering wings around,
till all our wanderings cease,
and at our Father's loved abode
our souls arrive in peace.

Philip Doddridge 1702-1751
John Logan 1748-1788
based on Genesis 28:20-22
This may be sung to Dundee 128

1 O God of Be - thel, by whose hand
thy peo - ple still are fed,
who through this wea - ry pil - grim - age
hast all our fa - thers led:

2 our vows, our prayers, we now present
before thy throne of grace.
God of our fathers, be the God
of their succeeding race.

3 Through each perplexing path of life
our wandering footsteps guide;
give us each day our daily bread,
and raiment fit provide.

4 O spread thy covering wings around,
till all our wanderings cease,
and at our Father's loved abode
our souls arrive in peace.

Philip Doddridge 1702-1751
John Logan 1748-1788
based on Genesis 28:20-22
This may be sung to Dundee 128

264

O GOD, WHOSE MIGHTY WISDOM MOVES

ASCENDIT DEUS 888 D

Johann Gottfried Schicht 1753–1823

1 O God, whose might-y wis-dom moves the minds of men to seek thy way,
by thee our fa-thers sought the law; Lord, keep us in that quest to-day,
that in thy light we yet may see the path that leads through truth to thee.

2 O God, whose perfect holiness
inspires our search to find thy will,
by thee the prophets spoke of old;
Lord, let us hear them speaking still,
that in thy light we yet may see
the path that leads through right to thee.

3 O God, whose tender, yearning heart
gave us thy Son, the living word,
by thee men sent the good news forth;
Lord, let this gospel now be heard,
that in thy light we yet may see
the path that leads through love to thee.

4 O God, whose surging Spirit stirs
within the minds of all on earth,
by thee the scriptures bring new life,
and hopes forgotten find rebirth;
Lord, grant us in thy light to see
the path that leads through all to thee.

George Brandon 1924–

265

COME, GRACIOUS SPIRIT

EISENACH 8 8 8 8

Johann Hermann Schein 1586-1630

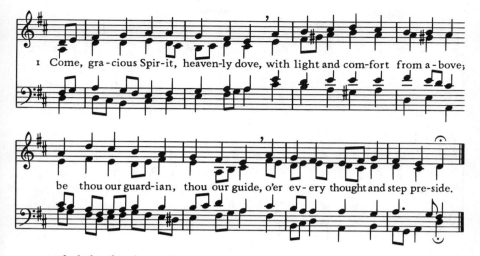

1 Come, gra-cious Spir-it, heaven-ly dove, with light and com-fort from a-bove;
be thou our guard-ian, thou our guide, o'er ev-ery thought and step pre-side.

2 The light of truth to us display,
   and make us know and choose thy way;
   plant holy fear in every heart,
   that we from God may ne'er depart.

3 Lead us to Christ, the living way,
   nor let us from his pastures stray;
   lead us to holiness, the road
   that we must take to dwell with God.

4 Lead us to heaven, that we may share
   fullness of joy for ever there;
   lead us to God, our final rest,
   to be with him for ever blest.

Simon Browne 1680-1732

266

JESUS, FRIEND OF LITTLE CHILDREN

FARNHAM 8 5 8 3

Gerald Wheeler 1929-

1 Je - sus, friend of lit-tle child-ren, be a friend to me;
take my hand, and ev - er keep me close to thee.

2 Teach me how to grow in goodness,
daily as I grow.
Thou has been a child, and surely
thou dost know.

3 Never leave me, nor forsake me;
ever be my friend;
for I need thee, from life's dawning
to its end.

Walter John Mathams 1853-1931

267

JESUS, SAVIOUR, PILOT ME   melody by John Edgar Gould 1822–1875

PILOT 777777   harmonized by Stanley L Osborne 1907–

1 Jesus, Saviour, pilot me over life's tempestuous sea;
un-known waves before me roll, hiding rock and treacherous shoal;
chart and compass come from thee, Jesus, Saviour, pilot me.

2   As a mother stills her child,
    thou canst hush the ocean wild;
    boisterous waves obey thy will
    when thou biddest them 'Be still.'
    Wondrous sovereign of the sea,
    Jesus, Saviour, pilot me.

3   When at last I near the shore,
    and the fearful breakers roar
    'twixt me and the peaceful land,
    still supported by thy hand,
    may I hear thee say to me,
    'Fear not, I will pilot thee.'

Edward Hopper 1818–1888

268

LEAD US, HEAVENLY FATHER

MANNHEIM 8 7 8 7 8 7   adapted from a chorale by Friedrich Filitz 1804–1876

1 Lead us, heaven-ly Fa-ther, lead us o'er the world's tem-pes-tuous sea;
guard us, guide us, keep us, feed us, for we have no help but thee;
yet pos-sess-ing ev-ery bless-ing if our God our Fa-ther be.

2 Saviour, breathe forgiveness o'er us;
all our weakness thou dost know;
thou didst tread this earth before us,
thou didst feel its keenest woe;
lone and dreary, faint and weary,
through the desert thou didst go.

3 Spirit of our God, descending,
fill our hearts with heavenly joy,
love with every passion blending,
pleasure that can never cloy;
thus provided, pardoned, guided,
nothing can our peace destroy.

James Edmeston 1791–1867

269

GUIDE ME, O THOU GREAT JEHOVAH

CWM RHONDDA 8 7 8 7 8 7 and repeat   John Hughes 1873-1932

1 Guide me, O thou great Je-ho-vah, pil-grim through this bar-ren land.

I am weak, but thou art migh-ty; hold me with thy power-ful hand.

Bread of hea-ven, bread of hea-ven, feed me till I want no more,

feed me till I want no more.

2 Open now the crystal fountain
whence the healing stream doth flow;
let the fiery cloudy pillar
lead me all my journey through.
Strong deliverer,
be thou still my strength and shield.

3 When I tread the verge of Jordan,
bid my anxious fears subside;
death of death, and hell's destruction,
land me safe on Canaan's side:
songs of praises
I will ever give to thee.

William Williams 1717-1791
tr. Peter Williams 1722-1796

270
LEAD, KINDLY LIGHT
ALBERTA 10 4 10 4 10 10

William Henry Harris 1883-

Unison

1 Lead, kind-ly light, a - mid the en-cir-cling gloom; lead thou me on.

The night is dark, and I am far from home; lead thou me on.

Keep thou my feet; I do not ask to see

the dis - tant scene — one step e - nough for me.

2 I was not ever thus, nor prayed that thou
   shouldst lead me on.
   I loved to choose and see my path; but now
   lead thou me on.
   I loved the garish day, and spite of fears
   pride ruled my will: remember not past years.

3 So long thy power hath blest me, sure it still
   will lead me on,
   o'er moor and fen, o'er crag and torrent, till
   the night is gone;
   and with the morn those angel faces smile,
   which I have loved long since, and lost awhile.

   John Henry Newman 1801–1890
   This may be sung to Sandon 129

271

O GOD OF LOVE, O KING OF PEACE

WILDERNESS 8 8 8 8

Reginald Sparshatt Thatcher 1888–1957

1 O God of love, O King of peace, make wars through-out the world to cease; the wrath of sin-ful man re-strain. Give peace, O God, give peace a-gain!

2 Remember, Lord, thy works of old,
the wonders that our fathers told;
remember not our sin's dark stain.
Give peace, O God, give peace again!

3 Whom shall we trust but thee, O Lord?
Where rest but on thy faithful word?
None ever called on thee in vain.
Give peace, O God, give peace again!

4 Where saints and angels dwell above,
all hearts are knit in holy love.
O bind us in that heavenly chain!
Give peace, O God, give peace again!

Henry Williams Baker 1821–1877

*The accidentals within the parentheses
refer to the final stanza only.

272

LORD OF OUR LIFE

ISTE CONFESSOR 11 11 11 5

Poitiers Vesperale 1746
harmonized by Healey Willan 1880-1968

Unison

1 Lord of our life, and God of our sal - va - tion,
star of our night, and hope of ev - ery na - tion:
hear and re - ceive thy church's sup - pli - ca - tion,
Lord God al - migh - ty.

2 Lord, thou canst help when earthly armour faileth;
Lord, thou canst save when deadly sin assaileth;
Lord, o'er thy church nor death nor hell prevaileth;
grant us thy peace, Lord:

3 peace in our hearts, our evil thoughts assuaging;
peace in thy church, where brothers are engaging;
peace, when the world its busy war is waging.
Calm thy foes' raging.

4 Grant us thy help till backward they are driven;
grant them thy truth, that they may be forgiven;
grant peace on earth, and, after we have striven,
peace in thy heaven.

Philip Pusey 1799-1855
based on Matthäus Apelles
von Löwenstern 1594-1648

273

GOD, THE OMNIPOTENT

RUSSIAN HYMN 11 10 11 9

Alexis Feodorovitch Lvov 1799–1871

1 God, the om-ni-po-tent! King, who or-dain-est great winds thy cla-ri-ons, light-nings thy sword: show forth thy pi-ty on high where thou reign-est; give to us peace in our time, O Lord.

2 God the all-merciful! earth hath forsaken
  meekness and mercy, and slighted thy word;
  bid not thy wrath in its terrors awaken;
  give to us peace in our time, O Lord.

3 God the all-righteous one! man hath defied thee;
  yet to eternity standeth thy word;
  falsehood and wrong shall not tarry beside thee;
  give to us peace in our time, O Lord.

4 God the all-wise! by the fire of thy chastening,
  earth shall to freedom and truth be restored;
  through the thick darkness thy kingdom is hastening;
  thou wilt give peace in thy time, O Lord.

5 So shall thy children, with thankful devotion,
  praise him who saved them from peril and sword,
  singing in chorus, from ocean to ocean,   Henry Fothergill Chorley 1808–1872
  peace to the nations, and praise to the Lord.   John Ellerton 1826–1893

274
LET THERE BE LIGHT

CONCORD 4776

Robert J B Fleming 1921–

1 Let there be light, let there be un - der - stand - ing,
let all the na - tions ga - ther, let them be face to face;

2 open our lips,
   open our minds to ponder,
   open the door of concord
   opening into grace;

3 perish the sword,
   perish the angry judgement,
   perish the bombs and hunger,
   perish the fight for gain;

4 hallow our love,
   hallow the deaths of martyrs,
   hallow their holy freedom,
   hallowed be thy name;

5 thy kingdom come,
   thy spirit turn to language,
   thy people speak together,
   thy spirit never fade;

6 let there be light,
   open our hearts to wonder,
   perish the way of terror,
   hallow the world God made.

Frances Wheeler Davis 1936–

275

O DAY OF GOD

BELLWOODS 6 6 8 6

James Hopkirk 1908–

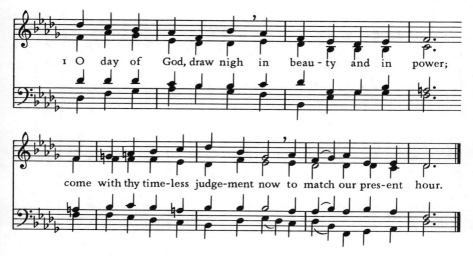

1 O day of God, draw nigh in beau-ty and in power;
come with thy time-less judge-ment now to match our pres-ent hour.

2 Bring to our troubled minds,
   uncertain and afraid,
   the quiet of a steadfast faith,
   calm of a call obeyed.

3 Bring justice to our land,
   that all may dwell secure,
   and finely build for days to come
   foundations that endure.

4 Bring to our world of strife
   thy sovereign word of peace,
   that war may haunt the earth no more
   and desolation cease.

5 O day of God, draw nigh,
   as at creation's birth;
   let there be light again, and set
   thy judgements in the earth.

Robert B Y Scott 1899–

276

THY KINGDOM COME, O GOD

ST CECILIA 6 6 6 6

Leighton George Hayne 1836-1883

1 Thy king-dom come, O God, thy rule, O Christ, be - gin;
break with thine i - ron rod the ty - ran-nies of sin.

2 Where is thy reign of peace,
and purity, and love?
When shall all hatred cease,
as in the realms above?

3 When comes the promised time
that war shall be no more,
and lust, oppression, crime
shall flee thy face before?

4 We pray thee, Lord, arise,
and come in thy great might;
revive our longing eyes,
which languish for thy sight.

5 Men scorn thy sacred name,
and wolves devour thy fold;
by many deeds of shame
we learn that love grows cold.

6 Where peoples near and far
in darkness linger yet,
arise, O morning star,
arise, and never set!

Lewis Hensley 1824-1905

277

ALMIGHTY FATHER, WHO DOST GIVE

IVYHATCH 8 8 8 8   Bertram Luard Selby 1853–1919

1 Al - migh-ty Fa - ther, who dost give the gift of life to all who live,
look down on all earth's sin and strife, and lift us to a nob-ler life.

2 Lift up our hearts, O King of kings,
  to brighter hopes and kindlier things,
  to visions of a larger good,
  and holier dreams of brotherhood.

3 Thy world is weary of its pain,
  of selfish greed and fruitless gain,
  of tarnished honour, falsely strong,
  and all its ancient deeds of wrong.

4 Hear thou the prayer thy servants pray,
  uprising from all lands today,
  and o'er the vanquished powers of sin,
  O bring thy great salvation in.

John Howard Bertram Masterman 1867–1933

278

THY KINGDOM COME—ON BENDED KNEE

IRISH 8 6 8 6   from 'Collection of Hymns and Sacred Poems,' Dublin 1749

1 Thy king - dom come - on bend - ed knee the pass - ing a - ges pray; and faith - ful souls have yearned to see on earth that king - dom's day.

2   But the slow watches of the night
     not less to God belong,
     and for the everlasting right
     the silent stars are strong.

3   And lo, already on the hills
     the flags of dawn appear;
     gird up your loins, ye prophet souls,
     proclaim the day is near:

4   the day in whose clear-shining light
     all wrong shall stand revealed,
     when justice shall be clothed with might,
     and every hurt be healed;

5   when knowledge, hand in hand with peace,
     shall walk the earth abroad;
     the day of perfect righteousness,
     the promised day of God.

Frederick Lucian Hosmer 1840-1929

279

FATHER ETERNAL, RULER OF CREATION

LANGHAM II IO II IO IO

Geoffrey Turton Shaw 1879-1943

Unison

1 Father e - ter - nal, rul - er of cre - a - tion,
Spir - it of life, which moved ere form was made,
through the thick dark - ness cov - ering ev - ery na - tion,
light to man's blind - ness, O be thou our aid:
thy king - dom come, O Lord, thy will be done.

2 Races and peoples, lo, we stand divided,
  and, sharing not our griefs, no joy can share;
  by wars and tumults love is mocked, derided;
  his conquering cross no kingdom wills to bear:
  thy kingdom come, O Lord, thy will be done.

3 Envious of heart, blind-eyed, with tongues confounded,
  nation by nation still goes unforgiven,
  in wrath and fear, by jealousies surrounded,
  building proud towers which shall not reach to heaven:
  thy kingdom come, O Lord, thy will be done.

4 Lust of possession worketh desolations;
  there is no meekness in the sons of earth;
  led by no star, the rulers of the nations
  still fail to bring us to the blissful birth:
  thy kingdom come, O Lord, thy will be done.

5 How shall we love thee, holy hidden being,
  if we love not the world which thou hast made?
  O give us brother-love for better seeing
  thy word made flesh, and in a manger laid:
  thy kingdom come, O Lord, thy will be done.

Laurence Housman 1865-1959

280

LORD OF LIGHT

ALLELUIA 8 7 8 7 D

Samuel Sebastian Wesley 1810–1876

1 Lord of light, whose name out-shin-eth all the stars and suns of space,

deign to make us thy co-work-ers in the king-dom of thy grace;

use us to ful - fil thy pur-pose in the gift of Christ thy Son:

Fa - ther, as in high - est hea-ven so on earth thy will be done.

2   By the toil of nameless workers
     in some far outlying field,
     by the courage where the radiance
     of the cross is still revealed,
     by the victories of meekness
     through reproach and suffering won:
     Father, as in highest heaven,
     so on earth thy will be done.

3   Grant that knowledge, still increasing,
     at thy feet may lowly kneel;
     with thy grace our triumphs hallow,
     with thy charity our zeal;
     lift the nations from the shadows
     to the gladness of the sun:
     Father, as in highest heaven
     so on earth thy will be done.

4   By the prayers of faithful watchmen,
     never silent day or night;
     by the cross of Jesus bringing
     peace to men, and healing light;
     by the love that passeth knowledge,
     making all thy children one:
     Father, as in highest heaven
     so on earth thy will be done.

Howell Elvet Lewis 1860–1953

AND THE FOLLOWING

281

WHEN IN HIS OWN IMAGE

WHITWORTH 6 5 6 5 D

Walter MacNutt 1910–

1 When in his own im - age God cre - a - ted man,

he in - clud - ed free - dom in cre - a - tion's plan.

For he loved us ev - en from be - fore our birth;

by his grace he made us free - men of this earth.

2 God to man entrusted
   life as gift and aim.
   Sin became our prison,
   turning hope to shame.
   Man against his brother
   lifted hand and sword,
   and the father's pleading
   went unseen, unheard.

3 Then in time, our maker
   chose to intervene,
   set his love in person
   in the human scene.
   Jesus broke the circle
   of repeated sin,
   so that man's devotion
   newly might begin.

4 Choose we now in freedom
   where we should belong,
   let us turn to Jesus;
   let our choice be strong.
   May the great obedience
   which in Christ we see
   perfect all our service:
   then we shall be free!

Frederik Herman Kaan 1929-

282

I FEEL THE WINDS OF GOD

KINGSFOLD 8 6 8 6 D

English and Irish traditional melody
harmonized by Ralph Vaughan Williams 1872–1958

1 I feel the winds of God to-day; to - day my sail I lift,

though hea-vy oft with drench-ing spray and torn with ma-ny a rift;

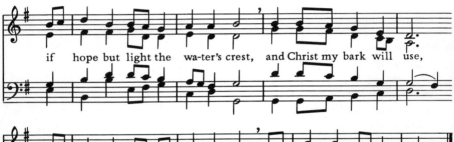

if hope but light the wa-ter's crest, and Christ my bark will use,

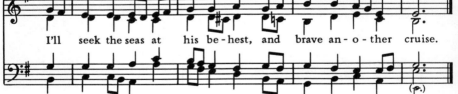

I'll seek the seas at his be-hest, and brave an - o - ther cruise.

2 It is the wind of God that dries
    my vain regretful tears,
    until with braver thoughts shall rise
    the purer, brighter years;
    if cast on shores of selfish ease
    or pleasure I should be,
    Lord, let me feel thy freshening breeze,
    and I'll put back to sea.

3 If ever I forget thy love
    and how that love was shown,
    lift high the blood-red flag above;
    it bears thy name alone.
    Great pilot of my onward way,
    thou wilt not let me drift.
    I feel the winds of God today;
    today my sail I lift.

Jessie Adams 1863–1954
for a higher setting see 202

283

WHO WOULD TRUE VALOUR SEE

MONK'S GATE 6 5 6 5 6 6 6 5

English traditional melody
arranged by Ralph Vaughan Williams 1872-1958

1 Who would true val-our see, let him come hith-er: here's one will con-stant be, come wind, come wea-ther. There's no dis-cour-age-ment shall make him once re-lent his first a-vowed in-tent to be a pil-grim.

2 Whoso beset him round
with dismal stories
do but themselves confound:
his strength the more is.
No lion can him fright,
he'll with a giant fight,
but he will have the right
to be a pilgrim.

3 Since, Lord, thou dost defend
him with thy Spirit,
he knows he at the end
shall life inherit.
Then fancies fly away!
I'll fear not what men say,
but labour night and day
to be a pilgrim.

John Bunyan 1628-1688
and others

284

JUST AS I AM

SAFFRON WALDEN 8 8 8 6   FIRST TUNE

Arthur Henry Brown 1830-1926

1 Just as I am, with - out one plea,

but that thy blood was shed for me,

and that thou bidd'st me come to thee,

O Lamb of God, I come.

2 Just as I am, poor, wretched, blind;
   sight, riches, healing of the mind,
   yea, all I need, in thee to find,
   O Lamb of God, I come.

3 Just as I am, though tossed about
   with many a conflict, many a doubt,
   fightings and fears within, without,
   O Lamb of God, I come.

4 Just as I am, and waiting not
   to rid my soul of one dark blot,
   to thee, whose blood can cleanse each spot,
   O Lamb of God, I come.

5 Just as I am – thy love unknown
   has broken every barrier down –
   now to be thine, yea, thine alone,
   O Lamb of God, I come.

Charlotte Elliott 1789-1871

melody by William Batchelder Bradbury 1816–1868

WOODWORTH 8 8 8 6 SECOND TUNE   harmonized by Stanley L Osborne 1907–

Unison

1 Just as I am, with-out one plea,

but that thy blood was shed for me,

and that thou bidd'st me come to thee,

O Lamb of God, I come, I come.

2 Just as I am, poor, wretched, blind;
  sight, riches, healing of the mind,
  yea, all I need, in thee to find,
  O Lamb of God, I come.

3 Just as I am, though tossed about
  with many a conflict, many a doubt,
  fightings and fears within, without,
  O Lamb of God, I come.

4 Just as I am, and waiting not
  to rid my soul of one dark blot,
  to thee, whose blood can cleanse each spot,
  O Lamb of God, I come.

5 Just as I am – thy love unknown
  has broken every barrier down –
  now to be thine, yea, thine alone,
  O Lamb of God, I come.

Charlotte Elliott 1789–1871

285

MY FAITH LOOKS UP TO THEE

DULWICH 664 6664   FIRST TUNE

Clement McWilliam 1934–

1 My faith looks up to thee, thou Lamb of Cal - va - ry,

Sav - iour di - vine. Now hear me while I pray;

take all my guilt a - way.

O let me from this day be whol - ly thine.

2 May thy rich grace impart
strength to my fainting heart,
my zeal inspire.
As thou hast died for me,
O may my love to thee
pure, warm, and changeless be,
a living fire.

3 While life's dark maze I tread,
and griefs around me spread,
be thou my guide,
bid darkness turn to day;
wipe sorrow's tears away;
nor let me ever stray
from thee aside.

melody from Lowell Mason 1792-1872
harmonized by Stanley L Osborne 1907-

My faith looks up to thee, thou Lamb of Cal - va-ry, Sav - iour di - vine. Now hear me while I pray; take all my guilt a-way. O let me from this day be whol - ly thine.

4 When ends life's transient dream,
   when death's cold sullen stream
   shall o'er me roll,
   blest Saviour, then, in love,
   fear and distrust remove;
   O bear me safe above,
   a ransomed soul.

Ray Palmer 1808-1887

286

THEE WILL I LOVE
PATER OMNIUM 888888

Henry James Ernest Holmes 1852-1938

1 Thee will I love, my strength, my tower;
thee will I love, my joy, my crown;
thee will I love with all my power
in all thy works, and thee a - lone;
thee will I love till sac - red fire
fills my whole soul with warm de - sire.

2   I thank thee, uncreated Sun,
     that thy bright beams on me have shined;
     I thank thee, who hast overthrown
     my foes, and healed my wounded mind;
     I thank thee, whose enlivening voice
     bids my freed heart in thee rejoice.

3   Uphold me in the doubtful race,
     nor suffer me again to stray;
     strengthen my feet with steady pace
     still to press forward in thy way,
     that all my powers, with all their might,
     in thy sole glory may unite.

4   Thee will I love, my joy, my crown;
     thee will I love, my Lord, my God;
     thee will I love, beneath thy frown
     or smile, thy sceptre or thy rod;
     what though my flesh and heart decay,
     thee shall I love in endless day.

Johann Scheffler 1624-1677
tr. John Wesley 1703-1791

287

O LORD AND MASTER OF US ALL

ST SWITHUN 8 6 8 6

Sydney Watson 1903–

1 O Lord and Mas-ter of us all, what - e'er our name or sign, we own thy sway, we hear thy call, we test our lives by thine.

2 Our thoughts lie open to thy sight;
and naked to thy glance
our secret sins are, in the light
of thy pure countenance.

3 Yet weak and blinded though we be,
thou dost our service own;
we bring our varying gifts to thee,
and thou rejectest none.

4 Apart from thee all gain is loss,
all labour vainly done;
the solemn shadow of thy cross
is better than the sun.

5 Our friend, our brother, and our Lord,
what may thy service be?
Nor name, nor form, nor ritual word,
but simply following thee.

6 We faintly hear; we dimly see;
in differing phrase we pray;
but dim or clear, we own in thee
the light, the truth, the way.

John Greenleaf Whittier 1807-1892

288

SAVIOUR, TEACH ME DAY BY DAY

INNOCENTS 7 7 7 7

William Henry Monk 1823-1899

1 Sav-iour, teach me day by day, love's sweet les-son: to o - bey;
sweet-er les-son can-not be, lov-ing him who first loved me.

2 With a childlike heart of love
   at thy bidding may I move,
   prompt to serve and follow thee,
   loving him who first loved me.

3 Teach me thus thy steps to trace,
   strong to follow in thy grace,
   learning how to love from thee,
   loving him who first loved me.

4 Love in loving finds employ,
   in obedience all her joy;
   ever new that joy will be,
   loving him who first loved me.

5 Thus may I rejoice to show
   that I feel the love I owe,
   singing, till thy face I see,
   of his love who first loved me.

Jane Eliza Leeson 1807-1882

AND THE FOLLOWING

98 Lord, be thy word my guide
294 Take my life and let it be
304 O Jesus, I have promised

289

THE EARTH, THE SKY, THE OCEANS

ORBIS TERRARUM 7676D

Frederick R C Clarke 1931-

1 The earth, the sky, the o-ceans and all that they con-tain; the world with all its sec-rets, they are the Lord's do-main. To rule his great cre-a-tion, God has en-dowed man-kind with gifts of strength and cour-age and an in-ven-tive mind.

2   To us from birth is given
      our stewardship and brief,
      to search for truth and purpose,
      to find the heart of life.
      God calls us to adventure
      with work of hand and brain,
      to share with all his people
      the profits we may gain.

3   For quest and exploration,
      our God has given the key
      to free the hidden forces
      and wealth of soil and sea.
      To new advance in science
      research to conquer pain,
      to growth in skill and knowledge,
      we are by God ordained.

4   We pledge ourselves to service,
      that with the help of Christ
      we may be able stewards
      of all that does exist.
      Whate'er we may discover,
      on earth, in outer space,
      God grant that we may use it
      to bless the human race.

Frederik Herman Kaan 1929-

290

YOUR WORK, O GOD, NEEDS MANY HANDS

KILMARNOCK 8 6 8 6

Neil Dougall 1776–1862

1 Your work, O God, needs man-y hands to help you ev-ery - where, and some there are who can-not serve un - less our gifts we share.

2 Because we love you and your work,
   our offering now we make:
   be pleased to use it as your own,
   we ask for Jesus' sake.

Calvin Weiss Laufer 1874–1938

291

ALMIGHTY FATHER, WHO FOR US THY SON DIDST GIVE

ANNUE CHRISTE 12 12 12 12

Cluny Antiphoner 1686
arranged by Alfred Whitehead 1887–

Unison

1 Al - migh - ty Fa - ther, who for us thy Son didst give,

that men and na-tions through his pre-cious death might live,

in mer-cy guard us, lest by sloth and self - ish pride
we cause to stum-ble those for whom the Sav - iour died.

2 We are thy stewards; thine our talents, wisdom, skill;
  our only glory, that we may thy trust fulfil,
  that we thy pleasure in our neighbours' good pursue,
  if thou but workest in us both to will and do.

3 On just and unjust thou thy care dost freely shower;
  make us, thy children, free from greed and lust for power,
  lest human justice, yoked with man's unequal laws,
  oppress the needy and neglect the humble cause.

4 Let not our worship blind us to the claims of love;
  but let thy manna lead us to the feast above,
  to seek the country which by faith we now possess,
  where Christ, our treasure, reigns in peace and righteousness.

George Bradford Caird 1917–

292
SON OF GOD, ETERNAL SAVIOUR
EVERTON 8 7 8 7 D

Henry Thomas Smart 1813-1879

1 Son of God, e - ter-nal Sav-iour, source of life and truth and grace, Son of man, whose birth a-mong us hal-lows all our hu-man race; thou our Head, who throned in glo-ry, for thine own dost ev - er plead: fill us with thy love and pi - ty; heal our ills and help our need.

2 As thou, Lord, hast lived for others,
so may we for others live;
freely have thy gifts been granted,
freely may thy servants give:
thine the gold and thine the silver,
thine the wealth of land and sea,
we but stewards of thy bounty
held in solemn trust for thee.

3 By thy patient years of toiling,
by thy silent hours of pain,
quench our fevered thirst for pleasure,
shame our selfish greed for gain.
Thou who prayedst, thou who willest
that thy people should be one,
grant, O grant our hope's fruition:
here on earth thy will be done.

Somerset Corry Lowry 1855-1932

293

THE WISE MAY BRING THEIR LEARNING

TYROL 7 6 7 6 D

Tyrolese carol

1 The wise may bring their learn-ing, the rich may bring their gold;
and some may bring their great-ness, and glo-ries new and old.
We too would bring our trea-sures to of-fer to the King;
we have no wealth nor wis-dom; what shall we child-ren bring?

2 We'll bring him hearts that love him,
we'll bring him thankful praise,
and young souls meekly striving
to walk in holy ways.
And these shall be the treasures
we offer to the King,
and these are gifts that even
the poorest child may bring.

3 We'll bring the little duties,
we have to do each day;
we'll try our best to please him
at home, at school, at play.
And better are these treasures
to offer to our King,
than richest gifts without them;
yet these a child may bring.

Author unknown c1881

294

TAKE MY LIFE AND LET IT BE

MOZART 7 7 7 7   adapted from Wolfgang Amadeus Mozart 1756-179?

2   Take my hands, and let them move
at the impulse of thy love;
take my feet, and let them be
swift and purposeful for thee.

3   Take my lips and let them be
filled with messages from thee;
take my intellect, and use
every power as thou shalt choose.

4   Take my will, and make it thine;
it shall be no longer mine;
take my heart, it is thine own;
it shall be thy royal throne.

5   Take my love: my Lord, I pour
at thy feet its treasure store;
take myself, and I will be
ever, only, all for thee.

Frances Ridley Havergal 1836-1879

295

LORD OF ALL GOOD

MORESTEAD 10 10 10 10   Sydney Watson 1903–

1 Lord of all good, our gifts we bring to thee,
use them thy ho- ly pur-pose to ful - fil;
to-kens of love and pled-ges they shall be
that our whole life is of-fered to thy will.

2 We give our mind to understand thy ways,
   hands, eyes and voice to serve thy great design;
   heart with the flame of thine own love ablaze,
   till for thy glory all our powers combine.

3 Father, whose bounty all creation shows,
   Christ, by whose willing sacrifice we live,
   Spirit, from whom all life in fullness flows,
   to thee with grateful hearts ourselves we give.

Albert Frederick Bayly 1901–

296

WE GIVE THEE BUT THINE OWN   Johann Balthasar König 1691-1758

FRANCONIA 6 6 8 6   adapted by William Henry Havergal 1793-1870

1 We give thee but thine own, what-e'er the gift may be:
all that we have is thine a-lone, a trust, O Lord, from thee.

2 May we thy bounties thus
   as stewards true receive,
   and gladly as thou blessest us
   to thee our first-fruits give.

3 To comfort and to bless,
   to God the lost to bring,
   to teach the way of life and peace,
   it is a Christ-like thing.

4 And we believe thy word,
   though dim our faith may be:
   whate'er for thine we do, O Lord,
   we do it unto thee.

William Walsham How 1823-1897
for a lower setting see 58

297

FOR THE CROWD OF THOUSANDS

GLENFINLAS 6 5 6 5   Kenneth George Finlay 1882–

1 For the crowd of thou - sands sit - ting on the ground,
se - ven is suf - fi - cient, se - ven will go round.

2 Seven is sufficient,
   fish and loaves of bread;
   Jesus, for our hunger,
   gives us life instead.

3 Jesus makes his offer:
   fish and bread as food.
   Make us truly thankful,
   make our living good.

4 If we give to Jesus
   bread to bless and break,
   five and two will feed us
   seven days a week.

5 What we give to Jesus,
   what with man we share,
   will at last be gathered:
   over and to spare!

Frederik Hermann Kaan 1929–

AND THE FOLLOWING

83 O Lord of every shining constellation
378 For beauty of prairies
380 Hear us, our Father, as we pray

298

A WORKMAN IN A VILLAGE HOME

TYNEMOUTH 868686

from Choron's 'Chants Chorals'

1 A workman in a village home, he toiled for daily bread, he spent his strength in honest work, with hands and heart and head. A King uncrowned, though no man knew, kingly he lived and true.

2 He healed the deaf, the dumb, the blind,
the maimed, the sick, the sad;
he gave to them his Father's strength,
the radiant strength he had.
They followed him, a King uncrowned,
new life with him they found.

3 He rode into Jerusalem,
they hailed him, 'David's Son';
yet when in danger of his life,
they left him, every one.
Though crowned with thorns and crucified,
as Lord and King he died.

4 O King uncrowned, thou Guide of men,
O Captain brave and true,
we praise thee for thy kingly life;
we would be kingly too.
To serve thee now, thou Saviour King,
our lives to thee we bring.

Author unknown c1930

299

O BROTHER MAN

WELWYN 11 10 11 10

Alfred Scott-Gatty 1847-1918

1 O brother man, fold to thy heart thy brother!
Where pity dwells, the peace of God is there;
to worship rightly is to love each other,
each smile a hymn, each kindly deed a prayer.

2 For he whom Jesus loved hath truly spoken:
the holier worship which he deigns to bless
restores the lost, and binds the spirit broken,
and feeds the widow and the fatherless.

3 Follow with reverent steps the great example
of him whose holy work was doing good;
so shall the wide earth seem our Father's temple,
each loving life a psalm of gratitude.

4 Then shall all shackles fall; the stormy clangour
of wild war-music o'er the earth shall cease;
love shall tread out the baleful fire of anger,
and in its ashes plant the tree of peace.

John Greenleaf Whittier 1807-1892

300

WE FIND THEE, LORD

WILFORD 8 7 8 7   adapted from a melody by George Gardner 1853–1925

1 We find thee, Lord, in o-thers' need, we see thee in our bro-thers; by lov-ing word and kind-ly deed we serve the man for o - thers.

2 We look around and see thy face
disfigured, marred, neglected;
we find thee, Lord, in every place,
sought for and unexpected.

3 We offer in simplicity
our loving gift and labour;
and what we do, we do to thee,
incarnate in our neighbour.

4 We love since we are loved by thee;
new strength from thee we gather;
and in thy service we shall be
made perfect with each other.

Giles Ambrose 1912–

301

O MASTER, LET ME WALK WITH THEE

MARYTON 8 8 8 8

melody by Henry Percy Smith 1825-1898
harmonized by Eric Harding Thiman 1900-

1 O Mas-ter, let me walk with thee
in low-ly paths of ser-vice free;
teach me thy se-cret, help me bear
the strain of toil, the fret of care.

2 Help me the slow of heart to move
with some clear, winning word of love;
teach me the wayward feet to stay,
and guide them in the homeward way.

3 Teach me thy patience; still with thee,
in closer, dearer company,
in work that keeps faith sweet and strong,
in trust that triumphs over wrong,

4 in hope that sends a shining ray
far down the future's broadening way,
in peace that only thou canst give,
with thee, O Master, let me live.

Washington Gladden 1836-1918

302

LORD, SPEAK TO ME
WINSCOTT 8 8 8 8

Samuel Sebastian Wesley 1810–1876

1 Lord, speak to me that I may speak

in liv - ing e - choes of thy tone;

as thou hast sought, so let me seek

thy err - ing child - ren lost and lone.

2   O lead me, Lord, that I may lead
     the wandering and the wavering feet;
     O feed me, Lord, that I may feed
     thy hungering ones with manna sweet.

3   O teach me, Lord, that I may teach
     the precious things thou dost impart;
     and wing my words, that they may reach
     the hidden depths of many a heart.

4   O fill me with thy fullness, Lord,
     until my very heart o'erflow
     in kindling thought and glowing word,
     thy love to tell, thy praise to show.

5   O use me, Lord, use even me
     just as thou wilt, and when, and where,
     until thy blessed face I see,
     thy rest, thy joy, thy glory share.

Frances Ridley Havergal 1836-1879
This may be sung to Melcombe 229 or 360

303

WHERE CROSS THE CROWDED WAYS OF LIFE

FULDA 8 8 8 8   Gardiner's 'Sacred Melodies' 1815

1 Where cross the crowd - ed ways of life,

where sound the cries of race and clan,

a - bove the noise of self - ish strife,

we hear thy voice, O Son of Man.

2　In haunts of wretchedness and need,
　　on shadowed thresholds, dark with fears,
　　from paths where hide the lures of greed,
　　we catch the vision of thy tears.

3　From tender childhood's helplessness,
　　from woman's grief, man's burdened toil,
　　from famished souls, from sorrow's stress,
　　thy heart has never known recoil.

4　The cup of water given for thee
　　still holds the freshness of thy grace;
　　yet long these multitudes to see
　　the strong compassion of thy face.

5　O Master, from the mountain side,
　　make haste to heal these hearts of pain;
　　among these restless throngs abide,
　　O tread the city's streets again,

6　till sons of men shall learn thy love
　　and follow where thy feet have trod,
　　till glorious from thy heaven above
　　shall come the city of our God.

Frank Mason North 1850-1935

304

O JESUS, I HAVE PROMISED

WOLVERCOTE 7676D

William Harold Ferguson 1874-1950

1 O Je - sus, I have pro - mised to serve thee to the end;

be thou for ev - er near me, my mas-ter and my friend:

I shall not fear the bat - tle if thou art by my side,

nor wan-der from the path - way if thou wilt be my guide.

2   O let me feel thee near me:
    the world is ever near;
    I see the sights that dazzle,
    the tempting sounds I hear;
    my foes are ever near me,
    around me and within;
    but, Jesus, draw thou nearer
    and shield my soul from sin.

3   O let me hear thee speaking
    in accents clear and still,
    above the storms of passion,
    the murmurs of self-will;
    O speak to reassure me,
    to hasten or control;
    O speak, and make me listen,
    thou guardian of my soul.

4   O Jesus, thou has promised
    to all who follow thee,
    that where thou art in glory
    there shall thy servant be;
    and Jesus, I have promised
    to serve thee to the end;
    O give me grace to follow,
    my master and my friend.

John Ernest Bode 1816–1874
This may be sung to Thornbury 152

AND THE FOLLOWING

305

LORD, AS WE RISE TO LEAVE

LOBET DEN HERREN 11 11 11 5

Johann Crüger 1598–1662

1 Lord, as we rise to leave this shell of wor - ship,
called to the risk of un - pro - tect - ed liv - ing,
will - ing to be at one with all your peo - ple,
we ask for cour - age.

2 For all the strain with living interwoven,
for the demands each day will make upon us,
and for the love we owe the modern city,
Lord, make us cheerful.

3 Give us an eye for openings to serve you;
make us alert when calm is interrupted,
ready and wise to use the unexpected;
sharpen our insight.

4 Lift from our life the blanket of convention;
give us the nerve to lose our life to others;
be with your church in death and resurrection,
Lord of all ages!

Frederik Herman Kaan 1929–

306

FORTH IN THY NAME, O LORD

SONG 34 8 8 8 8   Orlando Gibbons 1583-1625

1 Forth in thy name, O Lord, I go,
my dai-ly la-bour to pur-sue,
thee, on-ly thee, re-solved to know
in all I think, or speak, or do.

2 The task thy wisdom hath assigned
O let me cheerfully fulfil,
in all my works thy presence find,
and prove thy good and perfect will.

3 Thee may I set at my right hand,
whose eyes my inmost substance see,
and labour on at thy command
and offer all my works to thee.

4 Give me to bear thy easy yoke,
and every moment watch and pray,
and still to things eternal look,
and hasten to thy glorious day;

5 for thee delightfully employ
whate'er thy bounteous grace hath given,
and run my course with even joy,
and closely walk with thee to heaven.

Charles Wesley 1707-1788

307

FROM GLORY TO GLORY ADVANCING

ST KEVERNE 14 14 14 15

Craig Seller Lang 1891–

1 From glo-ry to glo-ry ad-vanc-ing we praise thee, O Lord;
thy name with the Fa-ther and Spir-it be ev-er a-dored.
From strength un-to strength we go for-ward on Zi-on's high-way,
to ap-pear be-fore God in the ci-ty of in-fi-nite day.

2 Thanksgiving, and glory, and worship, and blessing, and love,
one heart and one song have the saints upon earth and above,
O Lord, evermore to thy servants thy presence be nigh;
ever fit us by service on earth for thy service on high.

from the Liturgy of St James   tr. Charles W. Humphreys 1840–1921

Last line of v. 2

ev-er fit us by ser - vice on earth for thy ser-vice on high.

308

LORD, DISMISS US WITH THY BLESSING

ALLELUIA, DULCE CARMEN 8 7 8 7 8 7

Samuel Webbe 1740–1816

1 Lord, dis-miss us with thy bless-ing; fill our hearts with joy and peace;
let us each, thy love pos-sess-ing, tri-umph in re-deem-ing grace;
O re-fresh us, O re-fresh us, tra-velling through the wil-der-ness.

2 Thanks we give and adoration
for thy gospel's joyful sound;
may the fruits of thy salvation
in our hearts and lives abound;
may thy presence
with us evermore be found.

John Fawcett 1740-1816

309

MAY THE GRACE OF CHRIST

OMNI DIE 8 7 8 7

Corner's Gesangbuch 1631
arranged by William Smith Rockstro 1823–1895

1 May the grace of Christ our Saviour, and the Father's boundless love, with the Holy Spirit's favour, rest upon us from above.

2 Thus may we abide in union
with each other and the Lord,
and possess in rich communion
joys which earth cannot afford.

John Newton 1725–1807
This may be sung to Sharon 319

AND THE FOLLOWING

25 Eternal, Unchanging, we sing to thy praise
35 Ye servants of God, your Master proclaim
173 Lead on, O King eternal
195 King of glory, King of peace
252 Eternal ruler of the ceaseless round
304 O Jesus, I have promised

Sacraments and other acts

310

A LITTLE CHILD THE SAVIOUR CAME

PUER NOBIS NASCITUR 8 8 8 8

melody from Michael Praetorius 1571-1621
harmonized by Derek Holman 1931-

1 A lit - tle child the Sav - iour came,

the migh - ty God was still his name;

and an - gels wor - shipped as he lay

the help - less in - fant of a day.

2 He who, a little child, began
the life divine to show to man,
proclaims from heaven the message free,
'Let little children come to me.'

3 We bring them, Lord, and with the sign
of living water name them thine:
their souls with saving grace endow;
baptize them with thy Spirit now.

4 O give thine angels charge, good Lord,
them safely in thy way to guard;
thy blessing on their lives command,
and write their names upon thy hand.

5 O thou, who by an infant's tongue
dost hear thy perfect glory sung,
may these, with all the heavenly host,
praise Father, Son, and Holy Ghost.

William Robertson 1820-1864
for another setting see 100

311

JESUS, SON OF BLESSED MARY

SHIPSTON 8 7 8 7

English traditional melody
arranged by Ralph Vaughan Williams 1872–1958

1 Je-sus, Son of bless-ed Ma-ry, once on earth a lit-tle child,

pat-tern fair of ho-ly liv-ing, gra-cious, lov-ing, un-de-filed:

2 though thy eager heart was yearning
   heavy-laden souls to free,
   yet thou calledst little children
   in their happiness to thee.

3 Thy bright kingdom still they enter
   through this sacrament of grace;
   in thy loving arms enfold them;
   hands of blessing on them place.

4 From the power of sin delivered
   may they learn to live for God,
   guided by thy Holy Spirit,
   nourished with the living word.

5 Grant that we, like little children,
   free from pride and guile may be;
   cheerful, trusting, safe, protected
   by the blessed trinity.

Charles Edward Riley 1884–
for a higher setting see 381

3I2

O LORD OF LIFE

PIER PAUL irregular

H Barrie Cabena 1933–

1 O Lord of life, who wills new life to be through love cre-a-ted:
born a child, in hu-man fa-mi-ly,
shaped in your im-age, this lit-tle child we bring.
With glad thanks-giv-ing be-fore you now we sing.

2　O Lord of love, who gives this sign to be
the outward symbol
of your love,
the seal of unity
which binds our children
and ourselves to you:
hear now the promise
these parents make anew.

3 O Lord of power, whose Spirit you have sent
to be received here,
as a gift,
through word and sacrament,
empower your people
with steadfast intent;
give us high purpose
to keep this covenant.

Margaret Joyce Dickin 1918-

313

NOW IN THE NAME OF HIM
LOB SEI DEM ALLMÄCHTIGEN GOTT 8 8 8 8

Johann Crüger 1598-1662

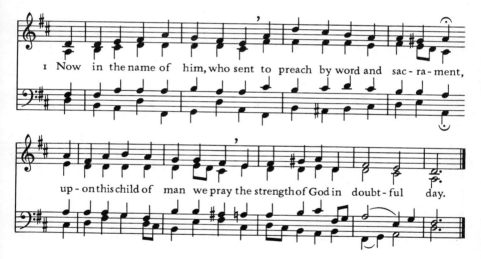

1 Now in the name of him, who sent to preach by word and sac-ra-ment,
up-on this child of man we pray the strength of God in doubt-ful day.

2 Our names are written in his hand;
he leads us to the promised land.
We rise in wonder from the flood
and love becomes our livelihood.

3 With Noah through disaster born,
with Moses from the river drawn,
with Jonah from the sea released,
we celebrate this rising feast.

4 The water is a seal and sign
of costly love that makes us clean.
This love we see in Christ portrayed,
who rose triumphant from the dead.

5 We sing our thanks that old and young
so to the church of Christ belong.
This is the covenant of grace;
we look salvation in the face.

Frederik Herman Kaan 1929-
This may be sung to Fulda 303

314

ETERNAL GOD, WE CONSECRATE

ARDEN 8 6 8 6

George Thomas Thalben-Ball 1896-

1 E - ter - nal God, we con - sec - rate

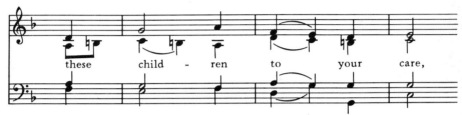

these child - ren to your care,

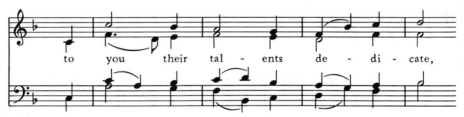

to you their tal - ents de - di - cate,

for they your im - age bear.

2 To them our solemn pledge we give,
   their lives by prayer to shield.
   May they in truth and honour live
   and to your guidance yield.

3 Your Spirit's power on them bestow,
   from sin their hearts preserve.
   In Christ their master may they grow
   and him for ever serve.

4 So may the waters of this rite
   become a means of grace,
   and these your children show the light
   that shone in Jesus' face.

Robert Dobbie 1901-

315

IN TOKEN THAT THOU SHALT NOT FEAR

BEDFORD 8 6 8 6

William Weale c1690–1727

1 In to-ken that thou shalt not fear
Christ cru-ci-fied to own,
we print the cross up-on thee here,
and stamp thee his a-lone.

2 In token that thou shalt not blush
   to glory in his name,
   we blazon here upon thy front
   his glory and his shame.

3 In token that thou shalt not flinch
   Christ's quarrel to maintain,
   but 'neath his banner manfully
   firm at thy post remain:

4 in token that thou too shalt tread
   the path he travelled by,
   endure the cross, despise the shame,
   and reign with him on high:

5 thus outwardly and visibly
   we seal thee for his own;
   and may the brow that wears his cross
   hereafter share his crown.

Henry Alford 1810-1871
This may be sung to
St Stephen 151 or 207

316

WE PRAISE YOU, LORD

DAYSPRING 8 6 8 6

Charles Harford Lloyd 1849–1919

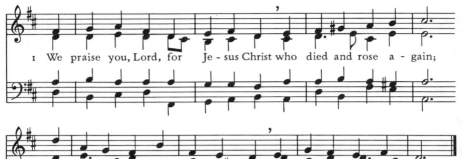

1 We praise you, Lord, for Je - sus Christ who died and rose a - gain;

he lives to break the power of sin and o - ver death to reign.

Organ

2 We praise you that this child now shares
   the freedom Christ can give,
   has died to sin with Christ, and now
   with Christ is raised to live.

3 We praise you, Lord, that now this child
   is grafted to the vine,
   is made a member of your house
   and bears the cross as sign.

4 We praise you, Lord, for Jesus Christ,
   he loves this child we bring:
   he frees, forgives, and heals us all,
   he lives and reigns as King.

Judith Beatrice O'Neill 1930–

317

WITH GRATEFUL HEARTS

GOTTLOB, ES GEHT 9 8 9 8

old German melody
harmonized by Stanley L Osborne 1907-

1 With grate-ful hearts our faith pro-fess-ing, we ask you, Fa-ther, grant us aid, that we our child-ren re-pos-sess-ing, may keep the vows that we have made.

2 We know that in your true providing
the young and old to Christ belong;
Lord, help us to be wise in guiding,
and make us in example strong.

3 Give to the parents love and patience,
each home with Christian graces fill;
protect our children in temptations,
and keep them safe in childhood's ill.

4 Accept, O Lord, our dedication
to fill with love the growing mind,
that in this church and congregation
the young a faith for life may find.

Frederik Herman Kaan 1929-
This may be sung to
Les Commandemens 225 or 366

318

LOBET DEN HERREN 11 11 11 5 irregular   Johann Crüger 1598-1662

1 Praise and thanks-giv-ing be to our Cre-a-tor,
source of this sac-ra-ment, Fa-ther, Med-i-a-tor.
Bapt-tize and make your own these who come be-fore you,
while we a-dore you.

2 Not our own holiness, nor that we have striven
brings us the peace which you, O Christ, have given.
Baptize and set apart; come, O risen Saviour,
with grace and favour.

3 Come, Holy Spirit; come in visitation:
you are the truth, our hope and our salvation.
Baptize with joy and power; give, O dove descending,
life never ending.

Frank Whiteley 1914-
Harold Francis Yardley 1911-

319

FATHER OF THE HUMAN FAMILY

SHARON 8 7 8 7   later form of a tune by William Boyce c1710-1791

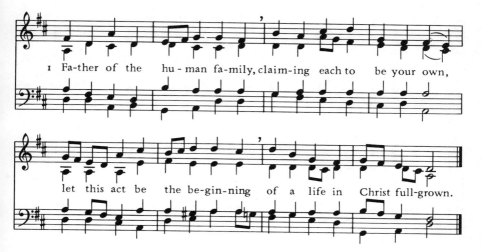

1 Father of the human family, claiming each to be your own,
let this act be the beginning of a life in Christ full-grown.

2 Grace and strength grant these young parents;
   of their call keep them aware;
   with your love surround these children,
   they your life of joy to share.

3 As the church we live your praises,
   marked for service in your name;
   with your Spirit born within us,
   we our worlds for Christ reclaim.

4 And from us, your gathered people,
   prayer and praise is offered new;
   by your grace we have been strengthened,
   greater works in faith to do.   Walter Henry Farquharson 1936-

AND THE FOLLOWING

4 Ye gates, lift up your heads on high
9 O praise ye the Lord
15 O come, let us sing to the Lord
23 The God of Bethlehem praise
29 Praise to the Lord, the Almighty, the King
31 O thou my soul, bless God the Lord
34 O Lord, thou art my God and King

39 At the name of Jesus
58 Blest are the pure in heart
141 My God, how endless is thy love
151 Behold the amazing gift of love
197 Now thank we all our God
253 Be thou my vision

320

HOLY SPIRIT, LORD OF LOVE

HEATHLANDS 7 7 7 7 7 7   Henry Thomas Smart 1813-1879

1 Holy Spir-it, Lord of love, thou who cam-est from a-bove,

gifts of bless-ing to be-stow on thy wait-ing church be-low:

once a-gain in love draw near to thy ser-vants ga-thered here.

2   Give them light thy truth to see,
    give them life to live for thee,
    daily power to conquer sin,
    patient faith the crown to win;
    shield them from temptation's breath,
    keep them faithful unto death.

3   When the sacred vow is made,
    when the hands are on them laid,
    come in this most solemn hour,
    with thy sevenfold gifts of power;
    come, thou blessed Spirit, come,
    make each eager heart thy home.

William Dalrymple Maclagan 1826-1910
for a lower setting see 234

321
LIFT HIGH THE CROSS
CRUCIFER 10 10 10 10

Sydney Hugh Nicholson 1875-1947

Lift high the cross ...

2 Led on their way by this triumphant sign,
the hosts of God in conquering ranks combine.

Lift high the cross ...

3 Each new-born soldier of the Crucified
bears on his brow the seal of him who died.

Lift high the cross ...

4 O Lord, once lifted on the glorious tree,
as thou hast promised, draw men unto thee.

Lift high the cross ...
5 So shall our song of triumph ever be
 praise to the Crucified for victory.
 Lift high the cross ...

George William Kitchin 1827-1912
Michael Robert Newbolt 1874-1956

322

O GOD, UNSEEN YET EVER NEAR

ST FLAVIAN 8 6 8 6

Day's Psalmes 1562

1 O God, un-seen yet ev-er near, re-veal thy pres-ence now while we in love that hath no fear, be-fore thy glo-ry bow.

2 Here may thy faithful people know
the blessings of thy love,
the streams that through the desert flow,
the manna from above.

3 We come, obedient to thy word,
to feast on heavenly food,
our meat the body of the Lord,
our drink his precious blood.

4 Thus may we all thy word obey,
for we, O God, are thine,
and go rejoicing on our way,
renewed with strength divine.

Edward Osler 1798-1863
for a lower setting see 59

323

THE SON OF GOD PROCLAIM

SUNDERLAND 6686

Henry Thomas Smart 1813-1879

1 The Son of God proclaim, the Lord of time and space;
the God who bade the light break forth now shines in Jesus' face.

2 Behold his outstretched hands;
   though all was in his power
   he took the towel and basin then,
   and serves us in this hour.

3 He, God's creative word,
   the church's Lord and head,
   here bids us gather as his friends,
   and share his wine and bread.

4 The Lord of life and death
   with wondering praise we sing;
   we break the bread at his command,
   and name him God and King.

5 We take this cup in hope:
   for he, who gladly bore
   the shameful cross, is risen again,
   and reigns for evermore.

Basil E Bridge 1927-

324

LORD, ENTHRONED IN HEAVENLY SPLENDOUR

ST OSMUND 8 7 8 7 4 7

proper melody from the Solesmes version
harmonized by Healey Willan 1880-1968

1 Lord, en-throned in heaven-ly splen-dour, first be-got-ten from the dead,

thou a - lone, our strong de-fend-er, lift-est up thy peo-ple's head.

Al - le - lu - ia, Je - sus, true and liv - ing bread!

2 Here our humblest homage pay we;
 here in loving reverence bow;
 here for faith's discernment pray we,
 lest we fail to know thee now.
 Alleluia,
 thou art here, we ask not how.

3 Though the lowliest form doth veil thee
 as of old in Bethlehem,
 here as there thine angels hail thee,
 branch and flower of Jesse's stem.
 Alleluia,
 we in worship join with them.

4 Paschal Lamb, thine offering, finished
 once for all when thou wast slain,
 in its fullness undiminished
 shall for evermore remain—
 alleluia—
 cleansing souls from every stain.

5 Life-imparting heavenly manna,
 stricken rock with streaming side,
 heaven and earth with loud hosanna
 worship thee, the Lamb who died—
 alleluia—
 risen, ascended, glorified!

George Hugh Bourne 1840–1925

325

LET US BREAK BREAD TOGETHER

NEGRO MELODY irregular

traditional

harmonized by Frederick R C Clarke 1931-

Unison

1 Let us break bread to-geth-er on our knees,
2 Let us drink wine to-geth-er on our knees,

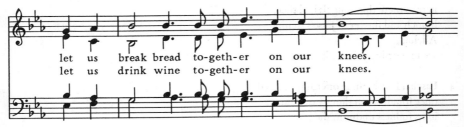

let us break bread to-geth-er on our knees.
let us drink wine to-geth-er on our knees.

When I fall down on my knees with my face to the ris-ing sun,

Oh, Lord, have mer-cy on me.

3 Let us praise God to-geth-er on our knees,

let us praise God to-geth-er on our knees.

When I fall down on my knees with my face to the ris-ing sun,

Oh, Lord, have mer-cy on me.

Negro Spiritual

326

BREAD OF THE WORLD
RENDEZ À DIEU 9898D

Genevan Psalter 1543
harmonized by Stanley L Osborne 1907

1 Bread of the world, in mer-cy bro - ken, wine of the
  Pain vi - vant don - né pour nos â - mes, vin pour nos

soul in mer - cy shed, by whom the words of life were
ê - tres ré - pan - du, pa - ro - les d'a-mour et de

spo - ken, and in whose death our sins are dead:
flam - mes, mort où l'es - poir nous est ren - du;

look on the heart by sor-row bro - ken, look on the tears by
vois no-tre des - tin mi - sé - ra - ble, les pleurs ver-sés sur

sin - ners shed; and be thy feast to us the
nos mal - heurs, nour - ris - nous à ta sain - te

to - ken that by thy grace our souls are fed.
ta - ble par ta bon - té, par tes dou - leurs.

Reginald Heber 1783-1826
tr. Henri Chapieu

327

MY GOD, AND IS THY TABLE SPREAD?

DAS WALT' GOTT VATER 8 8 8 8   probably by Daniel Vetter ?-c1730
harmonized by Stanley L Osborne 1907-

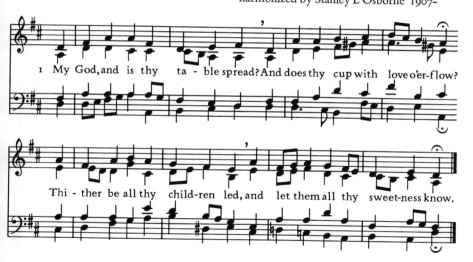

1 My God, and is thy ta - ble spread? And does thy cup with love o'er-flow?

Thi - ther be all thy child-ren led, and let them all thy sweet-ness know.

2 Let crowds approach with hearts prepared;
   with hearts inflamed let all attend,
   nor, when we leave our Father's board,
   the pleasure or the profit end.

3 O let thy table honoured be,
   and furnished well with joyful guests;
   and may each soul salvation see
   that here its sacred pledges tastes.

Philip Doddridge 1702-1751
This may be sung to Rockingham 109

328

I COME WITH JOY TO MEET MY LORD

TWYFORD 8686   Leonard James Blake 1907–

1 I come with joy to meet my Lord, for-giv-en, loved, and free,
in awe and won-der to re-call his life laid down for me.

2 I come with Christians far and near
to find, as we are fed,
man's true community of love
in Christ's communion bread.

3 As Christ breaks bread for men to share
each proud division ends.
That love that made us makes us one,
and strangers now are friends.

4 And thus with joy we meet our Lord,
His presence, always near,
is in such friendship better known:
we see, and praise him here.

5 Together met, together bound,
we'll go our different ways,
and as his people in the world,
we'll live and speak his praise.

Brian Arthur Wren 1936–

329

THEE WE ADORE, O HIDDEN SAVIOUR

ADORO TE 10 10 10 10   proper melody from the Solesmes version
arranged by Margaret Drynan 1915–

1 Thee we a-dore, O hid-den Sav-iour, thee,

who in thy sac - ra - ment dost deign to be;

both flesh and spir - it at thy pres - ence fail,

yet here thy pres - ence we de-vout - ly hail. A - men.

2   O blest memorial of our dying Lord,
    who living bread to men doth here afford,
    O may our souls for ever feed on thee,
    and thou, O Christ, for ever precious be.

3   Fountain of goodness, Jesus, Lord and God,
    cleanse us, unclean, with thy most cleansing blood;
    increase our faith and love, that we may know
    the hope and peace which from thy presence flow.

4   O Christ, whom now beneath a veil we see,
    may what we thirst for soon our portion be,
    to gaze on thee unveiled, and see thy face,
    the vision of thy glory and thy grace.

Thomas Aquinas 13th century
tr. James Russell Woodford 1820-1885

330

ONCE, ONLY ONCE, AND ONCE FOR ALL

ALBANO 8686 FIRST TUNE

Vincent Novello 1781-1861

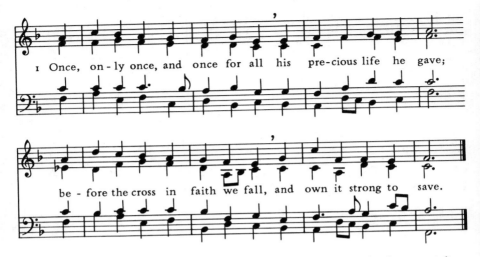

1 Once, on-ly once, and once for all his pre-cious life he gave;
be-fore the cross in faith we fall, and own it strong to save.

2 'One offering single and complete'
with lips and heart we say;
but what he never can repeat
he shows forth day by day.

3 For, as the priest of Aaron's line
within the holiest stood,
and sprinkled all the mercy-shrine
with sacrificial blood,

4 so he, who once atonement wrought,
our priest of endless power,
presents himself for those he bought
in that dark noontide hour.

5 His manhood pleads where now it lives
on heaven's eternal throne,
and where in mystic rite he gives
its presence to his own.

6 And so we show thy death, O Lord,
till thou again appear,
and feel, when we approach thy board,
we have an altar here.

7 All glory to the Father be,
all glory to the Son,
all glory, Holy Ghost, to thee,
while endless ages run.

William Bright 1824-1901

later form of a melody from
William Damon's Psalms 1591

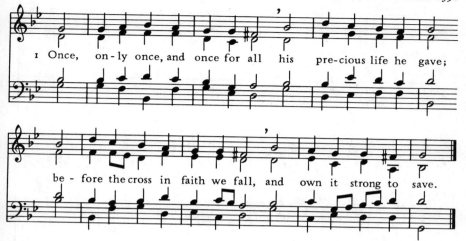

1 Once, on - ly once, and once for all   his   pre-cious life he   gave;

be - fore the cross in   faith we fall,   and   own it   strong to   save.

2 'One offering single and complete'
with lips and heart we say;
but what he never can repeat
he shows forth day by day.

3 For, as the priest of Aaron's line
within the holiest stood,
and sprinkled all the mercy-shrine
with sacrificial blood,

4 so he, who once atonement wrought,
our priest of endless power,
presents himself for those he bought
in that dark noontide hour.

5 His manhood pleads where now it lives
on heaven's eternal throne,
and where in mystic rite he gives
its presence to his own.

6 And so we show thy death, O Lord,
till thou again appear,
and feel, when we approach thy board,
we have an altar here.

7 All glory to the Father be,
all glory to the Son,
all glory, Holy Ghost, to thee,
while endless ages run.

William Bright 1824-1901

331

AND NOW, O FATHER, MINDFUL OF THE LOVE

SONG 4 10 10 10 10 10 10

Orlando Gibbons 1583-1625

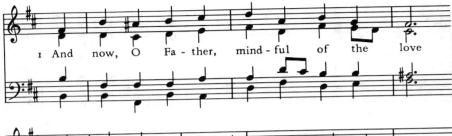

1 And now, O Fa-ther, mind-ful of the love

that bought us, once for all, on Cal-vary's tree,

and hav-ing with us him that pleads a-bove,

we here pre-sent, we here spread forth to thee

that on-ly of-fering per-fect in thine eyes,

the one true, pure, im-mor-tal sac-ri-fice.

2 Look, Father, look on his anointed face,
   and only look on us as found in him;
   look not on our misusings of thy grace,
   our prayer so languid, and our faith so dim:
   for lo! between our sins and their reward
   we set the passion of thy Son our Lord.

3 And then for those, our dearest and our best,
   by this prevailing presence we appeal;
   O fold them closer to thy mercy's breast,
   O do thine utmost for their souls' true weal;
   from tainting mischief keep them pure and clear,
   and crown thy gifts with strength to persevere.

4 And so we come; O draw us to thy feet,
   most patient Saviour, who canst love us still;
   and by this food, so awesome and so sweet,
   deliver us from every touch of ill:
   in thine own service make us glad and free,
   and grant us never more to part with thee.

William Bright 1824-1901

332
LET ALL MORTAL FLESH KEEP SILENCE
PICARDY 8 7 8 7 8 7

French traditional carol

1 Let all mor-tal flesh keep si - lence, and with awe and wel - come stand;
1 Oh! que tou-te chair se tai - se, fré-mis-sant d'un saint es - poir;

pon-der noth-ing earth-ly - mind-ed, for with bless-ing in his hand,
pen-seés é - phé - mè - res, vai - nes ah! quit - tez l'âme et le cœur.

Christ our God to us ap - proach - eth
Le Sei - gneur des - cend sur ter - re,

our full hom - age to de - mand.
Dieu lui don - ne tout pou - voir.

2 King of kings, yet born of Mary,
as of old on earth he stood,
Lord of lords, in human vesture,
in the body and the blood,
he will give to all the faithful
his own self for heavenly food.

3 Rank on rank the host of heaven
spreads its vanguard on the way,
as the Light of light descendeth
from the realms of endless day,
that the powers of hell may vanish
as the darkness clears away.

4 At his feet the six-winged seraph;
cherubim with sleepless eye
veil their faces to the presence,
as with ceaseless voice they cry,
Alleluia, alleluia,
alleluia, Lord most high.

from the Liturgy of St James
tr. Gerard Moultrie 1829-1885

2 Roi des rois, ton Fils, Marie,
aux jours de sa chair il vint
dans le pauvre corps des hommes,
des seigneurs pourtant Seigneur,
nourrir et sauver le monde,
dont il est le pain divin.

3 O Prince de paix, de grâce,
toi qui sais calmer la mer,
fais triompher la lumière,
fais tomber du ciel Satan!
Dans nos tristes cœurs, si lâches,
Christ, fais reculer l'enfer!

4 Tandis que le chœur des anges
chante, en se voilant les yeux:
gloire à celui qui se donne,
qui se rend obéissant
jusques à la mort infâme;
gloire au Christ venu des cieux!

tr. Suzanne Bidgrain c1880-1962

333

DECK THYSELF, MY SOUL, WITH GLADNESS

SCHMÜCKE DICH 8 8 8 8 D

Johann Crüger 1598-1662

1 Deck thy - self, my soul, with glad - ness,

leave the gloom - y haunts of sad - ness,

come in - to the day - light's splen - dour,

there with joy thy prais - es ren - der

un - to him, whose grace un - bound - ed

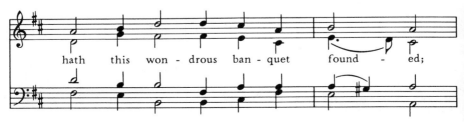

hath this won - drous ban - quet found - ed;

high o'er all the heavens he reign - eth,

yet to dwell with thee he deign - eth.

2 Now I sink before thee lowly,
   filled with joy most deep and holy,
   as with trembling awe and wonder
   on thy mighty works I ponder;
   how, by mystery surrounded,
   depths no man hath ever sounded,
   none may dare to pierce unbidden
   secrets that with thee are hidden.

3 Sun, who all my life dost brighten;
   Light, who dost my soul enlighten;
   Joy, the sweetest man e'er knoweth;
   Fount, whence all my being floweth:
   at thy feet I cry, my Maker,
   let me be a fit partaker
   of this blessed food from heaven,
   for our good, thy glory, given.

4 Jesus, Bread of life, I pray thee,
   let me gladly here obey thee;
   never to my hurt invited,
   be thy love with love requited;
   from this banquet let me measure,
   Lord, how vast and deep its treasure;
   through the gifts thou here dost give me,
   as thy guests in heaven receive me.

Johann Franck 1618-1677
tr. Catherine Winkworth 1829-1878

334

IN MEMORY OF THE SAVIOUR'S LOVE

ST ENODOC 8686   Craig Sellar Lang 1891–

1 In mem-ory of the Sav-iour's love
we keep the sac - red feast,
where ev-ery hum - ble, con - trite heart
is made a wel - come guest.

2 By faith we take the bread of life
  with which our souls are fed,
  the cup in token of his blood
  that was for sinners shed.

3 Under his banner thus we sing
  the wonders of his love,
  and thus anticipate by faith
  the heavenly feast above.

Thomas Cotterill 1779–1823
This may be sung to Evan 190

335

ON THIS DAY OF SHARING

PRESENCE 6 5 6 5

Stanley L Osborne 1907–

1 On this day of shar - ing glad - ly do we come
to the Lord's own ta - ble, ga-ther-ing as one.

2 See the table laden
with the bread and wine,
sign of Christ's own presence,
pledge of love divine!

3 Food and drink, symbolic
of his life on earth:
peace, good will to all men,
promised from his birth.

4 In the bread that's broken
in the wine that's poured,
be the name of Jesus
evermore adored!

5 Many urgent problems
face the human race –
war and vice and hunger:
God seems out of place.

6 Yet our Saviour sends us
to this world of sin,
calling men to Jesus:
'Let Christ enter in!'

7 Then, depart to serve him;
worship him as God;
follow as he leads us
in the way he trod.

David Kenneth Bentley 1948–
Doreen Margaret Jeal 1940–
Marsha Coburn Kahale 1947–
Robert Kyba 1949–

336

SONS OF GOD

SONS OF GOD irregular

James Thiem 1942–

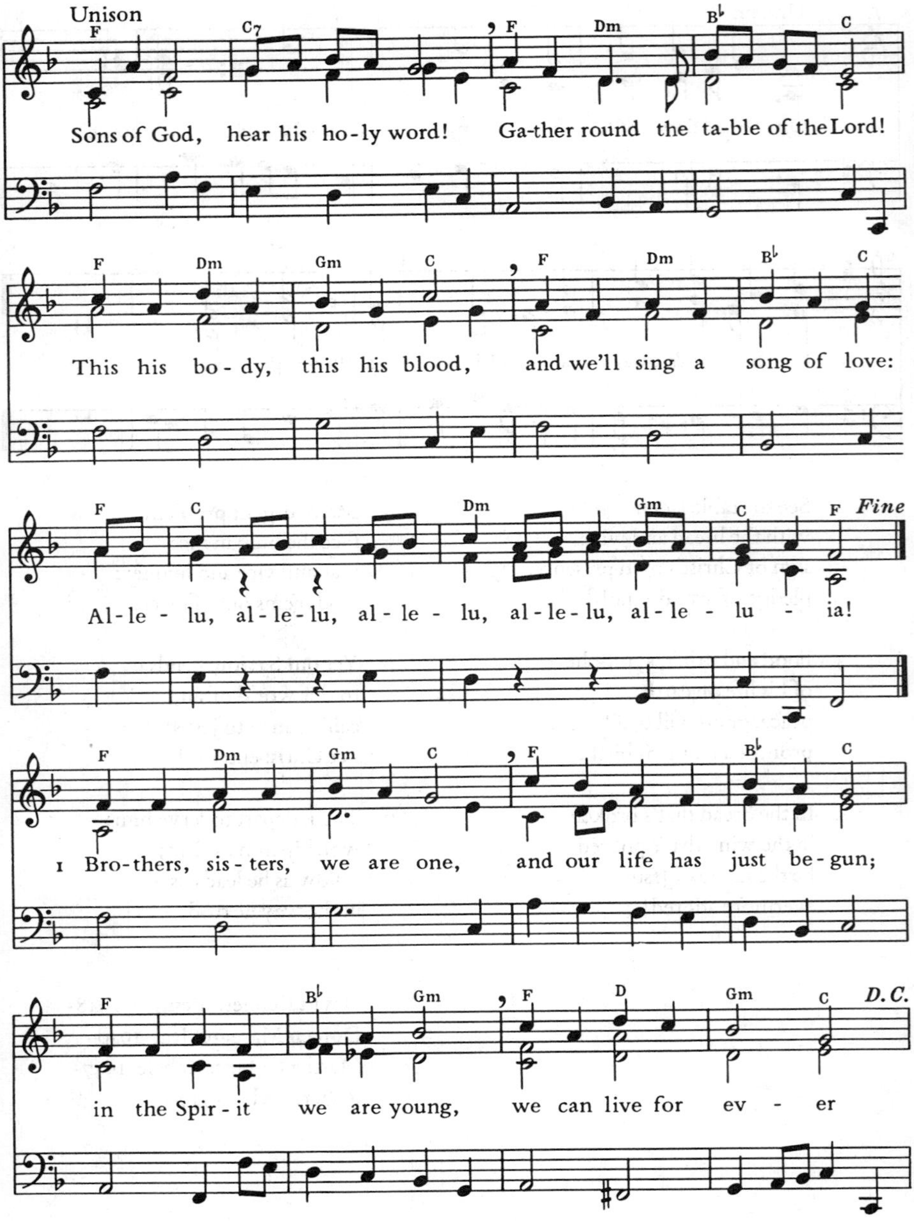
Unison
F C7 F Dm B♭ C
Sons of God, hear his ho-ly word! Ga-ther round the ta-ble of the Lord!
F Dm Gm C F Dm B♭ C
This his bo-dy, this his blood, and we'll sing a song of love:
F C Dm Gm C F Fine
Al-le-lu, al-le-lu, al-le-lu, al-le-lu, al-le-lu-ia!
F Dm Gm C F B♭ C
1 Bro-thers, sis-ters, we are one, and our life has just be-gun;
F B♭ Gm F D Gm C D.C.
in the Spir-it we are young, we can live for ev-er

2　Shout together to the Lord
　　who has promised our reward -
　　happiness a hundredfold;
　　and we'll live for ever
　　sons of God ...

3　If we want to live with him,
　　we must also die with him,
　　die to selfishness and sin,
　　and we'll rise for ever
　　sons of God ...

4　Make the world a unity,
　　make all men one family
　　joining with the trinity
　　to live with them for ever
　　sons of God ...

5　With the church we celebrate,
　　Jesus' coming we await;
　　so we make a holiday,
　　so we'll live for ever
　　sons of God ...

James Thiem 1942–
It is intended that 'allelu' be sung antiphonally.

337

WE HAIL THEE NOW
PASSION CHORALE 7 6 7 6 D

Hans Leo Hassler 1564-1612
harmonized by Johann Sebastian Bach 1685-1750

1 We hail thee now, O Jesus, thy presence here we own,
though sight and touch have failed us, and faith perceives alone;
thy love has veiled thy glory, and hid thy power divine,
in mercy to our weakness, beneath an earthly sign.

2 We hail thee now, O Jesus,
   in silence hast thou come,
   for all the hosts of heaven
   with wonderment are dumb—
   so great the condescension,
   so marvellous the love,
   which for our sakes, O Saviour,
   have drawn thee from above.

3 We hail thee now, O Jesus,
   for law and type have ceased,
   and thou in each communion
   art sacrifice and priest;
   we make this great memorial
   in union, Lord, with thee,
   and plead thy death and passion
   to cleanse and set us free.

4 We hail thee now, O Jesus,
  for death is ever near,
  and in thy presence only
  its terrors disappear;
  dwell with us, living Saviour,
  and guide us through the night,
  till shadows end in glory,
  and faith is lost in sight.

Frederick George Scott 1861-1944
for another setting see 452

338

HERE, LORD, WE TAKE THE BROKEN BREAD

ACH GOTT UND HERR 8 7 8 7   Christian Gall's 'As Hymnodus sacer' Leipzig 1625
                    adapted and harmonized by Johann Sebastian Bach 1685-1750

1 Here, Lord, we take the bro-ken bread and drink the wine, be - liev - ing
that by thy life our souls are fed, thy part-ing gifts re - ceiv - ing.

2 As thou hast given, so we would give
  ourselves for others' healing;
  as thou hast lived, so we would live,
  the Father's love revealing.

Charles Venn Pilcher 1879-1961
for a lower setting see 348

339

AS WE BREAK THE BREAD

MASSON 5 6 6 4

Stanley L Osborne 1907–

1 As we break the bread and drink the life of wine,
we bring to mind our Lord, man of all time.
scat-tered as grain.

2 Grain is sown to die;
   it rises from the dead,
   becomes through human toil
   our common bread.

3 Pass from hand to hand
   the living love of Christ!
   Machine and man provide
   bread for this feast.

4 Jesus binds in one
   our daily life and work;
   he is of all mankind
   symbol and mark.

5 Having shared the bread
   that died to rise again,
   we rise to serve the world,
   scattered as grain.

Frederik Herman Kaan 1929–

340

BREAD OF HEAVEN

JESU, MEINE ZUVERSICHT 777777

Johann Crüger 1598-1662
adapted by Johann Sebastian Bach 1685-1750

1 Bread of heaven, on thee we feed, for thy flesh is food in - deed;
ev - er may our souls be fed with this true and liv - ing bread,
day by day with strength sup-plied through the life of him who died.

2 Vine of heaven, thy blood supplies
   this blest cup of sacrifice;
   Lord, thy wounds our healing give,
   to thy cross we look and live;
   Jesus, may we ever be
   grafted, rooted, built in thee.

Josiah Conder 1789-1855

341

NOW, MY TONGUE, THE MYSTERY TELLING Mechlin plainsong
PANGE LINGUA 8 7 8 7 8 7 FIRST TUNE arranged by Margaret Drynan 1915–

1 Now, my tongue, the my-stery tell - ing, of the glo-rious bo - dy sing, and the blood, all price ex - cel - ling, which the na - tions' Lord and King, once on earth a-mong us dwell-ing, shed for this world's ran-som-ing.

A - men.

2 That last night, at supper lying
with the twelve, his chosen band,
Jesus with the law complying
keeps the feast its rites demand;
then, more precious food supplying,
gives himself with his own hand.

3 Word made flesh, by word he maketh
very bread his flesh to be;
man in wine Christ's blood partaketh:
and if senses fail to see,
faith alone the true heart waketh
to behold the mystery.

4 Therefore we, before him bending,
this great sacrament revere;
faith her aid to sight is lending;
though unseen, the Lord is near;
ancient types and shadows ending,
Christ our paschal Lamb is here.

5 Glory let us give, and blessing,
to the Father and the Son;
honour, thanks and praise addressing
while eternal ages run,
and the Spirit's power confessing,
who from both with both is one.

GRAFTON 8 7 8 7 8 7 SECOND TUNE   melody from 'Chants Ordinaires de l'Office Divin'
Paris 1881

1 Now, my tongue, the mystery telling, of the glorious body sing,

and the blood, all price excelling, which the nation's Lord and King,

once on earth among us dwelling, shed for this world's ransoming.

2 That last night, at supper lying
with the twelve, his chosen band,
Jesus with the law complying
keeps the feast its rites demand;
then, more precious food supplying,
gives himself with his own hand.

3 Word made flesh, by word he maketh
very bread his flesh to be;
man in wine Christ's blood partaketh:
and if senses fail to see,
faith alone the true heart waketh
to behold the mystery.

4 Therefore we, before him bending,
this great sacrament revere;
faith her aid to sight is lending;
though unseen, the Lord is near;
ancient types and shadows ending,
Christ our paschal Lamb is here.

5 Glory let us give, and blessing,
to the Father and the Son;
honour, thanks and praise addressing
while eternal ages run,
and the Spirit's power confessing,
who from both with both is one.

Thomas Aquinas 13th century
tr. Edward Caswall 1814-1878
and the compilers

342

O SAVIOUR VICTIM

JENA 8888 FIRST TUNE

melody from Melchior Vulpius c1560-1616
harmonized by Stanley L Osborne 1907-

1 O Saviour victim, opening wide
the gates of life to man below,
our foes press hard on every side:
your aid supply, your strength bestow.

2 To you our Lord both one and three
be glory ever, ever new,
whose mighty love has made us free
to share that land of life with you.

Thomas Aquinas 13th century
tr. Edward Caswall 1814-1878

arranged by A L Jacob (pseud.) c1890-c1950

VERBUM SUPERNUM 8 8 8 8   SECOND TUNE
Mechlin plainsong

1 O Sav - iour vic - tim, o - pening wide
the gates of life to man be - low,
our foes press hard on ev - ery side:
your aid sup - ply, your strength be - stow. A - men.

2 To you our Lord both one and three
be glory ever, ever new,
whose mighty love has made us free
to share that land of life with you.

Thomas Aquinas 13th century
tr. Edward Caswall 1814-1878

343

JESUS, THOU JOY OF LOVING HEARTS

MARYTON 8 8 8 8 FIRST TUNE

melody by Henry Percy Smith 1825–1898
harmonized by Eric Thiman 1900–

1 Je - sus, thou joy of lov - ing hearts,
thou fount of life, thou light of men,
from the best bliss that earth im - parts
we turn un - filled to thee a - gain.

2 Thy truth unchanged hath ever stood;
   thou savest those that on thee call:
   to them that seek thee thou art good,
   to them that find thee, all in all.

3 We taste thee, O thou living bread,
   and long to feast upon thee still;
   we drink of thee, the fountain-head,
   and thirst our souls from thee to fill.

for a lower setting see 301

plainsong melody c13th century arranged by Healey Willan 1880-1968

CHRISTE, REDEMPTOR OMNIUM 8 8 8 8   SECOND TUNE

Unison

1 Je - sus, thou joy of lov - ing hearts, thou fount of life, thou light of men, from the best bliss that earth im - parts we turn un - filled to thee a - gain. A - men.

4 Our restless spirits yearn for thee,
   where'er our changeful lot is cast,
   glad when thy gracious smile we see,
   blest when our faith can hold thee fast.

5 O Jesus, ever with us stay;
   make all our moments calm and bright;
   chase the dark night of sin away;
   shed o'er the world thy holy light.

Bernard of Clairvaux 12th century
tr. Ray Palmer 1808-1887

344

HERE, O MY LORD, I SEE THEE

FARLEY CASTLE 10 10 10 10 FIRST TUNE

Henry Lawes 1596-1662

1 Here, O my Lord, I see thee face to face;
here would I touch and han - dle things un - seen,
here grasp with firm - er hand the e - ter - nal grace,
and all my wear - i - ness up - on thee lean.

2 Here would I feed upon the bread of God,
here drink with thee the royal wine of heaven;
here would I lay aside each earthly load,
here taste afresh the calm of sin forgiven.

3 This is the hour of banquet and of song;
this is the heavenly table spread for me;
here let me feast, and feasting, still prolong
the brief bright hour of fellowship with thee.

Horatius Bonar 1808-1889

1 Here, O my Lord, I see thee face to face;
here would I touch and han-dle things un - seen,
here grasp with firm - er hand the e-ter - nal grace,
and all my wear-i-ness up - on thee lean.

2 Here would I feed upon the bread of God,
   here drink with thee the royal wine of heaven;
   here would I lay aside each earthly load,
   here taste afresh the calm of sin forgiven.

3 This is the hour of banquet and of song;
   this is the heavenly table spread for me;
   here let me feast, and feasting, still prolong
   the brief bright hour of fellowship with thee.

Horatius Bonar 1808-1889

345

THOU, WHO AT THY FIRST EUCHARIST DIDST PRAY

SONG I 10 10 10 10 10 10

Orlando Gibbons 1583–1625

1 Thou, who at thy first eu-char-ist didst pray
that all thy church might be for ev-er one,
grant us at ev-ery eu-char-ist to say
with long-ing heart and soul, Thy will be done.
O may we all one bread, one bo-dy be,
through this blest sac-ra-ment of u-ni-ty.

2   For all thy church, O Lord, we intercede;
make thou our sad divisions soon to cease;
draw us the nearer each to each, we plead,
by drawing all to thee, O Prince of peace;
thus may we all one bread, one body be,
through this blest sacrament of unity.

3   So, Lord, at length when sacraments shall cease,
may we be one with all thy church above,
one with thy saints in one unbroken peace,
one with thy saints in one unbounded love:
more blessed still, in peace and love to be
one with the trinity in unity.

William Henry Turton 1856-1938

346

O JESUS, KINDLY LORD

SCHÜTZ 81 8888

melody by Heinrich Schütz 1585-1672
harmonized by Frederick R C Clarke 1931-

1 O Je - sus, kind - ly Lord, to thee

my thanks be ev - er - last - ing - ly,

who with thy bo - dy and thy blood

re - freshed my soul, for thou art good.

2 Break forth, my soul, with joy, and say
how rich I have become this day;
my Saviour dwells within my heart;
thanks for the joy thou dost impart.

Thomas Kingo 1634-1703
tr. Roland Ford Palmer 1891-

347

LORD, AS THE GRAIN WHICH ONCE ON UPLAND ACRES

VICTORIA II IO II IO

Godfrey Ridout 1918-

1 Lord, as the grain which once on up-land ac - res
scat-tered a - broad, was ga-thered in - to one
in this one loaf where - of we are par - tak - ers,
in the blest fel - low - ship of thy dear Son:

2 so may thy church dispersed through all creation,
  seed of the living bread, thy holy Son,
  broken for us and for mankind's salvation,
  from the world's ends be gathered into one.

  from the Didache 2nd century
  tr. George Seaver 1890-

348

STRENGTHEN FOR SERVICE

ACH GOTT UND HERR 8 7 8 7   Christian Gall's 'As Hymnodus sacer', Leipzig 1625
adapted and harmonized by Johann Sebastian Bach 1685–1750

1 Strength-en for ser-vice, Lord, the hands that ho-ly things have tak - en;
Sei - gneur, daigne af-fer - mir ma main, car à la sain - te ta - ble

let ears that now have heard thy songs to cla-mour ne - ver wak - en.
j'ai pris le pain a - vec le vin, sa - cre-ment a - do - ra - ble.

2 Lord, may the tongues which 'Holy' sang
keep free from all deceiving;
the eyes which saw thy love be bright,
thy blessed hope perceiving.

2 Christ, que la voix qui t'a chanté
répugne à tout mensonge,
par ton amour, viens dissiper
le doute qui me ronge.

3 The feet that tread thy holy courts
from light do thou not banish;
the bodies by thy body fed
with thy new life replenish.

3 Quand nos pieds foulent tes parvis
accueille-nous, ô Père;
nourris nos corps de ton Esprit,
exauce nos prières.

from the Liturgy of Malabar
tr. Charles W Humphreys 1840-1921
Percy Dearmer 1867-1936

tr. Violette du Pasquier

for a higher setting see 338

AND THE FOLLOWING

349

O GOD, FROM WHOM MANKIND DERIVES ITS NAME

TEMISKAMING 10 10 10 10

William France 1912–

1 O God, from whom mankind derives its name,
whose co-ven-ant of grace re-mains the same,
be with these two who now be-fore you wait;
en-large the love they come to con-sec-rate.

2   May through their union other lives be blessed;
     their door be wide to stranger and to guest,
     Give them the understanding that is kind,
     grant them the blessing of an open mind.

3   Preserve their days from inwardness of heart;
     to each the gift of truthful speech impart.
     Their bond be strong against all strain and strife
     amid the changes of this earthly life.

4   From stage to stage on life's unfolding way
     bring to their mind the vows they make this day,
     your spirit be their guide in every move,
     their faith in Christ the basis of their love.

5   Lord, bless us all to whom this day brings joy,
     let no events our unity destroy,
     and help us, till all sense of time is lost,
     to live in love and not to count the cost.

Frederik Herman Kaan 1929-

350

O FATHER, ALL-CREATING

AURELIA 7 6 7 6 D

Samuel Sebastian Wesley 1810–1876

1 O Father, all-cre - a - ting, whose wis-dom, love, and power first bound two lives to - ge - ther in E-den's prim - al hour, to - day to these thy child - ren thine ear - liest gifts re - new, – a home by thee made hap - py, a love by thee kept true.

2 O Saviour, guest most bounteous
of old in Galilee,
reveal today thy presence
with these who call on thee;
their store of earthly gladness
transform to heavenly wine,
and teach them, in the tasting,
to know the gift is thine.

3 O Spirit of the Father,
breathe on them from above,
so mighty in thy pureness,
so tender in thy love;
that, guarded by thy presence,
from sin and strife kept free,
their lives may own thy guidance,
their hearts be ruled by thee.

4 Except thou build it, Father,
the house is built in vain;
except thou, Saviour, bless it,
the joy will turn to pain;
but nought can break the union
of hearts in thee made one;
and love thy Spirit hallows
is endless love begun.

John Ellerton 1826-1893
for a lower setting see 146

351

O PERFECT LOVE
O PERFECT LOVE 11 10 11 10

Joseph Barnby 1838–1896

1 O per-fect love, all hu-man thought tran - scend - ing,

low - ly we kneel in prayer be - fore thy throne,

that theirs may be the love that knows no end - ing,

whom thou for ev - er - more dost join in one.

2   O perfect life, be thou their full assurance
     of tender charity and steadfast faith,
     of patient hope, and quiet brave endurance,
     with childlike trust that fears nor pain nor death.

3   Grant them the joy which brightens earthly sorrow;
     grant them the peace which calms all earthly strife,
     and to life's day the glorious unknown morrow
     that dawns upon eternal love and life.

Dorothy Frances Gurney 1858-1932

AND THE FOLLOWING

LORD OF THE LIVING

AD TUUM NOMEN 11 11 11 5 FIRST TUNE

from the Chartres Antiphoner 1784

1 Lord of the liv-ing, in your name as-sem-bled,
we join to thank you for the life re-mem-bered.
Fa-ther, have mer-cy, to your child-ren giv-ing
hope in be-liev-ing.

2 Help us to treasure all that will remind us
of the enrichment in the days behind us.
Your love has set us in the generations,
God of creation.

3 May we, whenever tempted to dejection,
strongly recapture thoughts of resurrection.
You gave us Jesus to defeat our sadness
with Easter gladness.

4 Lord, you can lift us from the grave of sorrow
into the presence of your own tomorrow:
give to your people for the day's affliction
your benediction.

Frederik Herman Kaan 1929-

1 Lord of the liv-ing, in your name as-sem-bled,
we join to thank you for the life re-mem-bered.
Fa-ther, have mer-cy, to your child-ren giv-ing
hope in be-liev-ing.

AND THE FOLLOWING

353

POUR OUT THY SPIRIT FROM ON HIGH

HERR JESU CHRIST, MEIN'S LEBENS LICHT 8 8 8 8   'As Hymnodus sacer', Leipzig 1625

harmonized by Johann Sebastian Bach 1685–1750

1 Pour out thy Spir - it from on high;
Lord, thine as - sem - bled ser - vants bless;
gra - ces and gifts to each sup - ply,
and clothe thy priests with right - eous - ness.

2 Within thy temple when we stand,
    to teach the truth, as taught by thee,
    Saviour, like stars in thy right hand
    let all thy church's pastors be!

3 Wisdom and zeal and faith impart,
    firmness with meekness from above,
    to bear thy people on our heart,
    and love the souls whom thou dost love;

4 to watch and pray, and never faint;
    by day and night strict guard to keep;
    to warn the sinner, cheer the saint,
    nourish thy lambs, and feed thy sheep;

5 then, when our work is finished here,
    may we in hope our charge resign;
    when the chief Shepherd shall appear,
    O God, may they and we be thine.

James Montgomery 1771-1854
This may be sung to Melcombe 229 or 360

AND THE FOLLOWING

354

LORD GOD ALMIGHTY, KING OF ALL CREATION

ST OSYTH 11 10 11 10   Thomas Wood 1892–1950

1 Lord God al-migh-ty, King of all cre-a-tion, whose glo-ry fills the heavens and earth and sea, vis-it thy peo-ple joy-ous-ly as-sem-bled with-in this house now de-di-cate to thee.

2 Thou hast inspired the building of this temple;
  from thee the vision, gift and deed proceed;
  now grant to us the end of all our praying,
  thy love, thyself, the answer to all need.

3 To troubled souls grant peace of sins forgiven,
  to lonely souls grant thou a love divine;
  in minds and hearts confused by life's temptations
  thy gracious will with light and wisdom shine.

4 Here we would hear thy message clearly spoken,
  here at thy table share a grace divine,
  offer our lives to thee in humble service,
  go forth to tell thy love for all mankind.

James Raymond Hord 1918–1968

355

WE LOVE THE PLACE, O GOD

QUAM DILECTA 6666

Henry Lascelles Jenner 1820–1898

1 We love the place, O God, where-in thine hon-our dwells;
the joy of thine a - bode all earth-ly joy ex - cels.

2 It is the house of prayer,
  wherein thy servants meet;
  and thou, O Lord, art there
  thy chosen flock to greet.

3 We love the sacred font;
  for there the holy dove
  to pour is ever wont
  his blessing from above.

4 We love thine altar, Lord;
  O what on earth so dear?
  For there, in faith adored,
  we find thy presence near.

5 We love the word of life,
  the word that tells of peace,
  of comfort in the strife,
  and joys that never cease.

6 We love to sing below
  for mercies freely given;
  but O we long to know
  the triumph-song of heaven.

7 Lord Jesus, give us grace
  on earth to love thee more,
  in heaven to see thy face,
  and with thy saints adore.

William Bulloch 1798-1874
Henry Williams Baker 1821-1877

356

ONLY-BEGOTTEN, WORD OF GOD

ISTE CONFESSOR II II II 5

Poitiers Vesperale 1746
harmonized by Healey Willan 1880–1968

Unison

1 On - ly be - got - ten, word of God e - ter - nal,
Lord of cre - a - tion, mer - ci - ful and migh - ty,
list to thy ser - vants, when their tune-ful voi - ces
rise to thy pres - ence.

2 Thus in our solemn feast of dedication,
   graced with returning rites of due devotion,
   ever thy children, year by year rejoicing,
   chant in thy temple.

3 Here in our sickness healing grace aboundeth,
   light in our blindness, in our toil refreshment;
   sin is forgiven, hope o'er fear prevaileth,
   joy over sorrow.

4 Hallowed this dwelling where the Lord abideth,
   this is none other than the gate of heaven;
   strangers and pilgrims, seeking homes eternal,
   pass through its portal.

5 Lord we beseech thee, as we throng thy temple,
   by thy past blessings, by thy present bounty,
   smile on thy children, and with tender mercy
   hear our petitions.

6 God in three persons, Father everlasting,
   Son co-eternal, ever-blessed Spirit,
   thine be the glory, praise, and adoration,
   now and for ever.

from the Latin c 9th century
tr. Maxwell Julius Blacker 1822–1888

AND THE FOLLOWING

Times of worship

357

AWAKE, MY SOUL

MORNING HYMN 8 8 8 8   François Hippolyte Barthélémon 1741–1808

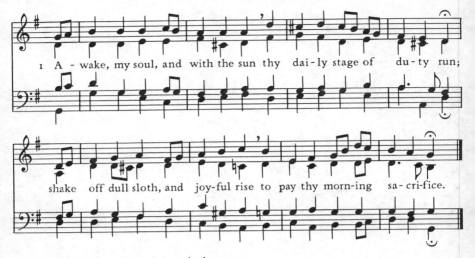

1 A - wake, my soul, and with the sun thy dai-ly stage of du-ty run; shake off dull sloth, and joy-ful rise to pay thy morn-ing sa-cri-fice.

2 Redeem thy mis-spent time that's past,
   and live this day as if thy last;
   improve thy talent with due care;
   for the great day thyself prepare.

3 Let all thy converse be sincere,
   thy conscience as the noon-day clear:
   think how all-seeing God thy ways
   and all thy secret thoughts surveys.

4 Wake, and lift up thyself, my heart,
   and with the angels bear thy part,
   who all night long unwearied sing
   glory to the eternal King.   Thomas Ken 1637-1711

358

GLORY TO THEE WHO SAFE HAST KEPT

MORNING HYMN 8 8 8 8

1   Glory to thee who safe hast kept,
    and hast refreshed me whilst I slept;
    grant, Lord, when I from earth shall wake
    I may of endless light partake.

2   Lord, I my vows to thee renew;
    scatter my sins as morning dew;
    guard my first springs of thought and will,
    and with thyself my spirit fill.

3   Direct, control, suggest, this day
    all I design or do or say,
    that all my powers with all their might
    in thy sole glory may unite.

4   Praise God, from whom all blessings flow;
    praise him, all creatures here below;
    praise him above, ye heavenly host;
    praise Father, Son, and Holy Ghost.   Thomas Ken 1637-1711

359

FATHER, WE PRAISE THEE
COELITES PLAUDANT 11 11 11 5

Rouen Church melody

Father, we praise thee, now the night is o - ver;
ac - tive and watch - ful stand we all be - fore thee;
sing - ing we of - fer prayer and med - i - ta - tion:
thus we a - dore thee.

2 Monarch of all things, fit us for thy mansions;
 banish our weakness, health and wholeness sending;
 bring us to heaven, where thy saints united
 joy without ending.

3 All-holy Father, Son and equal Spirit,
 trinity blessed, send us thy salvation;
 thine is the glory, gleaming and resounding
 through all creation.

ascribed to Gregory the Great 540–604
tr. Percy Dearmer 1867–1936

360

NEW EVERY MORNING
MELCOMBE 8 8 8 8

Samuel Webbe 1740–1816

1 New ev-ery morn-ing is the love our wak-ening and up - ris-ing prove;

through sleep and dark-ness safe - ly brought, re-stored to life, and power, and thought.

2 New mercies each returning day
hover around us while we pray;
new perils past, new sins forgiven,
new thoughts of God, new hopes of heaven.

3 If on our daily course our mind
be set to hallow all we find,
new treasures still of countless price
God will provide for sacrifice.

4 The trivial round, the common task,
will furnish all we ought to ask,
room to deny ourselves, a road
to bring us daily nearer God.

5 Only, O Lord, in thy dear love
fit us for perfect rest above;
and help us, this and every day,
to live more nearly as we pray.

John Keble 1792–1866
for a lower setting see 229

361

NOW THAT THE DAYLIGHT FILLS THE SKY

WARRINGTON 8 8 8 8

Ralph Harrison 1748–1810

1 Now that the day - light fills the sky,
we lift our hearts to God on high,
that he in all we do or say
may keep us free from harm to - day.

2   O guard our hearts and tongues from strife,
     from anger's din preserve our life,
     from sights unworthy turn our eyes,
     and close our ears from vanities.

3   Keep thou our inmost conscience pure,
     our thoughts from foolishness secure,
     and help us check the pride of sense
     by self-restraining abstinence.

4   So we, when this new day is gone
     and night in turn is drawing on,
     with conscience by the hours unstained,
     shall praise thy name for victory gained.

5   All praise to God the Father be,
     all praise, eternal Son, to thee,
     whom with the Spirit we adore,
     one God both now and evermore.

     from the Latin, 7th or 8th century
tr. John Mason Neale 1818-1866
     for a higher setting see 65

362

CHRIST WHOSE GLORY FILLS THE SKIES

RATISBON 7 7 7 7 7 7

Werner's Choralbuch 1815

1 Christ whose glo-ry fills the skies, Christ the true, the on-ly light,
sun of right-eous-ness, a-rise, tri-umph o'er the shades of night.
Day-spring from on high, be near; day-star, in my heart ap-pear.

2 Dark and cheerless is the morn
unaccompanied by thee;
joyless is the day's return,
till thy mercy's beams I see,
till they inward light impart,
glad my eyes and warm my heart.

3 Visit then this soul of mine,
pierce the gloom of sin and grief;
fill me, radiancy divine,
scatter all my unbelief;
more and more thyself display,
shining to the perfect day.

Charles Wesley 1707-1788

AND THE FOLLOWING

1 All creatures of our God and King
3 From all that dwell below the skies
8 O all ye far-spreading lakes
20 How shall I sing that majesty

141 My God, how endless is thy love
197 Now thank we all our God
365 O gladsome light st. 1,3

363

GLORY TO THEE, MY GOD

TALLIS'S CANON 8 8 8 8

Thomas Tallis c1505–1585

1 Glo-ry to thee, my God, this night for all the bless-ings of the light;
keep me, O keep me, King of kings, be-neath thine own al-migh-ty wings.

2 Forgive me, Lord, for thy dear Son,
the ill that I this day have done,
that with the world, myself, and thee
I ere I sleep at peace may be.

3 Teach me to live, that I may dread
the grave as little as my bed;
teach me to die, that so I may
rise glorious at the awful day.

4 O may my soul on thee repose,
and with sweet sleep mine eyelids close,
sleep that may me more vigorous make
to serve my God when I awake.

5 When in the night I sleepless lie,
my soul with heavenly thoughts supply;
let no ill dreams disturb my rest,
no powers of darkness me molest.

6 Praise God, from whom all blessings flow;
praise him, all creatures here below;
praise him above, ye heavenly host;
praise Father, Son, and Holy Ghost.

Thomas Ken 1637-1711

364

BLEST CREATOR OF THE LIGHT

VIENNA 7 7 7 7   Justin Heinrich Knecht 1752–1817

1 Blest Cre-a-tor of the light, mak-ing day with ra-diance bright,
thou didst o'er the form-ing earth give the gold-en light its birth.

2 Shade of eve with morning ray
took from thee the name of day;
darkness now is drawing nigh;
listen to our humble cry.

3 May we ne'er by guilt depressed
lose the way to endless rest;
nor with idle thoughts and vain
bind our souls to earth again.

4 Rather may we heavenward rise
where eternal treasure lies,
purified by grace within,
hating every deed of sin.

5 Holy Father, hear our cry
through thy Son our Lord most high,
whom our thankful hearts adore
with the Spirit evermore.

from the Latin 5th century
tr. John Chandler 1806-1876

365

O GLADSOME LIGHT

NUNC DIMITTIS 6 6 7 D

composed or adapted by Louis Bourgeois c1510–c1561
for the Genevan Psalter 1549
harmony chiefly from Claude Goudimel 1505–1572

1 O glad-some light, O grace of God, the Fa-ther's face,

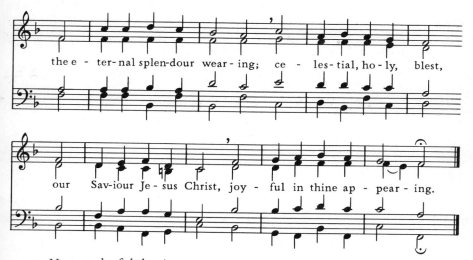

the e - ter - nal splen-dour wear - ing; ce - les - tial, ho - ly, blest,

our Sav-iour Je - sus Christ, joy - ful in thine ap - pear - ing.

2 Now, ere day fadeth quite,
   we see the evening light,
   our wonted hymn outpouring;
   Father of might unknown,
   thee, his incarnate Son,
   and Holy Spirit adoring.

3 To thee of right belongs
   all praise of holy songs,
   O Son of God, lifegiver;
   thee, therefore, O most high,
   the world doth glorify,
   and shall exalt for ever.

Greek hymn 3rd century
tr. Robert Seymour Bridges 1844-1930

366

THE DAY THOU GAVEST

LES COMMANDEMENS 9 8 9 8 FIRST TUNE

Louis Bourgeois c1510–c1561
harmonized by Stanley L Osborne 1907–

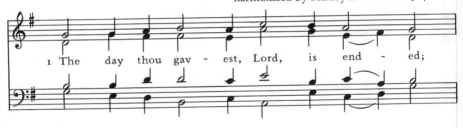

1 The day thou gav - est, Lord, is end - ed;

the dark - ness falls at thy be - hest;

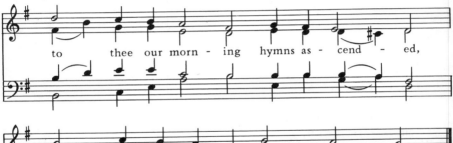

to thee our morn - ing hymns as - cend - ed,

thy praise shall sanc - ti - fy our rest.

2 We thank thee that thy church unsleeping,
while earth rolls onward into light,
through all the world her watch is keeping,
and rests not now by day or night.

3 As o'er each continent and island
the dawn leads on another day,
the voice of prayer is never silent,
nor dies the strain of praise away.

for another form of the tune see 225

1 The day thou gav - est, Lord, is end - ed;
the dark - ness falls at thy be - hest;
to thee our morn - ing hymns as - cend - ed,
thy praise shall sanc - ti - fy our rest.

4 The sun that bids us rest is waking
  our brethren 'neath the western sky,
  and hour by hour fresh lips are making
  thy wondrous doings heard on high.

5 So be it, Lord! Thy throne shall never,
  like earth's proud empires, pass away;
  thy kingdom stands and grows for ever,
  till all thy creatures own thy sway.

John Ellerton 1826-1893

367

NOW FROM THE ALTAR OF MY HEART

UNIVERSITY 8686   probably by Charles Collignon 1725–1785

1 Now from the al - tar of my heart let in-cense flames a - rise;

as - sist me, Lord, to of - fer up my eve-ning sac-ri - fice.

2 Awake, my love; awake, my joy;
  awake, my heart and tongue!
  Sleep not: when mercies loudly call,
  break forth into a song.

3 This day God was my sun and shield,
  my keeper and my guide;
  his care was on my frailty shown,
  his mercies multiplied.

4 New time, new favour, and new joys
  do a new song require;
  till I shall praise thee as I would,
  accept my heart's desire.   John Mason c1645–1694

368

NOW CHEER OUR HEARTS

ACH BLEIB BEI UNS 8 8 8 8

Geistliche Lieder, Leipzig 1589
arranged by Johann Sebastian Bach 1685–1750

1 Now cheer our hearts this ev - en - tide,
Lord Je - sus Christ, and with us bide,
thou that canst nev - er set in night,
our heaven - ly sun, our glo - rious light.

2   May we and all who bear thy name
by gentle love thy cross proclaim,
thy gift of peace on earth secure,
and for thy truth the world endure.

Nikolaus Selnecker 1532-1592
tr. Robert Seymour Bridges 1844-1930

369

NOW GOD BE WITH US

CHRISTE FONS JUGIS II II II 5

Rouen Church melody

Unison

1 Now God be with us, for the night is clos-ing;
the light and dark-ness are of his dis-pos-ing,
and 'neath his shad-ow here to rest we yield us,
for he will shield us.

2   Let evil thoughts and spirits flee before us;
     till morning cometh, watch, O Father, o'er us;
     in soul and body thou from harm defend us;
     thine angels send us.

3   Let holy thoughts be ours when sleep o'ertakes us;
     our earliest thoughts be thine when morning wakes us;
     all day serve thee, in all that we are doing
     thy praise pursuing.

4   We have no refuge; none on earth to aid us
     save thee, O Father, who thine own hast made us;
     but thy dear presence will not leave them lonely
     who seek thee only.

5   Father, thy name be praised, thy kingdom given,
     thy will be done on earth as 'tis in heaven;
     keep us in life, forgive our sins, deliver
     us now and ever.

    Petrus Herbert ?-1571
tr. Catherine Winkworth 1829-1878

370

SAVIOUR, AGAIN TO THY DEAR NAME

ELLERS 10 10 10 10

Edward John Hopkins 1818–1901

1 Saviour, again to thy dear name we raise
with one accord our parting hymn of praise;
we stand to bless thee ere our worship cease,
then, lowly kneeling, wait thy word of peace.

2   Grant us thy peace upon our homeward way;
    with thee began, with thee shall end the day;
    guard thou the lips from sin, the hearts from shame,
    that in this house have called upon thy name.

3   Grant us thy peace, Lord, through the coming night;
    turn thou for us its darkness into light;
    from harm and danger keep thy children free,
    for dark and light are both alike to thee.

4   Grant us thy peace throughout our earthly life,
    our balm in sorrow, and our stay in strife;
    then, when thy voice shall bid our conflict cease,
    call us, O Lord, to thine eternal peace.

John Ellerton 1826–1893
This may be sung to Adoro te 329

371

BEFORE THE ENDING OF THE DAY

TE LUCIS 8 8 8 8

plainsong melody
arranged by Healey Willan 1880–1968

1 Be - fore the end - ing of the day,
Cre - a - tor of the world, we pray
that with thy wont - ed fa - vour thou
wilt be our guard and keep - er now. A - men.

2   From all ill dreams defend our eyes,
    from nightly fears and fantasies;
    all harmful thoughts put thou to flight,
    that we refreshed may greet the light.

3   O Father, may this grace be shown
    through Jesus Christ, thine only Son,
    who with the Holy Ghost and thee
    doth live and reign eternally.

    from the Latin c 7th century
    tr. John Mason Neale 1818–1866
    This may be sung to Melcombe 229 or 360

372

HAIL THEE, FESTIVAL DAY!

SALVE, FESTA DIES irregular   Ralph Vaughan Williams 1872-1958

1 Hail thee, fes-ti-val day! blest day that art hal-lowed for ev - er, day where-in Christ a - rose, break-ing the king-dom of death.

vv. 2, 4
2 God the al-migh-ty the Lord, who rul-est the earth and the hea - vens, guard us from harm with-out, cleanse us from e - vil with-in.

vv. 3, 5
3 Com-fort-er, Spir-it of life, we praise thee, the fount of our be - ing, light that dost light - en all, life that in all dost a - bide.

4 Jesus the health of the world, enlighten our minds, thou Redeemer,
  Son of the Father supreme, only-begotten of God.
  Hail thee ...

5 God, who art giver of all good gifts and lover of concord,
  pour now thy balm on our souls, order our ways in thy peace.
  Hail thee ...

Venantius Fortunatus 530-609
tr. S P V

373
ON THIS DAY, THE FIRST OF DAYS
SCHÜTZ 19 7777   adapted from Heinrich Schütz 1585-1672
                                   harmonized by Frederick R C Clarke 1931-

1 On this day, the first of days, God the Fa-ther's name we praise,
  who, cre - a - tion's Lord and spring, did the world from dark-ness bring.

2 On this day the eternal Son
  over death his triumph won;
  on this day the Spirit came
  with his gifts of living flame.

3 Father, who didst fashion me
  image of thy self to be,
  fill me with thy love divine,
  let my every thought be thine.

4 Holy Jesus, may I be
  dead and buried here with thee;
  and, by love inflamed, arise
  unto thee a sacrifice.

5 Thou, who dost all gifts impart,
  shine, sweet Spirit, in my heart;
  best of gifts thyself bestow;
  make me burn thy love to know.

6 God, the blessed three in one,
  dwell within my heart alone;
  thou dost give thyself to me:
  may I give myself to thee.

from the Latin 18th century
tr. Henry Williams Baker 1821-1877

374

THE DAY OF RESURRECTION

KOMM, SEELE 7 6 7 6 D   melody by Johann Wolfgang Franck c1641–1688

1 The day of re - sur - rec - tion! Earth, tell it out a - broad;

the pass - o - ver of glad - ness, the pass - o - ver of God!

From death to life e - ter - nal, from earth un - to the sky,

our Christ hath brought us o - ver with hymns of vic - to - ry.

2 Our hearts be pure from evil,
   that we may see aright
   the Lord in rays eternal
   of resurrection light,
   and, listening to his accents,
   may hear so calm and plain
   his own 'All hail!' and, hearing,
   may raise the victor strain.

3 Now let the heavens be joyful,
   let earth her song begin,
   the round world keep high triumph,
   and all that is therein;
   let all things seen and unseen
   their notes of gladness blend,
   for Christ the Lord is risen,
   our Joy that hath no end.

   John of Damascus c 750
tr. John Mason Neale 1818-1866
   This may be sung to Ellacombe 216 or 448

375

THIS IS THE DAY WHEN LIGHT WAS FIRST CREATED

SCHOOL HOUSE 11 10 11 10   Thomas Wood 1892–1950

Unison

1 This is the day when light was first cre - a - ted,
sym - bol and gift of or - der and de - sign.
In light is God's in - ten - tion clear - ly sta - ted,
the break of day re - veals his lov - ing mind.

2   This is the day of man's complete surprising,
     repeat of Easter: Christ has come to life!
     Now in the feast of love's revolt and rising
     against the rule of hell and death and grief.

3   We join to praise, with every race and nation,
     the God who with mankind his Spirit shares;
     strong wind of change and earth's illumination,
     dispelling static thoughts and darkest fears.

4   This is the day of worship and of vision,
     great birthday of the church in every land.
     Let Christian men confess their sad division,
     and seek the strength again as one to stand.

5   We pray that this, the day of re-creation,
     may hallow all the week that is to come.
     Help us, O Lord, to lay a good foundation
     for all we do at work, at school, at home.

Frederik Herman Kaan 1929–

376

THIS IS THE DAY THE LORD HATH MADE

BROMSGROVE 8 6 8 6   later form of a melody from Psalmodia Evangelica 1789
harmonized by Hugh J McLean 1930–

1 This is the day the Lord hath made,

he calls the hours his own;

let heavens re - joice, let earth be glad,

and praise sur - round the throne.

2 Today he rose and left the dead,
  and Satan's empire fell;
  today the saints his triumphs spread,
  and all his wonders tell.

3 Hosanna to the anointed King,
  to David's holy Son!
  O help us, Lord, descend and bring
  salvation from thy throne.

4 Hosanna in the highest strains
  the church on earth can raise;
  the highest heavens in which he reigns
  shall give him nobler praise.

Isaac Watts 1674-1748
This may be sung to Nativity 47

AND THE FOLLOWING

377

FOR THY MERCY AND THY GRACE

SAVANNAH 7 7 7 7   Herrnhut 1740

1 For thy mer-cy and thy grace, faith-ful through an-oth-er year, hear our song of thank-ful-ness; Fa-ther and Re-deem-er, hear.

2 Lo! our sins on thee we cast,
thee, our perfect sacrifice,
and, forgetting all the past,
press towards our glorious prize.

3 Dark the future; let thy light
guide us, bright and morning star;
fierce our foes, and hard the fight;
arm us, Saviour, for the war.

4 In our weakness and distress,
rock of strength, be thou our stay;
in the pathless wilderness
be our true and living way.

5 Keep us faithful, keep us pure,
keep us evermore thine own;
help, O help us to endure:
fit us for the promised crown.   Henry Downton 1818–1885

378

FOR BEAUTY OF PRAIRIES

RADWELL II II II II   Hilary Philip Chadwyck-Healey 1889–

1 For beau-ty of prai-ries, for grand-eur of trees, for flow-ers of wood-lands, for crea-tures of seas, for all you cre-a-ted and trust-ed to man, we praise you, Cre-a-tor, ex-tol-ling your plan.

2 As stewards of beauty received at your hand,
   as creatures who hear your most urgent command,
   we turn from our wasteful destruction of life,
   confessing our failures, confessing our strife.

3 Teach men once again to be gardeners in peace;
   all nature around us is ours but on lease;
   your name we would hallow in all that we do,
   fulfilling our calling, creating with you.

Walter Henry Farquharson 1936–

379

AS COMES THE BREATH OF SPRING

DENBY 6 6 6 6 D

Charles J Dale c1875–c1950

1 As comes the breath of spring, with light, and mirth, and song,
so does God's Spir-it bring new days, brave, free and strong.
He comes with thrill of life to chase hence win-ter's breath,
to hush to peace the strife of sin that ends in death.

2 He comes like dawning day,
  with flaming truth and love,
  to chase all glooms away,
  to brace our wills to prove
  how wise, how good to choose
  the truth and its brave fight;
  to prize it, win or lose,
  and live on God's delight.

3 He comes like songs at morn
  that fill the earth with joy,
  till men of him new-born
  new strength in praise employ.
  He comes to rouse the heart
  from drifting to despair,
  through high hope to impart
  life, with an ampler air.

4 He breathes, and there is health;
  he moves, and there is power;
  he whispers, there is wealth
  of love, his richest dower.
  His presence is to men
  like summer in the soul;
  his joy shines forth, and then
  life blossoms to its goal.

David Lakie Ritchie 1865–1951

380

HEAR US, OUR FATHER

LANIGAN 8686

Lawrence Ritchey 1939–

1 Hear us, our Father, as we pray
for those who till the soil;
grant us a sense of growing worth,
give purpose to our toil. Amen.

2   The world has hungry people yet;
     our soils produce good grain.
     Lord, use our skills and practised arts
     to take away man's pain.

3   Our work, our knowledge, and our plans,
     we offer for your use;
     teach us to live in such a way
     this land knows no abuse.

4   Our heritage of fields and herds
     demands our thankful praise.
     Lord, bless our farming enterprise,
     the labour of our days.

5   Faithful with those who pioneered
     these fertile lands we till,
     we bless you, Father of mankind,
     whose purpose governs still.

Walter Henry Farquharson 1936–
This may be sung to St Flavian 59 or 322

381

GOD, WHOSE FARM IS ALL CREATION   English traditional melody

SHIPSTON 8 7 8 7   arranged by Ralph Vaughan Williams 1872–1958

1 God whose farm is all cre - a - tion, take the gra - ti - tude we give;

take the fin-est of our har-vest, crops we grow that men may live.

2 Take our ploughing, seeding, reaping,
hopes and fears of sun and rain,
all our thinking, planning, waiting,
ripening into fruit and grain.

3 All our labour, all our watching,
all our calendar of care,
in these crops of your creation,
take, O God: they are our prayer.

John Arlott 1914–
for a lower setting see 311

382

SING TO THE LORD OF HARVEST
WIE LIEBLICH IST DER MAIEN 7 6 7 6 D

Johann Steurlein 1547–1613
harmonized by Healey Willan 1880–1968

1 Sing to the Lord of har-vest, sing songs of love and praise,
with joy-ful hearts and voi-ces your hal-le-lu-jahs raise;
by him the rol-ling sea-sons in fruit-ful or-der move;
sing to the Lord of har-vest a joy-ful song of love.

2 By him the clouds drop fatness,
   the deserts bloom and spring,
   the hills leap up in gladness,
   the valleys laugh and sing;
   he filleth with his fullness
   all things with large increase;
   he crowns the year with goodness,
   with plenty and with peace.

3 Heap on his sacred altar
   the gifts his goodness gave,
   the golden sheaves of harvest,
   the souls he died to save:
   your hearts lay down before him
   when at his feet ye fall,
   and with your lives adore him
   who gave his life for all.

John Samuel Bewley Monsell
1811–1875

*Invert the soprano and tenor parts at this cadence of the final stanza.

383

WE PLOUGH THE FIELDS

WIR PFLÜGEN 7 6 7 6 D and refrain

Johann Abraham Peter Schulz 1747–1800

1 We plough the fields and scat-ter the good seed on the land, but it is fed and wa-tered by God's al-migh-ty hand; he sends the snow in win-ter, the warmth to swell the grain, the breez-es and the sun-shine, and soft re-fresh-ing rain.

Refrain

All good gifts a-round us are sent from heaven a-bove; then thank the Lord, O thank the Lord, for all his love.

2   He only is the maker
    of all things near and far;
    he paints the wayside flower,
    he lights the evening star;
    the winds and waves obey him;
    by him the birds are fed;
    much more to us, his children,
    he gives our daily bread.

3   We thank thee then, O Father,
    for all things bright and good,
    the seed-time and the harvest,
    our life, our health, our food;
    accept the gifts we offer
    for all thy love imparts,
    and, what thou most desirest,
    our humble, thankful hearts.

    All good gifts around us
    are sent from heaven above;
    then thank the Lord, O thank the Lord,
    for all his love.

Matthias Claudius 1740–1815
tr. Jane Montgomery Campbell 1817–1878

If desired, the refrain may be sung at the
conclusion of the third stanza only.

384

COME, YE THANKFUL PEOPLE, COME

ST GEORGE'S, WINDSOR 7 7 7 7 D

George Job Elvey 1816–1893

1 Come, ye thank-ful peo-ple, come, raise the song of har-vest-home!

All is safe-ly gath-ered in, ere the win-ter storms be-gin;

God, our mak-er, doth pro-vide for our wants to be sup-plied:

come to God's own tem-ple, come, raise the song of har-vest-home!

2　All the world is God's own field,
　　fruit unto his praise to yield;
　　wheat and tares together sown,
　　unto joy or sorrow grown;
　　first the blade, and then the ear,
　　then the full corn shall appear:
　　Lord of harvest, grant that we
　　wholesome grain and pure may be.

3　For the Lord our God shall come,
　　and shall take his harvest home;
　　from his field shall in that day
　　all offences purge away;
　　give his angels charge at last
　　in the fire the tares to cast;
　　but the fruitful ears to store
　　in his garner evermore.

4　Even so, Lord, quickly come
　　to thy final harvest-home!
　　Gather thou thy people in,
　　free from sorrow, free from sin;
　　there for ever purified,
　　in thy presence to abide:
　　come, with all thine angels, come,
　　raise the glorious harvest-home.

Henry Alford 1810–1871

385

GIVE THANKS, MY SOUL, FOR HARVEST

MUNICH 7 6 7 6 D

Meiningisches Gesangbuch 1693

1 Give thanks, my soul for har-vest, for store of fruit and grain;
but know the own-er giv-eth that we may share a-gain.
Where men are lone and hun-gry, or lit-tle child-ren cry,
with gifts from God's rich boun-ty may thank-ful-ness re-ply.

2 Give thanks, my soul, for riches
of woodland, mine, and hill;
but know that gold and timber
are the Creator's still.
God lends them to his stewards
to fashion and to share,
providing all earth's children
the blessing of his care.

3 Give thanks, my soul, for labours,
that strength and days employ;
but know the Master's purpose
brings toil as well as joy.
Show forth, O God, thy purpose;
direct our will and hand
to share thy love and bounty
with men in every land.

William Watkins Reid 1890–

386

PRAISE TO GOD, IMMORTAL PRAISE

ORIENTIS PARTIBUS 7 7 7 7

Mediæval French melody
harmonized by Derek Holman 1931-

1 Praise to God, im - mor - tal praise,
for the love that crowns our days;
boun - teous source of ev - ery joy,
let thy praise our tongues em - ploy:

2 for the blessings of the fields,
for the stores the garden yields,
flocks that whiten all the plain,
yellow sheaves of ripened grain:

3 all that spring with bounteous hand
scatters o'er the smiling land,
all that liberal autumn pours
from her rich o'erflowing stores.

4 These to thee, O God we owe,
source whence all our blessings flow;
and for these our souls shall raise
grateful vows and solemn praise.

Anna Laetitia Barbauld 1743-1825

387

NOW JOIN WE TO PRAISE THE CREATOR Irish traditional melody

CAILIN DEAS 9 8 9 8 D harmonized by Stanley L Osborne 1907-

1 Now join we to praise the Cre - a - tor,

our voi - ces in wor - ship and song;

we stand to re - call with thanks - giv - ing

that to him all sea - sons be - long.

We thank you, O God, for your good - ness,

for the joy and a - bund - ance of crops,

for food that is stored in our cup - boards,
for all we can buy in the shops.

2 But also of need and starvation
we sing with concern and despair,
of skills that are used for destruction,
of land that is burnt and laid bare.
We cry for the plight of the hungry
while harvests are left on the field,
for orchards neglected and wasting,
for produce from markets withheld.

3 The song grows in depth and in wideness:
the earth and its people are one.
There can be no thanks without giving,
no words without deeds that are done.
Then teach us, O Lord of the harvest,
to be humble in all that we claim;
to share what we have with the nations,
to care for the world in your name.

Frederik Herman Kaan 1929-

388

ALL BEAUTIFUL THE MARCH OF DAYS English traditional melody
FOREST GREEN 8 6 8 6 D harmonized by Ralph Vaughan Williams 1872–1958

1 All beau-ti-ful the march of days, as sea-sons come and go;

the hand that shaped the rose hath wrought the cry-stal of the snow,

hath sent the hoa-ry frost of heaven, the flow-ing wa-ters sealed,

and laid a si-lent love-li-ness on hill and wood and field.

2 O'er white expanses sparkling pure the radiant morns unfold;
the solemn splendours of the night burn brighter through the cold;
life mounts in every throbbing vein, love deepens round the hearth,
and clearer sounds the angel hymn, Good will to men on earth.

3 O thou from whose unfathomed law the year in beauty flows,
thyself the vision passing by in crystal and in rose;
day unto day doth utter speech, and night to night proclaim
in ever-changing words of light the wonder of thy name.

Frances Whitmarsh Wile 1878–1939
for a higher setting see 421

AND THE FOLLOWING

The Christian year

389

COME, THOU LONG-EXPECTED JESUS

STUTTGART 8 7 8 7   from a melody in Psalmodia Sacra, Gotha 1715

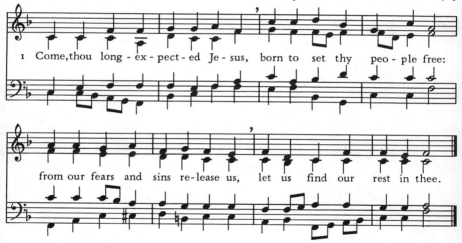

1 Come, thou long-ex-pect-ed Je-sus, born to set thy peo-ple free: from our fears and sins re-lease us, let us find our rest in thee.

2 Israel's strength and consolation,
hope of all the earth thou art,
dear desire of every nation,
joy of every longing heart.

3 Born thy people to deliver;
born a child and yet a King;
born to reign in us for ever;
now thy gracious kingdom bring.

4 By thine own eternal Spirit
rule in all our hearts alone;
by thine all-sufficient merit
raise us to thy glorious throne.

Charles Wesley 1707–1788
This may be sung to Hyfrydol 241

390

O COME, O COME, EMMANUEL

VENI EMMANUEL 8 8 8 8 and refrain

plainsong melody
arranged by Healey Willan 1880–1968

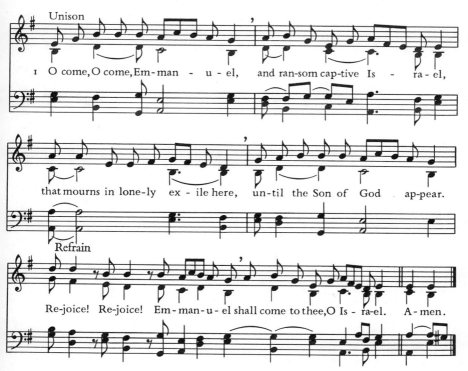

1 O come, O come, Em-man - u - el, and ran-som cap-tive Is - ra - el, that mourns in lone-ly ex - ile here, un-til the Son of God ap-pear.

Refrain

Re-joice! Re-joice! Em - man - u - el shall come to thee, O Is - ra - el. A - men.

2 O come, O come, thou Lord of might,
   who to thy tribes on Sinai's height
   in ancient times didst give the law
   in cloud and majesty and awe.

3 O come, thou rod of Jesse, free
   thine own from Satan's tyranny;
   from depths of hell thy people save,
   and give them victory o'er the grave.

4 O come, thou dayspring, come, and cheer
   our spirits by thine advent here;
   disperse the gloomy clouds of night,
   and death's dark shadows put to flight.

from the Latin 12th century
tr. John Mason Neale 1818–1866

391

ON JORDAN'S BANK
WINCHESTER NEW 8 8 8 8

Musikalisches Handbuch, Hamburg 1690

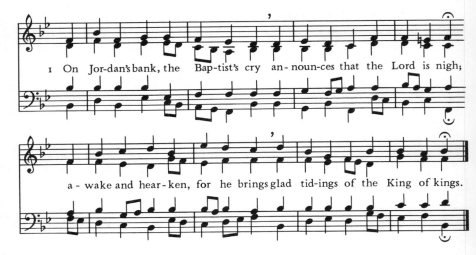

1 On Jordan's bank, the Baptist's cry announces that the Lord is nigh; a-wake and hear-ken, for he brings glad tid-ings of the King of kings.

2 Then cleansed be every breast from sin;
   make straight the way for God within;
   prepare we in our hearts a home,
   where such a mighty guest may come.

3 For thou art our salvation, Lord,
   our refuge, and our great reward;
   without thy grace we waste away,
   like flowers that wither and decay.

4 To heal the sick stretch out thine hand,
   and bid the fallen sinner stand;
   shine forth, and let thy light restore
   earth's own true loveliness once more.

5 All praise, eternal Son, to thee
   whose advent doth thy people free,
   whom with the Father we adore
   and Holy Ghost for evermore.

Charles Coffin 1676–1749
tr. John Chandler 1806–1876

392

HARK, A HERALD VOICE IS SOUNDING

MERTON 8 7 8 7 — William Henry Monk 1823–1889

1 Hark, a her-ald voice is sound-ing: 'Christ is nigh,' it seems to say, 'Cast a-way the dreams of dark-ness, O ye child-ren of the day!'

2 Wakened by the solemn warning,
let the earth-bound soul arise;
Christ her sun, all sloth dispelling,
shines upon the morning skies.

3 Lo, the Lamb, so long expected,
comes with pardon down from heaven;
let us all, with tears of sorrow,
pray that we may be forgiven,

4 that when next he comes with glory,
and the world is wrapped in fear,
with his mercy he may shield us,
and with words of love draw near.

5 Honour, glory, might and blessing
to the Father and the Son,
with the everlasting Spirit,
while eternal ages run.

from the Latin 6th century
tr. Edward Caswall 1814–1878

393

LO, HE COMES WITH CLOUDS DESCENDING

HELMSLEY 878747   English melody, 16th century as in Madan's Collection 1769

1 Lo, he comes with clouds de - scend - ing,
once for fa - voured sin - ners slain;
thou - sand thou - sand saints at - tend - ing
swell the tri - umph of his train:
al - le - lu - ia, al - le - lu - ia, al - le - lu - ia!
God ap - pears on earth to reign.

2 Every eye shall now behold him,
  robed in dreadful majesty;
  all who set at nought and sold him,
  pierced, and nailed him to the tree,
  deeply grieving,
  shall the true Messiah see.

3 Now redemption, long expected,
  see in solemn pomp appear;
  all his saints, by man rejected,
  thrill the trumpet sound to hear:
  hallelujah!
  See the day of God appear!

4 Yea, amen, let all adore thee,
  high on thine eternal throne;
  Saviour, take the power and glory,
  claim the kingdom for thine own:
  O come quickly!
  Hallelujah! Come, Lord, come!

John Cennick 1718–1755
Charles Wesley 1707–1788
Martin Madan 1726–1790

394

SLEEPERS, WAKE

WACHET AUF 898D 66488

melody ascribed to Philip Nicolai 1556–1608
harmonized by Johann Sebastian Bach 1685–1750

1 'Sleep - ers, wake!' the watch are call - ing,
Mid - night comes, no long - er slum - ber,

their notes from Zi - on's watch - tower fall - ing:
nor let dull sleep your sen - ses cum - ber.

'A - wake, a - wake, Je - ru - sa - lem!
Wise vir - gins, haste, or do you dream?

The bride - groom draw - eth near!

A - rise, your lamps show clear. Hal - le - lu - jah.

Your - selves ar - ray this mar - riage day

to meet the bride - groom on his way.'

2   Zion hears the watchmen singing,
    her heart within for joy is springing,
    she wakes, she speeds with glad surprise.
    For her Lord comes down all glorious,
    in grace most strong, in truth victorious,
    her light is come, her star doth rise.
    Welcome! thou worthy crown,
    Lord Jesus, God's dear Son,
    ho–osanna!
    We join the throng that streams along
    and fills thy banquet hall with song.

3   Let all creatures sound thy praises,
    now earth her voice with heaven raises,
    with harps' and cymbals' joyful tone.
    Gates of pearl swing wide before us,
    thy guests who join that blessed chorus
    of angels that surround thy throne.
    No eye hath seen, nor ear
    was yet so blest to hear
    such rejoicing!
    Henceforth may we eternally
    sing hallelujahs unto thee.

    Philip Nicolai 1556–1608
  tr. Jay Macpherson 1931–
    based on Isaiah 52:8, Matthew 25:1-13,
    Revelation 19:6-9

395

HARK THE GLAD SOUND!

BRISTOL 8 6 8 6

Ravenscroft Psalter 1621

1 Hark the glad sound! the Saviour comes, the Saviour promised long:
let every heart prepare a throne, and every voice a song.

2 He comes, the prisoners to release
in Satan's bondage held;
the gates of brass before him burst,
the iron fetters yield.

3 He comes, the broken heart to bind,
the bleeding soul to cure,
and with the treasures of his grace
to bless the humble poor.

4 Our glad hosannas, Prince of peace,
thy welcome shall proclaim;
and heaven's eternal arches ring
with thy beloved name.

Philip Doddridge 1702–1751
This may be sung to Richmond 147
based on Luke 4:18, 19

396

CREATOR OF THE STARS OF NIGHT   Sarum plainsong 7th century
CONDITOR ALME SIDERUM 8 8 8 8   harmonized by Robert Hunter Bell 1932–

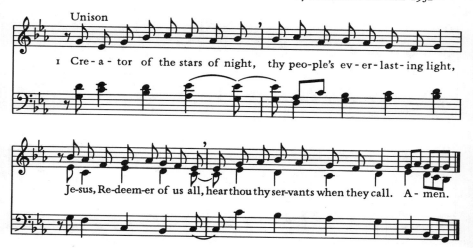

Unison

1 Cre-a-tor of the stars of night, thy peo-ple's ev-er-last-ing light,

Je-sus, Re-deem-er of us all, hear thou thy ser-vants when they call. A-men.

2   Thou, sorrowing at the helpless cry
of all creation doomed to die,
didst save our lost and guilty race
by healing gifts of heavenly grace.

3   When earth was near its evening hour,
thou didst in love's redeeming power,
like bridegroom from his chamber, come
forth from a maiden mother's womb.

4   At thy great name, exalted now,
all knees in lowly homage bow;
all things in heaven and earth adore,
and own thee King for evermore.

5   To thee, O holy one, we pray,
our judge in that tremendous day,
ward off, while yet we dwell below,
the weapons of our crafty foe.

6   To God the Father, God the Son,
and God the Spirit, three in one,
praise, honour, might and glory be
from age to age eternally.

from the Latin 6th century
tr. John Mason Neale 1818–1866
and the compilers
This may be sung to Eisenach 265

397

THE ADVENT OF OUR GOD

ST THOMAS 6686

Williams' New Universal Psalmodist 1770

1 The ad-vent of our God with eag-er prayers we greet,
and sing-ing haste up - on his road his com-ing reign to meet.

2 The everlasting Son
   came down to make us free;
   and he a servant's form put on
   to gain our liberty.

3 Daughter of Sion, rise
   to meet thy lowly King;
   nor let thy faithless heart despise
   the peace he comes to bring.

4 As judge, on clouds of light,
   he soon will come again,
   his scattered people to unite,
   with them in heaven to reign.

5 Then evil flee away
   before the rising dawn!
   Let this old Adam day by day
   God's image still put on.

6 Praise to the incarnate Son
   who comes to set us free,
   with Father, Spirit, ever one,
   to all eternity.

Charles Coffin 1676–1749
tr. John Chandler 1806–1876
   and others

398

JESUS CAME, THE HEAVENS ADORING

TANTUM ERGO 8 7 8 7 8 7

John Wade 1711–1786

1 Jesus came, the heavens adoring, came with peace from realms on high;
Jesus came for man's redemption, lowly came on earth to die,
alleluia! alleluia! came in deep humility.

2 Jesus comes again in mercy,
when our hearts are bowed with care.
Jesus comes again in answer
to our earnest heart-felt prayer,
alleluia! alleluia!
comes to save us from despair.

3 Jesus comes to hearts rejoicing,
bringing news of sins forgiven;
Jesus comes in sounds of gladness,
leading souls redeemed to heaven.
Alleluia! alleluia!
now the gate of death is riven.

4 Jesus comes on clouds triumphant,
when the heavens shall pass away;
Jesus comes again in glory:
let us then our homage pay,
alleluia! alleluia!
till the dawn of endless day.

Godfrey Thring 1823–1903
This may be sung to Richmond 147

399

TOMORROW CHRIST IS COMING

LITTLE BADDOW 7 6 7 6 D

Cecil Armstrong Gibbs 1889–1960

1 To-mor-row Christ is com - ing, as yes-ter-day he came; a child is born this mo - ment, we do not know his name. The world is full of dark - ness, a-gain there is no room; the sym-bols of ex - ist - ence are sta-ble, cross and tomb.

2 Tomorrow will be Christmas,
   the feast of love divine,
   but for the nameless millions
   the star will never shine.
   Still is the census taken
   and men are on the move;
   new infants born in stables
   are crying out for love.

3 There will be no tomorrows
   for many a baby born;
   Good Friday falls on Christmas
   when life is sown as corn.
   But Jesus Christ is risen
   and comes again in bread
   to still our deepest hunger
   and raise us from the dead.

4 Our Lord becomes incarnate
in every human birth.
Created in his image,
we must make peace on earth.
God will fulfil his purpose,
and this shall be the sign:
we shall find Christ among us
as child or youth or man.

Frederik Herman Kaan 1929–

400

GOOD CHRISTIAN MEN, REJOICE

IN DULCI JUBILO irregular

Klug's Gesangbuch 1535

harmonized by Frederick R C Clarke 1931–

Unison

1 Good Christ-ian men, re - joice with heart and soul and voice!

Give ye heed to what we say: News! News!

Je - sus Christ is born to - day.

Ox and ass be - fore him bow, and he is in the man-ger now.

Christ is born to - day, Christ is born to - day!

2   Good Christian men, rejoice
    with heart and soul and voice!
    Now ye hear of endless bliss:
    Joy! Joy!
    Jesus Christ was born for this.
    He hath oped the heavenly door,
    and man is blessed for evermore.
    Christ was born for this!

3   Good Christian men, rejoice
    with heart and soul and voice!
    Now ye need not fear the grave:
    Peace! Peace!
    Jesus Christ was born to save,
    calls you one and calls you all
    to gain his everlasting hall.
    Christ was born to save!

John Mason Neale 1818–1866

401

JOY TO THE WORLD

ANTIOCH 8 6 8 6 with repeat

melody from George Frederick Handel 1685–1759
adapted by Lowell Mason 1792–1872

1 Joy to the world! the Lord is come:
let earth re - ceive her King!
Let ev - ery heart pre - pare him room,
and heaven and na - ture sing, and heaven and na - ture
and heaven and na - ture sing, and
sing, and heaven, and heaven and na - ture sing.
heaven and na - ture sing,

2 Joy to the earth! the Saviour reigns:
  let men their songs employ,
  while fields and floods, rocks, hills and plains
  repeat the sounding joy.

3 No more let sins and sorrows grow,
  nor thorns infest the ground:
  he comes to make his blessings flow
  far as the curse is found.

4 He rules the earth with truth and grace,
  and makes the nations prove
  the glories of his righteousness
  and wonders of his love.

Isaac Watts 1674–1748
This may be sung to Nativity 47

402
BREAK FORTH, O BEAUTEOUS HEAVENLY LIGHT

ERMUNTRE DICH irregular

Johann Schop c1600–1665
harmonized by Johann Sebastian Bach 1685–1750

1 Break forth, O beau - teous heaven - ly light,

and ush - er in the morn - ing;

ye shep - herds, shrink not with af - fright,

but hear the an - gel's warn - ing.

This child, now born in in - fan - cy,

our con - fi - dence and joy shall be

the power of Sa - tan break - ing, our peace e - ter - nal mak - ing.

2   All blessing, thanks and praise to thee,
    Lord Jesus Christ, be given:
    thou hast our brother deigned to be,
    our foes in sunder riven.
    O grant us through our day of grace
    with constant praise to seek thy face;
    grant us ere long in glory
    with praises to adore thee.

    Johann Rist 1607–1677
tr. Arthur Tozer Russell 1806–1874
    and others

403

FROM EAST TO WEST

A SOLIS ORTUS CARDINE 8 8 8 8

plainsong melody
arranged by Healey Willan 1880-1968

1 From east to west, from shore to shore,
let ev - ery heart a - wake and sing
the ho - ly child whom Ma - ry bore,
the Christ, the ev - er - last - ing King. A - men.

2 Behold! the world's creator wears
the form and fashion of a slave;
our very flesh our maker shares,
his fallen creature, man, to save.

3 For this how wondrously he wrought!
A maiden, in her lowly place,
became, in ways beyond all thought,
the chosen vessel of his grace.

4 She bowed her to the angel's word
declaring what the Father willed,
and suddenly the promised Lord
that pure and hallowed temple filled.

5 He shrank not from the oxen's stall,
he lay within the manger bed;
and he whose bounty feedeth all
at Mary's breast himself was fed.

6 And while the angels in the sky
sang praise above the silent field,
to shepherds poor the Lord most high,
the one great Shepherd, was revealed.

7 All glory for this blessed morn
to God the Father ever be;
all praise to thee, O virgin-born,
all praise, O Holy Ghost, to thee.

Coelius Sedulius 5th century
tr. John Ellerton 1826-1893
This may be sung to Puer nobis nascitur 310

404

GO, TELL IT ON THE MOUNTAIN

NEGRO MELODY irregular

traditional

Go, tell it on the moun - tain, o-ver the hills and ev - ery - where.
Tell it
Tell it

Go, tell it on the moun - tain that Je - sus Christ is born.
Go, tell
Tell it

Fine

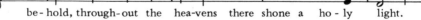

Solo

1 While shep-herds kept their watch - ing o'er si - lent flocks by night,

be - hold, through-out the hea-vens there shone a ho - ly light.

D.C.

2 The shepherds feared and trembled
  when lo, above the earth
  rang out the angel chorus
  that hailed our Saviour's birth!
  Go, tell it ...

3 Down in a lonely manger
  the humble Christ was born,
  and God sent our salvation
  that blessed Christmas morn.
  Go, tell it ...

Negro spiritual

405

WHILE SHEPHERDS WATCHED THEIR FLOCKS

WINCHESTER OLD 8 6 8 6

Este's Psalter 1592

1 While shep-herds watched their flocks by night all seat-ed on the ground, the an-gel of the Lord came down, and glo-ry shone a-round.

2 'Fear not,' said he, for mighty dread
   had seized their troubled mind;
   'Glad tidings of great joy I bring
   to you and all mankind.

3 'To you in David's town this day
   is born of David's line
   a Saviour, who is Christ the Lord;
   and this shall be the sign:

4 'The heavenly babe you there shall find
   to human view displayed,
   all meanly wrapped in swathing bands,
   and in a manger laid.'

5 Thus spake the seraph; and forthwith
   appeared a shining throng
   of angels praising God, who thus
   addressed their joyful song:

6 'All glory be to God on high,
   and to the earth be peace;
   good will henceforth from heaven to men
   begin, and never cease.'

Nahum Tate 1652-1715
based on Luke 2:8-14

406

ON A DAY WHEN MEN WERE COUNTED

KOREA 8 7 8 7 D

Korean carol

On a day when men were count-ed, God be-came the Son of Man;
that his name in ev-ery cen-sus should be en-tered was his plan.
God, the Lord of all cre-a-tion, hum-bly takes a crea-ture's place;
he whose form no man has wit-nessed has to-day a hu-man face.

2 On a night, while silent shepherds
   watched their flocks upon the plain,
   came a message with its summons
   brought by song of angel train:
   lo, in Bethlehem's little village
   has arrived the shepherd King,
   and each shepherd to his Master
   must his sheep as offering bring.

3 When there shone the star of David
   in the spangled eastern sky,
   kings arrived to pay their homage
   to the Christ, the Lord most high.
   Yet not all, for lo, there soundeth
   through the streets a fearful cry:
   for a King who will not worship
   has decreed that Christ must die.

4 Yet it's Christmas, and we greet him,
   coming even now to save;
   for the Lord of our salvation
   was not captive to the grave.
   Out of Egypt came the Saviour
   man's Immanuel to be –
   Christmas shines with Easter glory,
   glory of eternity.

Daniel Thambyrajah Niles 1908-1970

407

HARK! THE HERALD ANGELS SING

MENDELSSOHN 7 7 7 7 D and refrain

adapted from
Felix Mendelssohn Bartholdy 1809-1847
by William Hayman Cummings 1831-1915

1 Hark! the her-ald an-gels sing, Glo-ry to the new-born King,

peace on earth, and mer-cy mild, God and sin-ners re-con-ciled.

Joy-ful, all ye na-tions, rise, join the tri-umph of the skies;

with the an-gel-ic host pro-claim, 'Christ is born in Beth-le-hem'.

Refrain

Hark! the her-ald an-gels sing, Glo-ry to the new-born King.

Organ

2 Christ, by highest heaven adored,
   Christ, the everlasting Lord,
   late in time behold him come,
   offspring of a virgin's womb.
   Veiled in flesh the Godhead see;
   hail, the incarnate deity,
   pleased as Man with man to dwell,
   Jesus, our Emmanuel!

3 Hail, the heaven-born Prince of peace!
   Hail, the Sun of righteousness!
   Light and life to all he brings,
   risen with healing in his wings.
   Mild he lays his glory by,
   born that man no more may die,
   born to raise the sons of earth,
   born to give them second birth.

Charles Wesley 1707-1788

408

ANGELS, FROM THE REALMS OF GLORY

LARKIN 878787 FIRST TUNE

Walter MacNutt 1910-

1 Angels, from the realms of glory, wing your flight o'er all the earth; ye who sang creation's story, now proclaim Messiah's birth: come and worship, come and worship, worship Christ, the new-born King.

1 Angels, from the realms of glory, wing your flight o'er all the earth;

ye who sang creation's story, now proclaim Messiah's birth:

come and worship, come and worship, worship Christ, the new-born King.

2 Shepherds in the field abiding,
watching o'er your flocks by night,
God with man is now residing,
yonder shines the infant Light:
come and worship,
worship Christ, the new-born King.

3 Sages, leave your contemplations;
brighter visions beam afar;
seek the great desire of nations;
ye have seen his natal star:
come and worship,
worship Christ, the new-born King.

4 Saints before the altar bending,
watching long in hope and fear,
suddenly the Lord, descending,
in his temple shall appear:
come and worship,
worship Christ, the new-born King.

5 Though an infant now we view him,
he shall fill his Father's throne,
gather all the nations to him;
every knee shall then bow down:
come and worship,
worship Christ, the new-born King.

James Montgomery 1771-1854

409

SHEPHERDS IN THE FIELD ABIDING

IRIS 8 7 8 7 with refrain

French carol melody

harmony chiefly from Charles Wood 1866-1926

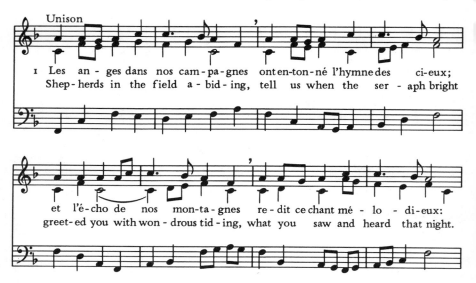

1 Les an-ges dans nos cam-pa-gnes ont en-ton-né l'hymne des ci-eux;
   Shep-herds in the field a-bid-ing, tell us when the ser-aph bright

et l'é-cho de nos mon-ta-gnes re-dit ce chant mé-lo-di-eux:
greet-ed you with won-drous tid-ing, what you saw and heard that night.

2 Bergers, pour qui cette fête?
  Quel est l'objet de tous ces chants?
  Quel vainqueur, quelle conquête
  mérite ces cris triomphants?
  Gloria in exelsis Deo!

2 We beheld – it is no fable –
  God incarnate, King of bliss,
  swathed and cradled in a stable,
  and the angel strain was this:
  Gloria in excelsis Deo.

3 Ils annoncent la naissance
  du libérateur d'Israël,
  et pleins de reconnaissance
  chantent en ce jour solennel.
  Gloria in excelsis Deo!

3 Choristers on high were singing
  Jesus and his virgin birth,
  heavenly bells the while a-ringing
  'Peace, good will to men on earth'.
  Gloria in excelsis Deo.

French carol 18th century

tr. George Ratcliffe Woodward 1848-1934

410

THE FIRST NOWELL

THE FIRST NOWELL irregular

English traditional carol c17th century

1 The first Now - ell the an - gel did say

was to cer - tain poor shep - herds in fields as they lay;

in fields where they lay a - keep - ing their sheep

on a cold win - ter's night that was so deep.

Refrain

Now - ell, Now - ell, Now - ell, Now - ell,

born is the King of Is - ra - el.

descant to refrain by Healey Willan 1880-1968

Now - ell, Now - ell, Now - ell, Now - ell,

born is the King of Is - ra - el.

2   They looked up and saw a star,
     shining in the east, beyond them far;
     and to the earth it gave great light,
     and so it continued both day and night.

3   And by the light of that same star
     three wise men came from country far;
     to seek for a King was their intent,
     and to follow the star wherever it went.

4   This star drew nigh to the north-west;
     o'er Bethlehem it took its rest,
     and there it did both stop and stay,
     right over the place where Jesus lay.

5   Then entered in those wise men three,
     full reverently upon their knee,
     and offered there in his presence
     their gold and myrrh and frankincense.

6   Then let us all with one accord
     sing praises to our heavenly Lord,
     that hath made heaven and earth of nought,
     and with his blood mankind hath bought.

English traditional carol c17th century

411

FROM HEAVEN ON HIGH

VOM HIMMEL HOCH 8 8 8 8   melody from Martin Luther 1483-1546

1 From heaven on high to earth I come to bring good news to ev-er-y home; such news of joy to all I bring, I glad-ly now both say and sing:

2 'To you this night is born a child
of Mary, chosen mother mild;
this tender child of lowly birth
shall be the joy of all the earth.'

3 Were earth ten thousand times so fair,
bedecked with gold and jewels rare,
she yet were far too poor to be
a narrow cradle, Lord, for thee.

4 Ah, dearest Jesus, holy child,
make thee a bed, soft, undefiled,
within my heart, that it may be
a quiet chamber kept for thee.

5 Glory to God in highest heaven,
who unto man his Son hath given:
the angels sing with joyful cheer,
and hail with us the glad new year.

Martin Luther 1483-1546
tr. Catherine Winkworth

412

'TWAS IN THE MOON OF WINTER TIME

JESOUS AHATONHIA irregular

arranged by H Barrie Cabena 1933–

1 'Twas in the moon of winter time, when all the birds had fled,
that mighty Gitchi Manitou sent angel choirs instead;
before their light the stars grew dim, and wondering hunters heard the hymn:
Jesus your King is born, Jesus is born, in excelsis gloria.

2 Within a lodge of broken bark
the tender babe was found,
a ragged robe of rabbit skin
enwrapped his beauty round;
but as the hunter braves drew nigh,
the angel song rang loud and high:
Jesus your King is born, Jesus is born,
in excelsis gloria.

3 O children of the forest free,
O sons of Manitou,
the holy child of earth and heaven
is born today for you.
Come, kneel before the radiant boy,
who brings you beauty, peace, and joy:
Jesus your King is born, Jesus is born,
in excelsis gloria.

Jean de Brébeuf 1593-1649
tr. Jesse Edgar Middleton 1872-1960

413
STARS OF ICE
CHINESE CAROL irregular

Fan T'ien-hsiang
harmonized by Frederick R C Clarke 1931-

1 Stars of ice, wheel of moon - light bright,
shine on sheep with sil - very light,
hum - ble shep - herds chat - ting, cir - cled round,
sit con - tent on grass - y heights.
Sud - den light! Hark, the an - gels sing!
Shep - herds crouch in awe.

'Mid the clouds the an - gels pro - claim
God's Son is born in Beth - le - hem.

2   Dies the song, stars and moon gently fade,
    shepherds leap for very joy;
    leave their quiet flocks, homeward quickly fly,
    worship then the holy boy.
    Wondrous news through the streets resounds;
    glad praises fill every home.
    Poor man's Saviour, peasant's friend,
    comes today to Bethlehem.

3   Learned men from far eastern lands
    kneel before the holy child,
    bring abundant gifts, rare, luxuriant,
    crowd the age-worn village inn.
    Miles on miles had they come to adore;
    no distance seemed too far.
    Boundless, saving, peaceful love   T'ien Ching-Fu
    now has come to Bethlehem.   tr. Bliss Wiant

414

SEE AMID THE WINTER'S SNOW

SEE AMID THE WINTER'S SNOW 7 7 7 7 with refrain

John Goss 1800–1880

1 See a-mid the win-ter's snow, born for us on earth be-low;

see the ten-der Lamb ap-pears, pro-mised from e - ter - nal years.

Refrain
Harmony

Hail, thou ev - er - bless-ed morn; hail, re-demp-tion's hap -py dawn;

sing through all Je - ru - sa-lem, Christ is born in Beth-le-hem.

2   Lo, within a manger lies
    he who built the starry skies;
    he who throned in height sublime
    sits amid the cherubim.

3   Say, ye holy shepherds, say
    what your joyful news today;
    wherefore have ye left your sheep
    on the lonely mountain steep?

4   'As we watched at dead of night,
    lo, we saw a wondrous light;
    angels singing 'Peace on earth'
    told us of the Saviour's birth'.

5   Sacred infant, all divine,
    what a mighty love was thine,
    thus to come from highest bliss
    down to such a world as this!

Edward Caswall 1814-1878
The refrain may be sung after
the final stanza only.

415

O COME, ALL YE FAITHFUL

ADESTE FIDELES *irregular*   attributed to John Francis Wade c1718–1786

A - des - te, fi - de - les, lae - ti tri - um - phan - tes, ve -
O come, all ye faith - ful, joy - ful and tri - um - phant, O

ni - te, ve - ni - te in Beth - le - hem:
come ye, O come ye to Beth - le - hem;

na - tum vi - de - te re - gem an - ge - lo - rum:
come and be - hold him, born the King of an - gels;

ve - ni - te a - do - re - mus, ve - ni - te a - do - re - mus,
O come, let us a - dore him, O come, let us a - dore him,

ve - ni - te a - do - re - mus Do - mi - num.
O come, let us a - dore him, Christ the Lord.

2 Deum de Deo, lumen de lumine,
  parturit virgo mater,
  Deum verum, genitum, non factum.
  Venite, adoremus Dominum.

God of God, light of light,
lo, he abhors not the virgin's womb;
very God, begotten not created:
O come, let us adore him, Christ the Lord.

3 Cantet nunc hymnos chorus angelorum;
  cantet nunc aula cælestium:
  gloria in excelsis Deo!
  Venite, adoremus Dominum.

Sing, choirs of angels, sing in exultation,
sing, all ye citizens of heaven above;
glory to God in the highest:
O come, let us adore him, Christ the Lord.

4 En grege relicto, – humiles ad cunas
  vocati pastores approperant:
  et nos ovanti gradu festinemus:
  venite, adoremus Dominum.

See how the shepherds summoned to his cradle,
leaving their flocks, draw nigh with lowly fear;
we too will thither bend our joyful footsteps;
O come, let us adore him, Christ the Lord.

5 Ergo qui natus die hodierna,
  Jesu, tibi sit gloria:
  Patris aeterni verbum caro factum.
  Venite, adoremus Dominum.

Yea, Lord, we greet thee, born this happy morning;
Jesus, to thee be glory given;
word of the Father, now in flesh appearing:
O come, let us adore him, Christ the Lord.

attributed to John Francis Wade
c1710–1786

tr. Frederick Oakeley 1802–1880
William T Brooke 1848–1917
and others

descant by Stanley L Osborne 1907–

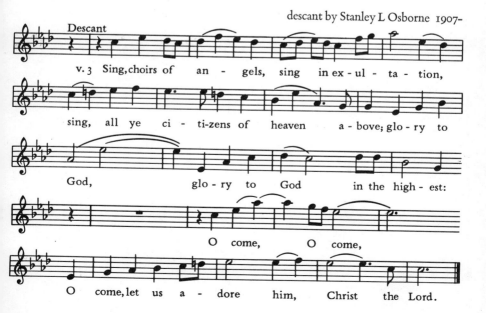

416

SILENT NIGHT! HOLY NIGHT!

<small>STILLE NACHT</small> irregular

Franz Gruber 1787-1863

1 Si - lent night! ho - ly night! All is calm, all is bright

round yon vir - gin moth-er and child. Ho - ly in-fant so ten-der and mild,

sleep in hea - ven-ly peace, sleep in hea - ven-ly peace!

2   Silent night! holy night!
     Shepherds quake at the sight:
     glories stream from heaven afar,
     heavenly hosts sing Alleluia,
     Christ, the Saviour, is born!

3   Silent night! holy night!
     Son of God, love's pure light
     radiant beams from thy holy face,
     with the dawn of redeeming grace,
     Jesus, Lord, at thy birth.

Joseph Mohr 1792–1848
tr. Jane Montgomery Campbell 1817–1878
  and others

417

ALL POOR MEN AND HUMBLE

OLWEN 6 6 8 6 6 8 ter

Welsh carol

arranged by Erik Routley 1917–

1 All poor men and hum-ble, all lame men who stum-ble, come haste ye, and feel not a-fraid; for Je-sus, our trea-sure, whose love pass-es mea-sure, in low-ly poor man-ger was laid. Though wise men who found him laid rich gifts a-round him, yet ox-en they gave him their hay; and Je-sus in beau-ty ac-cept-ed their du-ty: con-tent-ed in man-ger he lay.

Then haste we to show him the prais-es we owe him; our ser-vice he ne'er can des - pise, whose love still is a - ble to show us that sta-ble, where soft-ly in man-ger he lies.

2   The Christ child will lead us,
    the good shepherd feed us
    and with us abide till his day.
    Then hatred he'll banish,
    then sorrow will vanish,
    and death and despair flee away.
    And he shall reign ever,
    and nothing shall sever
    from us the great love of our King.
    His peace and his pity
    shall bless his fair city;
    his praises we ever shall sing.
    Then haste we to show him
    the praises we owe him;
    our service he ne'er can despise,
    whose love still is able
    to show us that stable,
    where softly in manger he lies.

Katharine Emily Roberts 1877-
William Thomas Pennar Davies 1911-

418

IN THE BLEAK MID-WINTER

CRANHAM irregular

Gustavus Theodor Holst 1874-1934

1 In the bleak mid-winter, frost-y wind made moan, earth stood hard as ir-on, wa-ter like a stone; snow had fal-len, snow on snow, snow on snow, in the bleak mid-win-ter, long a-go.

2 Heaven cannot hold him, nor earth sustain;
heaven and earth shall flee away when he comes to reign;
in the bleak mid-winter a stable place sufficed
the Lord God almighty, Jesus Christ.

3 Angels and archangels may have gathered there;
cherubim and seraphim thronged the air;
but his mother only, in her maiden bliss,
worshipped the beloved with a kiss.

4 What can I give him, poor as I am?
If I were a shepherd, I would bring a lamb;
if I were a wise man, I would do my part;
yet what I can I give him – give my heart.

Christina Georgina Rossetti
1830-1894

419

AWAY IN A MANGER

CRADLE SONG II II II II

melody from William James Kirkpatrick 1838-1921
harmonized by Stanley L Osborne 1907-

1 A - way in a man - ger, no crib for a bed,
the lit - tle Lord Je - sus laid down his sweet head.
The stars in the bright sky looked down where he lay,
the lit - tle Lord Je - sus a - sleep on the hay.

2 The cattle are lowing, the baby awakes,
but little Lord Jesus no crying he makes.
I love you, Lord Jesus; look down from the sky,
and stay by my side until morning is nigh.

3 Be near me, Lord Jesus, I ask you to stay
close by me for ever, and love me, I pray.
Bless all the dear children in your tender care,
and fit us for heaven, to live with you there.

Author unknown

420

GENTLE MARY LAID HER CHILD

GWYNNE 7 6 7 6 D and repeat

Stanley L Osborne 1907–

Unison

1 Gen-tle Ma-ry laid her child, low-ly in a man-ger;
there he lay, the un-de-filed, to the world a stran-ger.
Such a babe in such a place, can he be the Sav-iour?
Ask the saved of all the race who have found his fa-vour,
who have found his fa-vour.

2 Angels sang about his birth,
wise men sought and found him;
heaven's star shone brightly forth,
glory all around him.
Shepherds saw the wondrous sight,
heard the angels singing;
all the plains were lit that night,
all the hills were ringing.

3 Gentle Mary laid her child
lowly in a manger;
he is still the undefiled,
but no more a stranger.
Son of God of humble birth,
beautiful the story;
praise his name in all the earth;
hail the King of glory!

Joseph Simpson Cook 1859-1933

421

O LITTLE TOWN OF BETHLEHEM

FOREST GREEN 86867686

English traditional melody
harmonized by Ralph Vaughan Williams 1872-1958

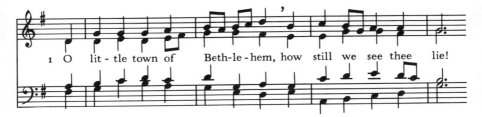

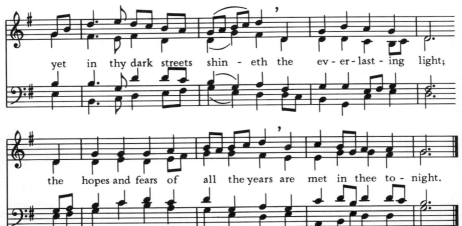

1 O lit-tle town of Beth-le-hem, how still we see thee lie!
A-bove thy deep and dream-less sleep the si-lent stars go by;
yet in thy dark streets shin-eth the ev-er-last-ing light;
the hopes and fears of all the years are met in thee to-night.

2 For Christ is born of Mary;
and, gathered all above,
while mortals sleep, the angels keep
their watch of wondering love.
O morning stars, together
proclaim the holy birth,
and praises sing to God the King,
and peace to men on earth.

3 How silently, how silently,
the wondrous gift is given!
So God imparts to human hearts
the blessings of his heaven.
No ear may hear his coming;
but in this world of sin,
where meek souls will receive him, still
the dear Christ enters in.

for a lower setting see 388

1 O lit-tle town of Beth-le-hem, how still we see thee lie!

A - bove thy deep and dream-less sleep the si - lent stars go by;

yet in thy dark streets shin - eth the ev - er - last - ing light;

the hopes and fears of all the years are met in thee to-night.

4   O holy child of Bethlehem,
     descend to us, we pray;
     cast out our sin, and enter in;
     be born in us today.
     We hear the Christmas angels
     the great glad tidings tell;
     O come to us, abide with us,
     our Lord Emmanuel.

Phillips Brooks 1835-1893

422

LOVE CAME DOWN AT CHRISTMAS

HERMITAGE 6 7 6 7

Reginald Owen Morris 1886-1948

1 Love came down at Christ - mas, love all love-ly, love di - vine;
love was born at Christ-mas, stars and an-gels gave the sign.

2 Worship we the Godhead,
   love incarnate, love divine;
   worship we our Jesus:
   but wherewith for sacred sign?

3 Love shall be our token,
   love be yours and love be mine,
   love to God and all men,
   love for plea and gift and sign.

Christina Georgina Rossetti 1830-1894

423

UNTO US A BOY IS BORN

PUER NOBIS NASCITUR 76777

from Piae Cantiones 1582
harmonized by Hugh J McLean 1930-

1 Un - to us a boy is born! King of all cre - a - tion, came he to a world for - lorn, the Lord of ev - ery na - tion, the Lord of ev - ery na - tion.

2 Cradled in a stall was he
with sleepy cows and asses;
but the very beasts could see
that he all men surpasses.

3 Herod then with fear was filled:
'A prince' he said 'in Jewry!'
All the little boys he killed
at Bethlehem in his fury.

4 Now may Mary's Son, who came
so long ago to love us,
lead us all with hearts aflame
unto the joys above us.

5 Omega and Alpha he!
Let the organ thunder
while the choir with peals of glee
doth rend the air asunder.

from the Latin c15th century
tr. Percy Dearmer 1867-1936

424

A STABLE LAMP IS LIGHTED

TOLLEFSON 7676 6676

Paulette Tollefson 1950-

1 A sta-ble lamp is light-ed whose glow shall wake the sky; the stars shall bend their voic-es, and ev-ery stone shall cry. And ev-ery stone shall cry, and straw like gold shall shine; a barn shall har-bour heav-en, a stall be-come a shrine.

2 This child through David's city
    shall ride in triumph by;
    the palm shall strew its branches,
    and every stone shall cry.
    And every stone shall cry,
    though heavy, dull, and dumb,
    and lie within the roadway
    to pave his kingdom come.

3 Yet he shall be forsaken,
    and yielded up to die;
    the sky shall groan and darken,
    and every stone shall cry.
    And every stone shall cry
    for stony hearts of men:
    God's blood upon the spearhead,
    God's blood refused again.

4 But now, as at the ending,
    the low is lifted high;
    the stars shall bend their voices,
    and every stone shall cry.
    And every stone shall cry
    in praises of the child
    by whose descent among us
    the worlds are reconciled.

Richard Wilbur 1921–

425

DOWN TO EARTH, AS A DOVE — melody from Piae Cantiones 1582
THEODORIC 6 6 6 6 6 and refrain — harmonized by Frederick R C Clarke 1931-

1 Down to earth, as a dove, came to man holy love:
Jesus Christ from above bringing great salvation
meant for every nation.

Refrain
Let us sing, sing, sing, dance and spring, spring, spring;
Christ is here, ever near! Gloria in excelsis.

2 This is love come to light,
now is fear put to flight.
God defeats darkest night,
giving for our sorrows
hope of new tomorrows.

3 Christ the Lord comes to feed
hungry men in their need;
in the house there is bread:
Jesus in a stable,
in the church a table.

Frederik Herman Kaan
1929-

426

NO CROWDED EASTERN STREET

HERITAGE 668887

Robert J B Fleming 1921–

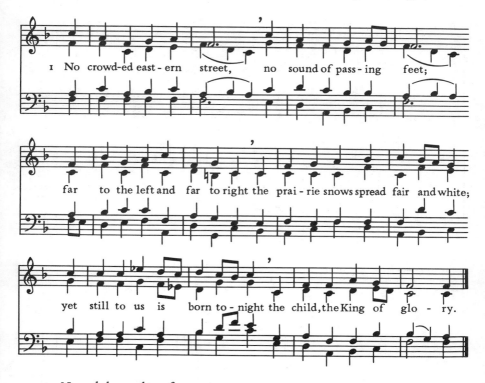

1 No crowd-ed east-ern street, no sound of pass-ing feet;
far to the left and far to right the prai-rie snows spread fair and white;
yet still to us is born to-night the child, the King of glo-ry.

2 No rock-hewn place of peace
   shared with the gentle beasts,
   but sturdy farm house, stout and warm,
   with stable, shed, and great red barn;
   and still to us is born tonight
   the child, the King of glory.

3 No blaze of heavenly fire,
   no bright celestial choir,
   only the starlight as of old,
   crossed by the planes' flash, red and gold;
   yet still to us is born tonight
   the child, the King of glory.

4 No king with gold and grain,
   no stately camel train:
   yet in his presence all may stand
   with loving heart and willing hand;
   for still to us is born tonight
   the child, the King of glory.

Frieda Major 1891–

427

IT CAME UPON THE MIDNIGHT CLEAR English traditional melody
NOEL 8 6 8 6 D FIRST TUNE   arranged by Arthur Seymour Sullivan 1842–1900

1 It came up-on the mid-night clear, that glo-rious song of old,
from an-gels bend-ing near the earth to touch their harps of gold:
'Peace on the earth, good will to men, from heaven's all-gra-cious King!'
The world in sol-emn still-ness lay to hear the an-gels sing.

2 Still through the cloven skies they come
  with peaceful wings unfurled;
  and still their heavenly music floats
  o'er all the weary world;
  above its sad and lowly plains
  they bend on hovering wing,
  and ever o'er its Babel sounds
  the blessed angels sing.

3 But with the woes of sin and strife
  the world has suffered long;
  beneath the angel strain have rolled
  two thousand years of wrong;
  and man, at war with man, hears not
  the love song which they bring;
  O hush the noise, ye men of strife,
  and hear the angels sing.

1 It came up-on the mid-night clear, that glo-rious song of old,

from an-gels bend-ing near the earth to touch their harps of gold,

'Peace on the earth, good will to men, from heaven's all - gra-cious King!'

The world in sol-emn still-ness lay to hear the an-gels sing.

4 For, lo! the days are hastening on,
   by prophet bards foretold,
   when with the ever-circling years
   comes round the age of gold,
   when peace shall over all the earth
   its ancient splendours fling,
   and the whole world give back the song
   which now the angels sing.

Edmund Hamilton Sears 1810–1876

428

EVERY STAR SHALL SING A CAROL
CAROL 878767

Sydney Carter 1915-

1 Ev-ery star shall sing a car-ol! Ev-ery crea-ture, high or low, come and praise the King of hea-ven by what-ev-er name you know. God a-bove, Man be-low, ho-ly is the name I know. ho-ly is the name I know.

2   When the King of all creation
    had a cradle on the earth,
    holy was the human body,
    holy was the human birth.
    God above, Man below,
    holy is the name I know.

3   Who can tell what other cradle,
    high above the milky way,
    still may rock the King of heaven
    on another Christmas day?
    God above, Man below,
    holy is the name I know.

4   Who can count how many crosses,
    still to come or long ago,
    crucify the King of heaven?
    Holy is the name I know.
    God above, Man below,
    holy is the name I know.

5   Who can tell what other body
    he will hallow for his own?
    I will praise the Son of Mary,
    brother of my blood and bone.
    God above, Man below,
    holy is the name I know.

6   Every star and every planet,
    every creature high and low,
    come and praise the King of heaven
    by whatever name you know.
    God above, Man below,
    holy is the name I know.

Sydney Carter 1915-

429

OF THE FATHER'S LOVE BEGOTTEN plainsong melody c12th century

DIVINUM MYSTERIUM 8787877 arranged by Healey Willan 1880-1968

Unison

1 Of the Fa-ther's love be-got-ten ere the worlds be-gan to be,

he is Al-pha and O-me-ga, he the source, the end-ing he,

of the things that are and have been, and that fu-ture years shall see,

ev-er-more and ev-er-more. A - men.

2 At his word the worlds were framed.
He commanded, it was done:
heaven and earth and depths of ocean
in their threefold order one;
all that grows beneath the shining
of the moon and burning sun,
evermore and evermore.

3 O that birth for ever blessed!
When the virgin, full of grace,
by the Holy Ghost conceiving,
bare the Saviour of our race,
and the babe, the world's redeemer,
first revealed his sacred face,
evermore and evermore.

4 This is he whom seers in old time
chanted of with one accord,
whom the voices of the prophets
promised in their faithful word;
now he shines, the long-expected;
let creation praise its Lord,
evermore and evermore.

5 O ye heights of heaven, adore him;
angel hosts, his praises sing;
all dominions, bow before him,
and extol our God and King;
let no tongue on earth be silent,
every voice in concert ring,
evermore and evermore.

6 Christ, to thee, with God the Father,
and, O Holy Ghost, to thee,
hymn and chant and high thanksgiving
and unwearied praises be,
honour, glory and dominion
and eternal victory,
evermore and evermore.

Aurelius Clemens Prudentius 348-413
tr. John Mason Neale 1818-1866

AND THE FOLLOWING

430

THE RACE THAT LONG IN DARKNESS PINED

DUNFERMLINE 8 6 8 6   Scottish Psalter 1615

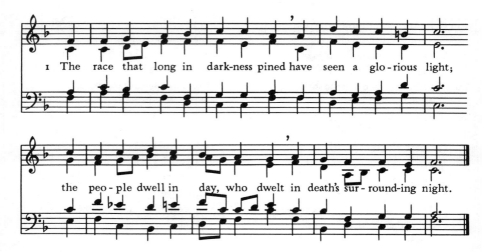

1 The race that long in darkness pined have seen a glorious light;
the people dwell in day, who dwelt in death's surrounding night.

2   To hail thy rise, thou better Sun!
     the gathering nations come,
     joyous as when the reapers bear
     the harvest treasures home.

3   To us a child of hope is born,
     to us a Son is given;
     him shall the tribes of earth obey,
     him all the hosts of heaven.

4   His name shall be the Prince of Peace,
     for evermore adored,
     the Wonderful, the Counsellor,
     the great and mighty Lord.

5   His power increasing still shall spread,
     his reign no end shall know;
     justice shall guard his throne above,
     and peace around below.

John Morison c1750-1798
Scottish Paraphrases 1781
based on Isaiah 9:2-8
for a lower setting see 453

431

EARTH HAS MANY A NOBLE CITY

STUTTGART 8 7 8 7   from a melody in Psalmodia Sacra, Gotha 1715

1 Earth has many a no-ble ci-ty; Beth-le-hem, thou dost all ex-cel:
out of thee the Lord from hea-ven came to rule his Is - ra-el.

2   Fairer than the sun at morning
    was the star that told his birth,
    to the world its God announcing
    seen in fleshly form on earth.

3   Eastern sages at his cradle
    make oblation rich and rare;
    see them give, in deep devotion,
    gold, and frankincense, and myrrh.

4   Sacred gifts of mystic meaning:
    incense doth their God disclose,
    gold the King of kings proclaimeth,
    myrrh his sepulchre foreshows.

5   Jesus, whom the Gentiles worshipped
    at thy glad epiphany,
    unto thee, with God the Father
    and the Spirit, glory be.

Aurelius Clemens Prudentius 348-413
tr. Edward Caswall 1814-1878
for a lower setting see 398

432
BRIGHTEST AND BEST OF THE SONS OF THE MORNING
STELLA ORIENTIS 11 10 11 10   Healey Willan 1880-1968

1 Bright-est and best of the sons of the morn - ing,
dawn on our dark-ness, and lend us thine aid;
star of the east, the ho - ri - zon a - dorn - ing,
guide where our in - fant Re - deem - er is laid.

2   Cold on his cradle the dew-drops are shining;
    low lies his head with the beasts of the stall;
    angels adore him in slumber reclining,
    maker and monarch and saviour of all.

3   Say, shall we yield him, in costly devotion,
    odours of Edom, and offerings divine,
    gems of the mountain and pearls of the ocean,
    myrrh from the forest or gold from the mine?

4   Vainly we offer each ample oblation,
    vainly with gifts would his favour secure:
    richer by far is the heart's adoration;
    dearer to God are the prayers of the poor.

5   Brightest and best of the sons of the morning,
    dawn on our darkness and lend us thine aid;
    star of the east, the horizon adorning,
    guide where our infant Redeemer is laid.

Reginald Heber 1783-1826
This may be sung to Liebster Immanuel 57

433

SONGS OF THANKFULNESS

SALZBURG 7 7 7 7 D

melody from Jakob Hintze 1622-1702
harmonized by Johann Sebastian Bach 1685-1750

1 Songs of thank-ful-ness and praise, Je-sus, Lord, to thee we raise,
man-i-fest-ed by the star to the sag-es from a-far,
branch of roy-al Da-vid's stem in thy birth at Beth-le-hem;
an-thems be to thee ad-dressed, God in man made man-i-fest.

2 Manifest at Jordan's stream,
   prophet, priest, and king supreme;
   and at Cana wedding-guest
   in thy Godhead manifest;
   manifest in power divine,
   changing water into wine;
   anthems be to thee addressed,
   God in man made manifest.

3 Manifest in making whole
   palsied limbs and fainting soul;
   manifest in valiant fight,
   overcoming evil's might;
   manifest in gracious will,
   ever bringing good from ill;
   anthems be to thee addressed,
   God in man made manifest.

4 Sun and moon shall darkened be,
   stars shall fall, the heavens shall flee;
   Christ will then like lightning shine,
   all will see his glorious sign;
   all will then the trumpet hear,
   all will see the judge appear;
   thou by all wilt be confessed,
   God in man made manifest.

5 Grant us grace to see thee, Lord,
   mirrored in thy holy word;
   may we imitate thee now,
   and be pure, as pure art thou,
   that we like to thee may be
   at thy great epiphany;
   and may praise thee, ever blest,
   God in man made manifest.

Christopher Wordsworth 1807-1885
This may be sung to St George's, Windsor 384

434

WHEN CHRIST'S APPEARING WAS MADE KNOWN

HOSTIS HERODIS IMPIE 8 8 8 8   plainsong melody arranged by Healey Willan 1880-1968

1 When Christ's ap-pear-ing was made known,
King He-rod trem-bled for his throne;
but he who of-fers heaven-ly birth
sought not the king-doms of this earth. A - men.

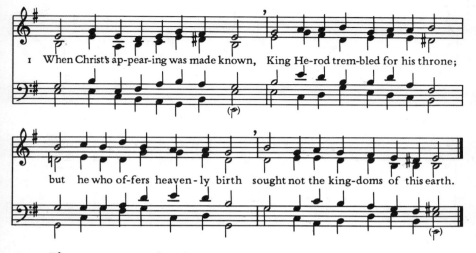

1 When Christ's ap-pear-ing was made known, King He-rod trem-bled for his throne;

but he who of-fers heaven-ly birth sought not the king-doms of this earth.

2 The eastern sages saw from far
  and followed on his guiding star;
  by light their way to light they trod,
  and by their gifts confessed their God.

3 Within the Jordan's sacred flood
  the heavenly Lamb in meekness stood,
  that he, to whom no sin was known,
  might cleanse his people from their own.

4 And O what miracle divine,
  when water reddened into wine!
  He spake the word, and forth it flowed
  in streams that nature ne'er bestowed.

5 All glory, Jesus, be to thee
  for this thy glad epiphany:
  whom with the Father we adore
  and Holy Ghost for evermore.

Coelius Sedulius c5th century
tr. John Mason Neale 1818-1866
and the compilers

435

AS WITH GLADNESS MEN OF OLD

DIX 777777   abridged from a chorale by Konrad Kocher 1786-1872

1 As with gladness men of old did the guiding star behold,
as with joy they hailed its light, leading onward, beaming bright,
so, most gracious Lord, may we evermore be led to thee.

2 As with joyful steps they sped,
Saviour, to thy lowly bed,
there to bend the knee before
thee, whom heaven and earth adore,
so may we with willing feet
ever seek thy mercy-seat.

3 As they offered gifts most rare
at that cradle rude and bare,
so may we with holy joy,
pure and free from sin's alloy,
all our costliest treasures bring,
Christ, to thee our heavenly King.

4 Holy Jesus, every day
keep us in the narrow way;
and, when earthly things are past,
bring our ransomed souls at last
where they need no star to guide,
where no clouds thy glory hide.

5 In the heavenly country bright
need they no created light;
thou its light, its joy, its crown,
thou its sun which goes not down;
there for ever may we sing
alleluias to our King.

William Chatterton Dix 1837-1898

AND THE FOLLOWING

436

GIVER OF THE PERFECT GIFT

SONG 13 7777 FIRST TUNE

Orlando Gibbons 1583-1625

1 Giv-er of the per-fect gift, on-ly hope of hu-man race,
hear the prayer our hearts up-lift, ga-thered at thy throne of grace.

2 Though the accusing voice within
speaks of many a wrong to thee,
thou canst cleanse from every sin,
thou canst set the conscience free.

3 Who can save us, Lord, but thou?
Let thy mercy show thy power;
lo, we plead thy promise now,
now, in this the accepted hour.

4 Oh, may these our lenten days,
blest by thee, with thee be passed,
that with purer, nobler praise
we may keep thy feast at last.

5 God the holy trinity,
grant the mercy we implore;
God the one, all praise to thee
through the ages evermore.

from the Latin c11th century
tr. John Ellerton 1826-1893

1 Giv-er of the per-fect gift, on-ly hope of hu-man race,
hear the prayer our hearts up-lift, ga-thered at thy throne of grace.

2 Though the accusing voice within
  speaks of many a wrong to thee,
  thou canst cleanse from every sin,
  thou canst set the conscience free.

3 Who can save us, Lord, but thou?
  Let thy mercy show thy power;
  lo, we plead thy promise now,
  now, in this the accepted hour.

4 Oh, may these our lenten days,
  blest by thee, with thee be passed,
  that with purer, nobler praise
  we may keep thy feast at last.

5 God the holy trinity,
  grant the mercy we implore;
  God the one, all praise to thee   from the Latin c11th century
  through the ages evermore.   tr. John Ellerton 1826–1893

437

O KIND CREATOR

plainsong melody arranged by Healey Willan 1880-1968

AUDI BENIGNE CONDITOR 8 8 8 8   FIRST TUNE

1 O kind Cre - a - tor, bow thine ear
to mark the cry, to know the tear
be - fore thy throne of mer - cy spent
in this thy ho - ly fast of lent. A - men.

2 Our hearts are open, Lord, to thee:
thou knowest our infirmity;
pour out on all who seek thy face
abundance of thy pardoning grace.

3 Our sins are many, this we know;
spare us, good Lord, thy mercy show;
and for the honour of thy name
our fainting souls to life reclaim.

4 Give us the self-control that springs
from discipline of outward things,
that fasting inward secretly
the soul may purely dwell with thee.

5 We pray thee, holy trinity,
one God, unchanging unity,
that we from this our abstinence
may reap the fruit of penitence.

Gregory the Great 540-604
tr. Thomas Alexander Lacey 1853-1931

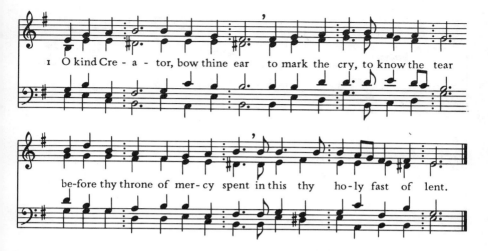

1 O kind Cre-a-tor, bow thine ear to mark the cry, to know the tear
before thy throne of mer-cy spent in this thy ho-ly fast of lent.

2 Our hearts are open, Lord, to thee:
thou knowest our infirmity;
pour out on all who seek thy face
abundance of thy pardoning grace.

3 Our sins are many, this we know;
spare us, good Lord, thy mercy show;
and for the honour of thy name
our fainting souls to life reclaim.

4 Give us the self-control that springs
from discipline of outward things,
that fasting inward secretly
the soul may purely dwell with thee.

5 We pray thee, holy trinity,
one God, unchanging unity,
that we from this our abstinence
may reap the fruit of penitence.

Gregory the Great 540–604
tr. Thomas Alexander Lacey 1853–1931

438

FORTY DAYS AND FORTY NIGHTS

HEINLEIN 7777   ascribed to Martin Herbst 1654–1681

1 For-ty days and for-ty nights thou wast fast-ing in the wild; for-ty days and for-ty nights tempt-ed, and yet un-de-filed;

2 sunbeams scorching all the day,
chilly dew-drops nightly shed;
prowling beasts about thy way;
stones thy pillow, earth thy bed.

3 Shall not we thy trial share,
and from earthly joys abstain,
fasting with unceasing prayer,
strong with thee to suffer pain?

4 And if Satan, vexing sore,
flesh or spirit should assail,
thou, his vanquisher before,
grant we may not faint nor fail.

5 So shall we have peace divine;
holier gladness ours shall be;
round us too shall angels shine,
such as ministered to thee.

6 Keep, O keep us, Saviour dear,
ever constant by thy side;
that with thee we may appear
at the eternal Eastertide.

George Hunt Smyttan 1822–1870
Francis Pott 1832–1909

439

LORD, FROM THE DEPTHS TO THEE I CRIED

COLESHILL 8 6 8 6

Barton's Psalms 1706

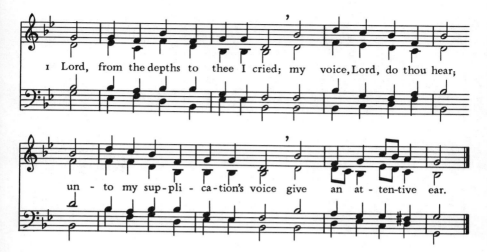

1 Lord, from the depths to thee I cried; my voice, Lord, do thou hear;
un - to my sup - pli - ca - tion's voice give an at - ten-tive ear.

2 Lord, who shall stand, if thou, O Lord,
shouldst mark iniquity?
But yet with thee forgiveness is,
that feared thou mayst be.

3 I wait for God, my soul doth wait;
my hope is in his word.
More than they that for morning watch,
my soul waits for the Lord;

4 I say, more than they that do watch
the morning light to see.
Let Israel hope in the Lord,
for with him mercies be.

5 Redemption also plenteous
is ever found with him,
and from all his iniquities
he Israel shall redeem.

Scottish Psalter 1650
based on Psalm 130

440

BENEATH THE CROSS OF JESUS
ST CHRISTOPHER 7 6 8 6 8 6 8 6

Frederick Charles Maker 1844-1927

1 Beneath the cross of Jesus I fain would take my stand: the shadow of a mighty rock within a weary land, a home within the wilderness, a rest upon the way, from the burning of the noon-tide heat and the burden of the day.

2 Upon the cross of Jesus
   mine eye at times can see
   the very dying form of one
   who suffered there for me;
   and from my smitten heart, with tears,
   two wonders I confess,
   the wonder of his glorious love,
   and my unworthiness.

3 I take, O cross, thy shadow
   for my abiding-place;
   I ask no other sunshine than
   the sunshine of his face,
   content to let the world go by,
   to know no gain nor loss,
   my sinful self my only shame,
   my glory all, the cross.

Elizabeth Cecilia Clephane 1830-1869

441

SWEET THE MOMENTS

ELLERKER 8 7 8 7   Johann Thommen's 'Christenschatz' 1745

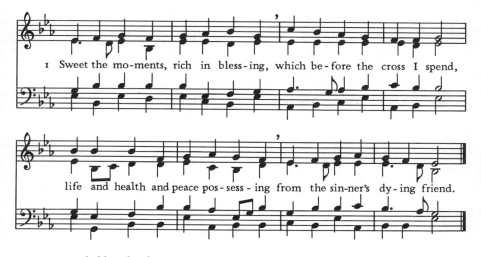

1 Sweet the mo-ments, rich in bless-ing, which be-fore the cross I spend,
life and health and peace pos-sess-ing from the sin-ner's dy-ing friend.

2 Truly blessed is the station
low before his cross to lie,
while I see divine compassion
beaming in his gracious eye.

3 Lord, in ceaseless contemplation
fix our hearts and eyes on thee,
till we taste thy full salvation,
and thy unveiled glory see.

4 For thy sorrows we adore thee,
for the griefs that wrought our peace;
gracious Saviour! we implore thee,   Walter Shirley 1725-1786
in our hearts thy love increase.   and others

442

MY SONG IS LOVE UNKNOWN

CROSSMAN 66664444 FIRST TUNE

Godfrey Ridout 1918–

1 My song is love un-known, my Sav-iour's love to me;
love to the love-less shown, that they might love-ly be.
O who am I, that for my sake
my Lord should take frail flesh, and die?

2 He came from his blest throne
salvation to bestow;
but men made strange, and none
the longed-for Christ would know:
but O my friend,
my friend indeed,
who at my need
his life did spend!

3 Sometimes they strew his way,
and his sweet praises sing,
resounding all the day
hosannas to their King;
then 'Crucify!'
is all their breath,
and for his death
they thirst and cry.

4 They rise and needs will have
  my dear Lord made away;
  a murderer they save,
  the prince of life they slay.
  Yet cheerful he
  to suffering goes,
  that he his foes
  from thence might free.

5 Here might I stay and sing,
  no story so divine;
  never was love, dear King,
  never was grief like thine!
  This is my friend,
  in whose sweet praise
  I all my days
  could gladly spend.

Samuel Crossman 1624-1683

WESLEY 66664444 SECOND TUNE   Composer unknown

1 My song is love un-known, my Sav-iour's love to me;
love to the love-less shown, that they may love-ly be.
O who am I, that for my sake my Lord should take frail flesh, and die?

443

AH, HOLY JESUS

HERZLIEBSTER JESU 11 11 11 5

melody by Johann Crüger 1598–1662
adapted by Johann Sebastian Bach 1685–1750

1 Ah, ho - ly Je - sus, how hast thou of - fend - ed,
that man to judge thee hath in hate pre - tend - ed?
By foes de - rid - ed, by thine own re - ject - ed,
O most af - flict - ed.

2 Who was the guilty? Who brought this upon thee?
Alas, my treason, Jesus, hath undone thee;
'twas I, Lord Jesus, I it was denied thee,
I crucified thee.

3 Lo, the good shepherd for the sheep is offered;
the slave hath sinnèd, and the Son hath suffered;
for man's atonement, while he nothing heedeth,
God intercedeth.

4 For me, kind Jesus, was thy incarnation,
thy mortal sorrow, and thy life's oblation;
thy death of anguish and thy bitter passion,
for my salvation.

5 Therefore, kind Jesus, since I cannot pay thee,
I do adore thee, and will ever pray thee,
think on thy pity and thy love unswerving,
not my deserving.

Johann Heermann 1585-1647
tr. Robert Seymour Bridges 1844-1930

444
MAN OF SORROWS
ABERYSTWYTH 7 7 7 7 D

Joseph Parry 1841-1903

1 Man of sor-rows, wrapt in grief, bow thine ear to our re-lief;

thou for us the path hast trod of the right-eous wrath of God;

thou the cup of fire hast drained till its light a - lone re-mained.

Lamb of love! we look to thee: hear our mourn-ful li - ta - ny.

2 By the garden, fraught with woe,
   whither thou full oft wouldst go;
   by thine agony of prayer
   in the desolation there;
   by the dire and deep distress
   of that mystery fathomless;
   Lord, our tears in mercy see:
   hearken to our litany.

3 By the chalice brimming o'er
   with disgrace and torment sore;
   by those lips which fain would pray
   that it might but pass away;
   by the heart which drank it dry,
   lest a rebel race should die;
   by thy pity, Lord, our plea:
   hear our solemn litany.

4 Man of sorrows! let thy grief
   purchase for us our relief;
   Lord of mercy! bow thine ear,
   slow to anger, swift to hear;
   by the cross's royal road
   lead us to the throne of God,
   there for aye to sing to thee
   heaven's triumphant litany.

   Matthew Bridges 1800–1894

AND THE FOLLOWING

445

THE FLAMING BANNERS

VEXILLA REGIS 8 8 8 8 FIRST TUNE

Sarum plainsong 7th century
arranged by Healey Willan 1880-1968

Unison

1 The flam - ing ban - ners of our King
ad-vance through his self - of - fer - ing.
He lived to rob death of its sting;
he died e - ter - nal life to bring. A - men.

2 A Roman soldier drew a spear
to mix his blood with water clear.
That blood retains its living power:
the water cleanses to this hour.

3 The crowd would have been satisfied
to see a prophet crucified.
They stumbled on a mystery:
Messiah reigning from a tree.

1 The flam-ing ban-ners of our King
ad-vance through his self-of-fer-ing.
He lived to rob death of its sting;
he died e-ter-nal life to bring. A - men.

4 With what strange light the rough trunk shone,
   its purple limbs a royal throne,
   its load a royal treasury:
   the ransom of a world set free.

5 The best are shamed before that wood;
   the worst gain power to be good.
   O grant, most blessed trinity,
   that all may share the victory.

Venantius Fortunatus 530-609
tr. John Webster Grant 1919-

446

SING, MY TONGUE, THE GLORIOUS BATTLE   Sarum plainsong
PANGE LINGUA 878787 FIRST TUNE   arranged by Robert H Bell 1932–

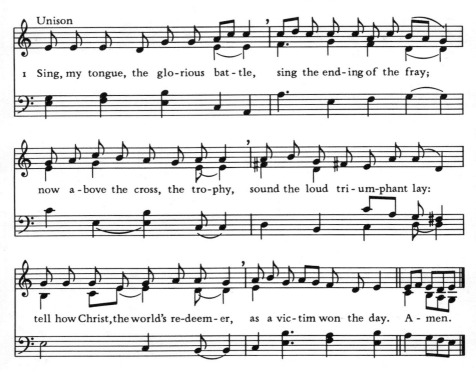

1 Sing, my tongue, the glo-rious bat-tle, sing the end-ing of the fray; now a-bove the cross, the tro-phy, sound the loud tri-um-phant lay: tell how Christ, the world's re-deem-er, as a vic-tim won the day. A-men.

2 Tell how, when at length the fullness
of the appointed time was come,
he, the word, was born of woman,
left for us his Father's home,
showed to men the perfect manhood,
shone as light amidst the gloom.

3 Thus, with thirty years accomplished,
went he forth from Nazareth,
destined, dedicate, and willing,
wrought his work, and met his death;
like a lamb he humbly yielded
on the cross his dying breath.

4 Faithful cross, thou sign of triumph,
now for man the noblest tree,
none in foliage, none in blossom,
none in fruit thy peer may be;
symbol of the world's redemption
for the weight that hung on thee!

5 Unto God be praise and glory;
to the Father and the Son,
to the eternal Spirit, honour
now and evermore be done:
praise and glory in the highest,
while the timeless ages run.

Venantius Fortunatus 530–609
tr. Percy Dearmer 1867–1936

Casper Ett in 'Cantica Sacra' 1840

1 Sing, my tongue, the glorious battle, sing the ending of the fray;
now above the cross, the trophy, sound the loud triumphant lay:
tell how Christ, the world's redeemer, as a victim won the day.

2 Tell how, when at length the fullness
of the appointed time was come,
he, the word, was born of woman,
left for us his Father's home,
showed to men the perfect manhood,
shone as light amidst the gloom.

3 Thus, with thirty years accomplished,
went he forth from Nazareth,
destined, dedicate, and willing,
wrought his work, and met his death;
like a lamb he humbly yielded
on the cross his dying breath.

4 Faithful cross, thou sign of triumph,
now for man the noblest tree,
none in foliage, none in blossom,
none in fruit thy peer may be;
symbol of the world's redemption
for the weight that hung on thee!

5 Unto God be praise and glory;
to the Father and the Son,
to the eternal Spirit, honour
now and evermore be done:
praise and glory in the highest,
while the timeless ages run.

Venantius Fortunatus 530-609
tr. Percy Dearmer 1867-1936

447

ALL GLORY, LAUD AND HONOUR
ST THEODULPH 7676D

Melchior Teschner c1615

1 All glo-ry, laud and hon-our to thee, Re-deem-er, King,
to whom the lips of child-ren made sweet ho-san-nas ring.
Thou art the King of Is-rael, thou Da-vid's roy-al Son,
who in the Lord's name com-est, the King and bless-ed one.

2 All glory ... ring.
The company of angels
are praising thee on high,
and mortal men and all things
created make reply.

3 All glory ... ring.
The people of the Hebrews
with palms before thee went;
our praise and prayer and anthems
before thee we present.

4 All glory ... ring.
To thee before thy passion
they sang their hymns of praise;
to thee now high exalted
our melody we raise.

5 All glory ... ring.
Thou didst accept their praises;
accept the prayers we bring,
who in all good delightest,
thou good and gracious King.

Theodulph of Orleans ?-821
tr. John Mason Neale 1818-1866

448

HOSANNA, LOUD HOSANNA

ELLACOMBE 7 6 7 6 D

from Xavier Ludwig Hartel's
'Vollständige Sammlung' 1833

1 Ho - san - na, loud ho - san - na the lit - tle child-ren sang;
through pil - lared court and tem - ple the love-ly an-them rang;
to Je - sus, who had blessed them close fold - ed to his breast,
the child-ren sang their prais - es, the sim - plest and the best.

2 From Olivet they followed
'mid an exultant crowd,
the victor palm-branch waving,
and chanting clear and loud;
the Lord of men and angels
rode on in lowly state,
nor scorned that little children
should on his bidding wait.

3 'Hosanna in the highest!'
That ancient song we sing,
for Christ is our Redeemer,
the Lord of heaven our King.
O may we ever praise him
with heart and life and voice,
and in his blissful presence
eternally rejoice!

Jennette Threlfall 1821-1880

449

RIDE ON! RIDE ON IN MAJESTY!

THE KING'S MAJESTY 8 8 8 8

Graham George 1912-

1 Ride on! ride on in majesty! Hark! all the tribes hosanna cry: O Saviour meek, pursue thy road with palms and scattered garments strowed.

2 Ride on! ride on in majesty!
In lowly pomp ride on to die;
O Christ, thy triumphs now begin
o'er captive death and conquered sin.

3 Ride on! ride on in majesty!
The winged squadrons of the sky
look down with sad and wondering eyes
to see the approaching sacrifice.

4 Ride on! ride on in majesty!
Thy last and fiercest strife is nigh;
the Father on his sapphire throne
awaits his own anointed Son.

5   Ride on! ride on in majesty!
In lowly pomp ride on to die;
bow thy meek head to mortal pain,
then take, O God, thy power, and reign.

Henry Hart Milman 1791–1868
based on John 12:12-15
This may be sung to Winchester New 391

450

THE GLORY OF OUR KING
MORNING SONG 8 6 8 6

early American melody
harmonized by C Winfred Douglas 1867–1944

1 The glo-ry of our King was seen when he came rid-ing by,
and all the child-ren waved and sang, Ho-san-na, King most high!

2   The glory of our King was seen
when, with his arms stretched wide
to show his love to everyone,
Jesus was crucified.

3   The glory of our King was seen
on the first Easter day,
when Christ rose up, set free from death,
to love, to guide, to stay.

Margaret B Cropper c1905–

451
GO TO DARK GETHSEMANE
NICHT SO TRAURIG 7 7 7 7 7 7

Johann Sebastian Bach 1685-1750

1 Go to dark Geth-sem-a - ne, ye that feel the tempt-er's power;

your Re-deem-er's con-flict see; watch with him one bit - ter hour;

turn not from his griefs a-way: learn from him to watch and pray.

2 See him at the judgement-hall,
beaten, bound, reviled, arraigned;
see him meekly bearing all;
love to man his soul sustained.
Shun not suffering, shame, or loss:
learn of Christ to bear the cross.

3 Calvary's mournful mountain view;
there the Lord of glory see,
made a sacrifice for you,
dying on the accursed tree.
'It is finished,' hear his cry:
trust in Christ and learn to die.

James Montgomery 1771-1854
This may be sung to Redhead No. 76   79

452

O SACRED HEAD

PASSION CHORALE 7 6 7 6 D

melody by Hans Leo Hassler 1564-1612
arranged by Johann Sebastian Bach 1685-1750

1 O sa-cred head, sore wound-ed, with grief and shame weighed down;
now scorn-ful-ly sur-round-ed with thorns, thine on-ly crown:
how art thou pale with an-guish, with sore a-buse and scorn;
how does that vis-age lan-guish, which once was bright as morn!

2   Thy grief and bitter passion
      were all for sinners' gain;
      mine, mine was the transgression,
      but thine the cruel pain.
      Lo, here I fall, my Saviour,
      turn not from me thy face;
      but look on me with favour,
      vouchsafe to me thy grace.

3   What language shall I borrow
      to thank thee, dearest friend,
      for this thy dying sorrow,
      thy pity without end?
      O make me thine for ever;
      and, should I fainting be,
      Lord, let me never, never
      outlive my love to thee.

4   Be near when I am dying,
      O show thy cross to me;
      and for my succour flying,
      come, Lord, to set me free.
      These eyes, new faith receiving,
      from thee shall not remove,
      for he who dies believing
      dies safely through thy love.

Paul Gerhardt 1607–1676
tr. James Waddell Alexander 1804–1859
  and others
for another setting see 337

453

O DEAREST LORD

DUNFERMLINE 8 6 8 6

Scottish Psalter 1615

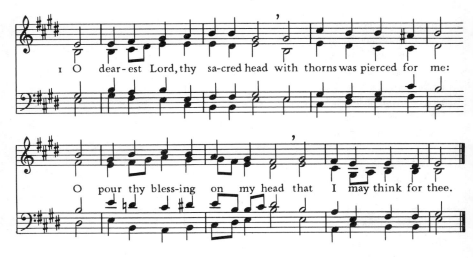

1 O dear-est Lord, thy sa-cred head with thorns was pierced for me:
O pour thy bless-ing on my head that I may think for thee.

2 O dearest Lord, thy sacred hands
with nails were pierced for me:
O shed thy blessing on my hands
that they may work for thee.

3 O dearest Lord, thy sacred feet
with nails were pierced for me:
O pour thy blessing on my feet
that they may follow thee.

4 O dearest Lord, thy sacred heart
with spear was pierced for me:
O pour thy Spirit in my heart
that I may live for thee.

Henry Ernest Hardy 1869-1946
for a higher setting see 430

454

ALONE THOU GOEST FORTH

BANGOR 8 6 8 6

Tans'ur's 'Compleat Melody' 1734

1 A - lone thou go-est forth, O Lord, in sa-cri-fice to die: is this thy sor - row naught to us who pass un-heed-ing by?

2 Our sins, not thine, thou bearest, Lord;
make us thy sorrow feel,
till through our pity and our shame
love answers love's appeal.

3 This is earth's darkest hour, but thou
dost light and life restore;
then let all praise be given thee
who livest evermore.

4 Give us compassion with thee, Lord,
that, as we share this hour,
thy cross may bring us to thy joy
and resurrection power.

Peter Abelard 1079-1142
tr. Francis Bland Tucker 1895-

455

AT THE CROSS HER VIGIL KEEPING

STABAT MATER 8 8 7

Mainz Gesangbuch 1661

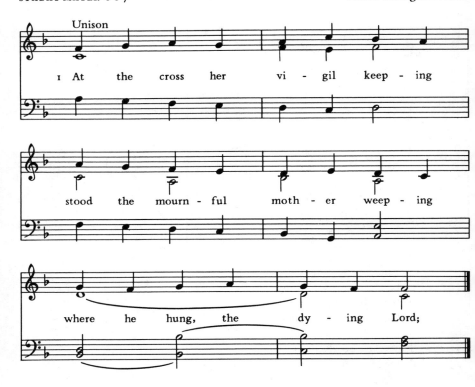

1 At the cross her vigil keeping
stood the mourn-ful moth-er weep-ing
where he hung, the dy-ing Lord;

2   through her soul of joy bereaved,
bowed with sorrow, deeply grieved,
passed the sharp and piercing sword.

3   Who upon that mother gazing,
in her anguish so amazing,
born of woman, would not weep?

4   Who, of Christ's dear mother thinking
while her Son that cup is drinking,
would not share her sorrow deep?

5   For his people's sins chastised
she beheld her Son despised,
scourged, and crowned with thorns entwined,

6   saw him then from judgement taken,
and in death by all forsaken,
till his spirit he resigned.

7   Near thy cross, O Christ, abiding,
grief and love my heart dividing,
I with her would take my place:

8   by thy saving cross uphold me,
in thy dying, Christ, enfold me,
with the deathless arms of grace.

Jacopone da Todi ?-1306
tr. Edward Caswall 1814-1878
and others

456

MY LORD, MY MASTER

DONNE SECOURS 11 10 11 10

Genevan Psalter 1551

1 My Lord, my mas - ter, at thy feet a - dor - ing,
I see thee bowed be - neath thy load of woe:
for me, a sin - ner, is thy life-blood pour - ing;
for thee, my Sav - iour, scarce my tears will flow.

2 Thine own disciple to thy foes has sold thee,
   with friendship's kiss and loyal word he came:
   how oft of faithful love my lips have told thee,
   while thou hast seen my falsehood and my shame!

3 With taunts and scoffs they mock what seems thy weakness,
   with blows and outrage adding pain to pain;
   thou art unmoved and steadfast in thy meekness:
   when I am wronged how quickly I complain!

4 O victim of thy love, O pangs most healing,
   O saving death, O wounds that I adore,
   O shame most glorious! Christ, before thee kneeling,
   I pray thee keep me thine for evermore.

   Jacques Bridaine 1701-1767
   tr. Thomas Benson Pollock 1836-1896

457

THRONED UPON THE AWFUL TREE   Christopher Tye ?-c1573

GETHSEMANE 777777   adapted by William Henry Monk 1823-1889

1 Throned up-on the aw-ful tree, King of grief, I watch with thee;
dark-ness veils thine an-guished face; none its lines of woe can trace;
none can tell what pangs un-known hold thee si-lent and a-lone:

2 silent through those three dread hours,
   wrestling with the evil powers,
   left alone with human sin,
   gloom around thee and within,
   till the appointed time is nigh,
   till the Lamb of God may die.

3 Hark, that cry that peals aloud
   upward through the whelming cloud!
   Thou, the Father's only Son,
   thou his own anointed one,
   thou dost ask him – can it be? –
   'Why hast thou forsaken me?'

4 Lord, should fear and anguish roll
   darkly o'er my sinful soul,
   thou, who once wast thus bereft
   that thine own might ne'er be left,
   teach me by that bitter cry
   in the gloom to know thee nigh.

John Ellerton 1826–1893
This may be sung to Nicht so traurig 451

458

O COME AND MOURN WITH ME A WHILE

ST CROSS 8 8 8 8   John Bacchus Dykes 1823-1876

1 O come and mourn with me a while;

O come ye to the Sav - iour's side;

O come, to - geth - er let us mourn:

Je - sus, our Lord, is cru - ci - fied.

2 Have we no tears to shed for him,
   while soldiers scoff and foes deride?
   Ah! look how patiently he hangs:
   Jesus, our Lord, is crucified.

3 Seven times he spake, seven words of love;
   and all three hours his silence cried
   for mercy on the souls of men:
   Jesus, our Lord, is crucified.

4 O break, O break, hard heart of mine!
   Thy weak self-love and guilty pride
   his Pilate and his Judas were:
   Jesus, our Lord, was crucified.

5 O love of God! O sin of man!
   In his dread act your strength is tried,
   and victory remains with love:
   Jesus, our Lord, is crucified.

Frederick William Faber 1814-1863

459
O CRUCIFIED REDEEMER
LLANGLOFFAN 7 6 8 6 D

Welsh hymn melody

1 O cru-ci-fied Re-deem-er, whose life-blood we have split,
to you we raise our guil-ty hands, and hum-bly own our guilt.
To-day we see your pas-sion spread o-pen to our gaze;
the crowd-ed town, the coun-try road, its Cal-va-ry dis-plays.

2   Wherever love is outraged,
    wherever hope is killed,
    where man still wrongs his brother man,
    your passion is fulfilled.
    We see your tortured body,
    we see the wounds that bleed,
    where brotherhood hangs crucified,
    nailed to the cross of greed.

3   We hear your cry of anguish,
    we see your life outpoured,
    where battlefield runs red with blood,
    our brothers' blood, O Lord.
    And in that bloodless battle,
    the fight for daily bread,
    where might is right and self is king,
    we see your thorn-crowned head.

4   The groaning of creation
    wrung out by pain and care,
    the anguish of a million hearts
    that break in dumb despair:
    O crucified Redeemer,
    these are your cries of pain.
    O may they break our selfish hearts,
    and love come in to reign.

Timothy Rees 1874-1939

460

WERE YOU THERE
NEGRO MELODY irregular

traditional

Choir

1 Were you there when they cru - ci - fied my Lord? Were you there?

Congregation

Were you there when they cru - ci - fied my Lord?

Choir

Oh! Oh!

Congregation

Some-times it caus - es me to trem - ble, trem-ble, trem - ble:

were you there when they cru - ci - fied my Lord?

2 Were you there when they nailed him to the tree?

3 Were you there when they pierced him in the side?

4 Were you there when the sun refused to shine?

5 Were you there when they laid him in the tomb?

6 Were you there when he burst the bonds of death?

Negro spiritual

461

HAIL THEE, FESTIVAL DAY

SALVE, FESTA DIES irregular

Ralph Vaughan Williams 1872–1958

Unison

1 Hail thee, fes-ti-val day! blest day that art hal-lowed for ev - er,

Fine

day where-in Christ a - rose, break-ing the king-dom of death.

vv. 2 & 4

2 Lo, the fair beau-ty of earth, from the death of the win-ter a - ris - ing,

D. C.

ev - ery good gift of the year now with its mas-ter re - turns.

vv. 3 & 5

3 He who was nailed to the cross is God and the rul - er of all things;

D. C.

all things cre - a - ted on earth wor-ship the mak - er of all.

For accompaniment to this tune see 372

4   Mourning they laid thee to rest, who art author of life and creation;
    treading the pathway of death, life thou bestowedst on man.
    Hail thee, festival day! ...

5   God of all pity and power, let thy word be assured to the doubting;
    light on the third day returns: rise, Son of God, from the tomb!
    Hail thee, festival day! ...

Venantius Fortunatus 530-609
tr. Maurice Frederick Bell 1862-1947

462

WELCOME, HAPPY MORNING

LAUS TIBI, CHRISTE 11 11 11 11   from a German melody 14th century

1 'Wel-come, hap-py morn-ing!' age to age shall say,
'Hell to-day is van-quished, heaven is won to-day.'
Lo! the dead is liv-ing, God for ev-er - more:
him, their true Cre - a - tor, all his works a - dore.

2 Earth with joy confesses, clothing her for spring,
all good gifts return with her returning King;
bloom in every meadow, leaves on every bough,
speak his sorrows ended, hail his triumph now.

3 Months in due succession, days of lengthening light,
hours and passing moments, praise thee in their flight;
brightness of the morning, sky, and fields, and sea,
vanquisher of darkness, bring their praise to thee.

4 Thou, of life the author, death didst undergo,
   tread the path of darkness, saving strength to show;
   come then, true and faithful, now fulfil thy word;
   'tis thine own third morning: rise, O buried Lord!

Venantius Fortunatus 530-609
tr. John Ellerton 1826-1893

463

YE CHOIRS OF NEW JERUSALEM
ST FULBERT 8 6 8 6

John Henry Gauntlett 1805-1876

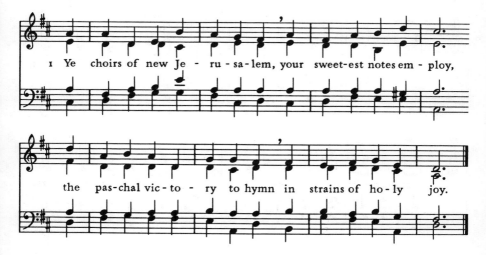

1 Ye choirs of new Je - ru - sa - lem, your sweet-est notes em - ploy,
the pas-chal vic-to - ry to hymn in strains of ho-ly joy.

2 For Judah's lion bursts his chains,
   crushing the serpent's head,
   and cries aloud through death's domains
   to wake the imprisoned dead.

3 Devouring depths of hell their prey
   at his command restore;
   his ransomed hosts pursue their way
   where Jesus goes before.

4 Triumphant in his glory now
   to him all power is given;
   to him in one communion bow
   all saints in earth and heaven.

5 All glory to the Father be,
   all glory to the Son,
   all glory, Holy Ghost, to thee,
   while endless ages run.

Fulbert of Chartres ?-1028
tr. Robert Campbell 1814-1868

464

COME, YE FAITHFUL, RAISE THE STRAIN

CAROL 7 6 7 6 D and alleluias FIRST TUNE   Johann Hermann Schein 1586-1630

1 Come, ye faith-ful, raise the strain   of tri-um-phant glad-ness:

God hath brought his   Is-ra-el   in-to joy from sad-ness,

loosed from Phar-aoh's bit-ter yoke   Ja-cob's sons and daugh-ters,

led them with un-moist-ened foot   through the Red Sea wa-ters.

Al-le-lu-ia, al-le-lu-ia, al-le-al-le-lu-ia!

2 'Tis the spring of souls today,
  Christ hath burst his prison,
  and from three days' sleep in death
  as a sun hath risen:
  all the winter of our sins,
  long and dark, is flying
  from his light, to whom we give
  laud and praise undying.

3 Now the queen of seasons, bright
  with the day of splendour,
  with the royal feast of feasts,
  comes its joy to render,
  comes to glad Jerusalem,
  who with true affection
  welcomes in unwearied strains
  Jesus' resurrection!

4 Neither might the gates of death,
  nor the tomb's dark portal,
  nor the watchers, nor the seal,
  hold thee as a mortal;
  but today amidst the twelve
  thou didst stand, bestowing
  that thy peace which evermore
  passeth human knowing.

5 Alleluia now we cry
  to our King immortal,
  who triumphant burst the bars
  of the tomb's dark portal:
  alleluia, with the Son
  God the Father praising,
  alleluia yet again
  to the Spirit raising.

John of Damascus 8th century
tr. John Mason Neale 1818-1866

COME, YE FAITHFUL, RAISE THE STRAIN

AVE VIRGO VIRGINUM 7676 D SECOND TUNE   Leisentritt's Gesangbuch 1584

1 Come, ye faith-ful, raise the strain of tri-um-phant glad-ness:
God hath brought his Is-ra-el in-to joy from sad-ness,
loosed from Phar-aoh's bit-ter yoke Ja-cob's sons and daugh-ters,
led them with un-moist-ened foot through the Red Sea wa-ters.

2   'Tis the spring of souls today,
    Christ hath burst his prison,
    and from three days' sleep in death
    as a sun hath risen:
    all the winter of our sins,
    long and dark, is flying
    from his light, to whom we give
    laud and praise undying.

3   Now the queen of seasons, bright
    with the day of splendour,
    with the royal feast of feasts,
    comes its joy to render,
    comes to glad Jerusalem,
    who with true affection
    welcomes in unwearied strains
    Jesus' resurrection!

4   Neither might the gates of death,
    nor the tomb's dark portal,
    nor the watchers, nor the seal,
    hold thee as a mortal;
    but today amidst the twelve
    thou didst stand, bestowing
    that thy peace which evermore
    passeth human knowing.

5   Alleluia now we cry
    to our King immortal,
    who triumphant burst the bars
    of the tomb's dark portal:
    alleluia, with the Son
    God the Father praising,
    alleluia yet again
    to the Spirit raising.

John of Damascus 8th century
tr. John Mason Neale 1818-1866

465

JESUS CHRIST IS RISEN TODAY

EASTER HYMN 7 7 7 7 and alleluias

Lyra Davidica 1708

1 Jesus Christ is risen today, Alleluia!
  Aujourd'hui, jour de mé-moi-re, Allé-lu-ia!

our triumphant holy day, Alleluia!
du tombeau le roi de gloire Allé-lu-ia!

who did once, upon the cross, Alleluia!
est sorti victorieux Allé-lu-ia!

suffer to redeem our loss. Alleluia!
pour triompher dans les cieux. Allé-lu-ia!

2 Hymns of praise then let us sing,
unto Christ our heavenly King,
who endured the cross and grave,
sinners to redeem and save.

3 But the pains which he endured
our salvation have procured;
now above the sky he's King,
where the angels ever sing.

4 Sing we to our God above,
praise eternal as his love;
praise him, all ye heavenly host,
Father, Son, and Holy Ghost.

Lyra Davidica 1708
and others

2 Célébrons par nos louanges
Jésus-Christ, le Roi des anges;
avec lui portons la croix;
avec lui nous serons rois.

3 Pour nous ce Dieu de clémence,
rempli d'un amour immense,
a succombé sous les coups.
Il mourut, ce fut pour nous.

4 Levons-nous de la poussière,
du Christ suivons la bannière,
loin de ce monde agité,
Jésus est ressuscité.

traducteur inconnu

This hymn may be sung antiphonally,
one group of voices taking only the Alleluias.

466

CHRIST THE LORD IS RISEN TODAY   R Williams c1781-1821

LLANFAIR 7 7 7 7 and alleluias   harmonized by John Roberts 1822-1877

1 'Christ the Lord is risen to-day', Al - le - lu - ia!

sons of men and an - gels say; Al - le - lu - ia!

raise your joys and tri-umphs high; Al - le - lu - ia!

Unison

sing, ye heavens, and earth re - ply: Al - le - lu - ia!

2   Love's redeeming work is done,
      fought the fight, the battle won:
      lo, our sun's eclipse is o'er!
      lo, he sets in blood no more!

3   Vain the stone, the watch, the seal,
      Christ has burst the gates of hell;
      death in vain forbids his rise,
      Christ has opened paradise.

4   Lives again our glorious King:
      where, O death, is now thy sting?
      Once he died, our souls to save:
      where thy victory, O grave?

5   Soar we now where Christ has led,
      following our exalted head;
      made like him, like him we rise:
      ours the cross, the grave, the skies.

6   Hail, the Lord of earth and heaven,
      praise to thee by both be given!
      Thee we greet triumphant now:
      hail, the resurrection thou!

Charles Wesley 1707-1788

This hymn may be sung antiphonally,
one group of voices taking only the Alleluias.

467

O SONS AND DAUGHTERS
O FILII ET FILIAE 8 8 8 with alleluias

French carol c16th century
arranged by Frederick R C Clarke 1931-

Alleluia, alleluia, alleluia!

1 O sons and daughters, let us sing!

The King of heaven, the glorious King,

o'er death today rose triumphing.

Alleluia!

2   That night the apostles met in fear;
     amidst them came their Lord most dear,
     and said, 'My peace be on all here.'
     Alleluia!

3   When Thomas first the tidings heard,
     he doubted if it were their Lord,
     until he came and spake the word.
     Alleluia!

4   'My pierced side, O Thomas, see;
     behold my hands, my feet,' said he;
     'not faithless but believing be.'
     Alleluia!

5   No longer Thomas then denied;
     he saw the feet, the hands, the side;
     'Thou art my Lord and God,' he cried.
     Alleluia!

6   How blest are they who have not seen,
     and yet whose faith hath constant been,
     for they eternal life shall win.
     Alleluia!

7   On this most holy day of days,
     to God your hearts and voices raise
     in laud and jubilee and praise.
     Alleluia!

Jean Tisserand ?-1494
tr. John Mason Neale 1818-1866

The threefold Alleluia serves as an introduction,
and is therefore sung only at the beginning of the hymn.

468

THE STRIFE IS O'ER

VULPIUS 8 8 8 and alleluias FIRST TUNE

Melchior Vulpius 1560–1616
arranged by Ernest Campbell Macmillan 1893–

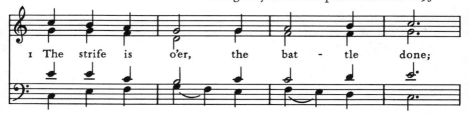

1 The strife is o'er, the bat - tle done;

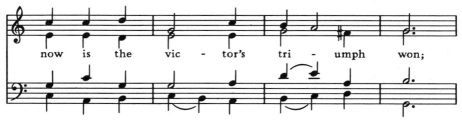

now is the vic - tor's tri - umph won;

O let the song of praise be sung,

Al - le - lu - ia, al - le - lu - ia, al - le - lu - ia!

2 Death's mightiest powers have done their worst,
and Jesus hath his foes dispersed;
let shouts of praise and joy outburst,
Alleluia!

3 He closed the ancient gates of hell,
the bars from heaven's high portals fell;
let songs of praise his triumph tell,
Alleluia!

4 On the third morn he rose again,
glorious in majesty to reign;
O let us swell the joyful strain,
Alleluia!

5 Lord, by the stripes which wounded thee,
from death's dread sting thy servants free,
that we may live, and sing to thee,
Alleluia!

from the Latin 17th century
tr. Francis Pott 1832–1909

VICTORY 8 8 8 and alleluia SECOND TUNE

adapted by
William Henry Monk 1823-1899
from Giovanni Pierluigi da Palestrina c1525-1592

1 The strife is o'er, the bat - tle done;
now is the vic - tor's tri - umph won;
O let the song of praise be sung,
Al - le - lu - ia!

2 Death's mightiest powers have done their worst,
and Jesus hath his foes dispersed;
let shouts of praise and joy outburst,
Alleluia!

3 He closed the ancient gates of hell,
the bars from heaven's high portals fell;
let songs of praise his triumph tell,
Alleluia!

4 On the third morn he rose again,
glorious in majesty to reign;
O let us swell the joyful strain,
Alleluia!

5 Lord, by the stripes which wounded thee,
from death's dread sting thy servants free,
that we may live, and sing to thee,
Alleluia!

from the Latin 17th century
tr. Francis Pott 1832-1909

469
GOOD CHRISTIAN MEN, REJOICE AND SING
AGINCOURT 8 8 8 8   English melody 15th century

1 Good Christ - ian men, re - joice and sing!

Now is the tri - umph of our King!

To all the world glad news we bring:

Al - le - lu - ia! Al - le - lu - ia!

2 The Lord of life is risen today;
   bring flowers of song to strew his way;
   let all mankind rejoice and say:
   Alleluia! Alleluia!

3 Praise we in songs of victory
   that love, that life which cannot die,
   and sing with hearts uplifted high:
   Alleluia! Alleluia!

4 Thy name we bless, O risen Lord,
   and sing today with one accord
   the life laid down, the life restored:
   Alleluia! Alleluia!

Cyril Argentine Alington 1872-1955

470

WALK SOFTLY IN SPRINGTIME

MARCHE DOUCEMENT 11 11 11 11

Frederick Alan Reesor 1935-

1 Walk soft-ly in spring-time, to hear the grass sing its whis-per-ing ca-rols to Je-sus our King, to see the new flow-ers bright col-ours dis-play, to tell all the child-ren of glad Eas-ter day.

2 Sing gently in springtime, and join with the birds,
who warble their music, a song without words,
that floats through the air and that reaches the sky,
a message of love to the Father on high.

3 Praise gladly in springtime when earth seems to glow
with new life and colour in all things that grow;
for all nature's children are happy to say,
Rejoice, for the Saviour is risen today.

Edna Fay Grant 1905-

471

THIS JOYFUL EASTERTIDE

EASTERTIDE 6 7 6 7 and refrain

Dutch carol

harmonized by Stanley L Osborne 1907-

1 This joy-ful Eas-ter-tide, a-way with sin and sor - row! My love, the cru-ci - fied, hath sprung to life this mor - row.

Refrain

Had Christ, that once was slain, ne'er burst his three-day pris-on, our faith had been in vain: but now hath Christ a-ris-en, a-ris-en, a-ris-en, a-ris - en!

2   My flesh in hope shall rest,
    and for a season slumber,
    till trump from east to west
    shall wake the dead in number.
    Had Christ ...

3   Death's flood hath lost his chill,
    since Jesus crossed the river:
    lover of souls, from ill
    my passing soul deliver.
    Had Christ ...

from David's Psalmen, Amsterdam 1685
Cowley Carol Book 1902

472
THE LAMB'S HIGH BANQUET

AD COENAM AGNI PROVIDI 8 8 8 8

plainsong melody
arranged by Healey Willan 1880-1968

2 Upon the altar of the cross
his body hath redeemed our loss;
and, tasting of his precious blood,
our life is hid with him in God.

3 Protected in the paschal night
from the destroying angel's might,
in triumph went the ransomed free
from Pharoah's cruel tyranny.

4 Now Christ our passover is slain,
the Lamb of God without a stain;
his flesh, the true unleavened bread,
is freely offered in our stead.

5 O all sufficient sacrifice,
beneath thee hell defeated lies;
thy captive people are set free,
and endless life restored in thee.

melody from the Paris Antiphoner 1681
harmonized by Charles Peaker 1900-

1 The Lamb's high ban - quet called to share,
ar - rayed in gar - ments white and fair,
the Red Sea past, we fain would sing
to Je - sus our tri - um - phant King.

6 We hymn thee rising from the grave,
   from death returning, strong to save;
   thine own right hand the tyrant chains,
   and paradise for man regains.

7 All praise be thine, O risen Lord,
   from death to endless life restored;
   all praise to God the Father be
   and Holy Ghost eternally.

from the Latin 6th century
tr. John Mason Neale 1818-1866

473

LIGHT'S GLITTERING MORN

LASST UNS ERFREUEN 8 8 8 8 and alleluias   Geistliche Kirchengesänge, Cologne 1623

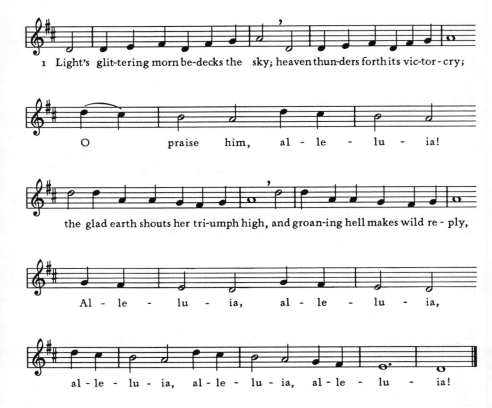

1 Light's glit-tering morn be-decks the sky; heaven thun-ders forth its vic-tor-cry;

O   praise him, al - le - lu - ia!

the glad earth shouts her tri-umph high, and groan-ing hell makes wild re - ply,

Al - le - lu - ia, al - le - lu - ia,

al - le - lu - ia, al - le - lu - ia, al - le - lu - ia!

2 while he, the King, the mighty King,
despoiling death of all its sting
and trampling down the powers of night,
brings forth his ransomed souls to light.

3 His tomb of late the threefold guard
of watch and stone and seal had barred;
but now in pomp and triumph high
he comes from death to victory.

4 The pains of hell are loosed at last;
the days of mourning now are past;
an angel robed in light hath said,
'The Lord is risen from the dead.'

5 From every weapon death can wield
thine own redeemed for ever shield:
O Lord of all, with us abide
in this our joyful Eastertide.

from the Latin c7th century
tr. John Mason Neale 1818-1866
for accompaniment to this tune
see 1 or 7

474

THAT EASTERTIDE WITH JOY WAS BRIGHT
LASST UNS ERFREUEN 8 8 8 8 and alleluias

1   That Eastertide with joy was bright,
the sun shone out with fairer light,
when, to their longing eyes restored,
the apostles saw their risen Lord.

2   He bade them see his hands, his side,
where yet the glorious wounds abide;
the tokens true which made it plain
their Lord indeed was risen again.

3   Jesus, the King of gentleness,
do thou thyself our hearts possess,
that we may give thee all our days
the tribute of our grateful praise.

4   From every weapon death can wield
thine own redeemed for ever shield:
O Lord of all, with us abide
in this our joyful Eastertide.

from the Latin c7th century
tr. John Mason Neale 1818-1866

475

HE'S BACK IN THE LAND OF THE LIVING

LAND OF THE LIVING 9 8 9 8 D irregular · Hugh J McLean 1930–

1 He's back in the land of the liv - ing, the man we de-cid-ed to kill;
he's stand-ing a-mong us, for-giv - ing our guilt of Good Fri - day hill.
He calls us to share in his ris - ing, to a - ban-don the grave of our past;
he of - fers us pres-ent and fu - ture, a world that is o-pen and vast.

2 He's back in a world where the living
are robbing each other of joy,
where men for prestige and destruction
the powers of nature employ.
From lofty respectable motives
are crosses erected today,
for people put people on trial
and evil is having its way.

3 But crosses are also the symbols
of love that is given and spent;
the signs of our hope and survival,
of Easter defeating our Lent.
Through men of compassion, responding
to rise against hunger and hell,
new life shall arise from the ashes
of hatred, and all shall be well!

Frederik Herman Kaan 1929–

AND THE FOLLOWING

476

HAIL THEE, FESTIVAL DAY

SALVE, FESTA DIES irregular

Ralph Vaughan Williams 1872-1958

Unison

1 Hail thee, fes-ti-val day! blest day that art hal-lowed for ev - er,

day when our God as - cends high in the hea - vens to reign.

vv. 2 & 4

2 Lo, the fair beau-ty of earth, from the death of the win-ter a - ris - ing;

ev - ery good gift of the year now with its mas-ter re - turns.

vv. 3 & 5

3 Dai-ly the love-li-ness grows, a-dorned with the glo - ry of blos - som;

hea-ven her gates un - bars, fling-ing her in - crease of light.

For accompaniment to this tune see 372

4 Christ in his triumph ascends, who hath vanquished the devil's dominion;
gay is the woodland with leaves, bright are the meadows with flowers.
Hail thee, festival day! ...

5 Jesus the health of the world, enlighten our minds, thou Redeemer,
Son of the Father supreme, only-begotten of God!
Hail thee, festival day! ...

Venantius Fortunatus 530-609
tr. Percy Dearmer 1867-1936

477

HAIL THE DAY THAT SEES HIM RISE

CHISLEHURST 7 7 7 7 and alleluias   FIRST TUNE   Sydney Hugo Nicholson 1875-1947

1 Hail the day that sees him rise Al-le-lu-ia! to his throne a-bove the skies; Al-le-lu-ia! Christ, a-while to mor-tals given, re-as-cends his na-tive heaven. Al-le-lu-ia, al-le-lu-ia, al-le-lu-ia!

2 There for him high triumph waits;
lift your heads, eternal gates;
he has conquered death and sin;
take the King of glory in.

3 Highest heaven its Lord receives,
yet he loves the earth he leaves:
though returning to his throne,
still he calls mankind his own.

4 See, he lifts his hands above.
See, he shows the prints of love.
Hark, his gracious lips bestow
blessings on his church below.

5 Still for us he intercedes,
his prevailing death he pleads,
near himself prepares our place,
he the first-fruits of our race.

6 There we shall with thee remain,
partners of thy endless reign;
there thy face unclouded see,
find our heaven of heavens in thee.

Charles Wesley 1707-1788

1 Hail the day that sees him rise Al - le - lu - ia!
to his throne a - bove the skies; Al - le - lu - ia!
Christ, a - while to mor-tals given, Al - le - lu - ia!
re - as - cends his na - tive heaven. Al - le - lu - ia!

2 There for him high triumph waits;
lift your heads, eternal gates;
he has conquered death and sin;
take the King of glory in.

3 Highest heaven its Lord receives,
yet he loves the earth he leaves:
though returning to his throne,
still he calls mankind his own.

4 See, he lifts his hands above.
See, he shows the prints of love.
Hark, his gracious lips bestow
blessings on his church below.

5 Still for us he intercedes,
his prevailing death he pleads,
near himself prepares our place,
he the first-fruits of our race.

6 There we shall with thee remain,
partners of thy endless reign;
there thy face unclouded see,
find our heaven of heavens in thee.

Charles Wesley 1707-1788
If desired, the Alleluias may
be sung antiphonally.

478

HAIL, THOU ONCE-DESPISED JESUS

EIFIONYDD 8 7 8 7 D

John Ambrose Lloyd 1815-1874

1 Hail, thou once-des-pis-ed Je-sus! Hail, thou Ga-li - le-an King!

Thou didst suf-fer to re-lease us; thou didst free sal - va-tion bring.

Hail, thou u - ni - ver-sal Sav-iour! Thou hast borne our sin and shame;

by thy mer-its we find fa-vour; life is giv-en through thy name.

2 Paschal Lamb, by God appointed,
   all our sins on thee were laid;
   by almighty love anointed,
   thou hast full atonement made.
   All thy people are forgiven,
   through the virtue of thy blood;
   opened is the gate of heaven,
   peace is made 'twixt man and God.

3 Jesus, hail! enthroned in glory,
   there for ever to abide;
   all the heavenly host adore thee,
   seated at thy Father's side.
   Worship, honour, power, and blessing
   thou art worthy to receive;
   loudest praises, without ceasing,
   meet it is for us to give.

John Bakewell 1721-1819
and others
This may be sung to Hyfrydol 49 or 241

479

ETERNAL MONARCH

ANDERNACH 8 8 8 8

from the Andernach Gesangbuch 1608

Unison

1 E-ter-nal Mon-arch, King most high,
whose blood hath brought re-demp-tion nigh,
by whom the death of death was wrought,
and con-quering gra-ce's bat-tle fought:

2 ascending to the throne of might,
 and seated at the Father's right,
 all power in heaven is Jesus' own
 that here his manhood had not known.

3 Yea, angels tremble when they see
 how changed is our humanity,
 that flesh hath purged what flesh had stained,
 and God, the flesh of God, hath reigned.

4 Be thou our joy and strong defence,
 who art our future recompense:
 so shall the light that springs from thee
 be ours through all eternity.

5 O risen Christ, ascended Lord,
 all praise to thee let earth accord,
 who art, while endless ages run,
 with Father and with Spirit one.

from the Latin 5th century
tr. John Mason Neale 1818–1866
 This may be sung to Deus tuorum militum 32 or 78

480

CROWN HIM WITH MANY CROWNS

DIADEMATA 6686D   George Job Elvey 1816-1893

1 Crown him with ma-ny crowns, the Lamb up-on his throne:
hark, how the heaven-ly an-them drowns all mu-sic but its own!
A-wake, my soul, and sing of him who died for thee,
and hail him as thy match-less King through all e-ter-ni-ty.

2 Crown him the Lord of life,
   who triumphed o'er the grave,
   and rose victorious in the strife
   for those he came to save.
   His glories now we sing
   who died and rose on high,
   who died eternal life to bring,
   and lives that death may die.

3 Crown him the Lord of peace,
   whose power a sceptre sways
   from pole to pole, that wars may cease,
   absorbed in prayer and praise.
   His reign shall know no end;
   and round his pierced feet
   fair flowers of Paradise extend
   their fragrance ever sweet.

4 Crown him the Lord of love;
   behold his hands and side,
   rich wounds yet visible above,
   in beauty glorified.
   All hail, Redeemer, hail!
   for thou hast died for me;
   thy praise shall never, never fail
   throughout eternity.

Matthew Bridges 1800–1894
Godfrey Thring 1823–1903

AND THE FOLLOWING

481

HAIL THEE, FESTIVAL DAY

SALVE, FESTA DIES irregular

Ralph Vaughan Williams 1872–1958

1 Hail thee, fes-ti-val day! blest day that art hal-lowed for ev - er,

day where-in God from heaven shone on the world with his grace.

vv. 2 & 4

2 Lo, in the like-ness of fire, on them that a-wait his ap - pear - ing

he whom the Lord fore-told sud-den-ly, swift-ly, des - cends.

vv. 3 & 5

3 Forth from the Fa-ther he comes with his seven-fold mys - ti-cal dow-ry,

pour-ing on hu - man souls in - fi-nite rich - es of God.

For accompaniment to this tune see 372

4   Hark! in a hundred tongues Christ's own, his chosen apostles,
    preach to a hundred tribes Christ and his wonderful works.
    Hail thee, festival day! ...

5   Praise to the Spirit of life, all praise to the fount of our being,
    light that dost lighten all, life that in all dost abide.
    Hail thee, festival day! ...

from the Latin c14th century
tr. George Gabriel Scott Gillett 1873-1948

482

LORD GOD, THE HOLY GHOST

SOUTHWELL 6686

melody from Damon's Psalmes 1579
harmonized by Stanley L Osborne 1907–

1 Lord God, the Ho-ly Ghost, in this ac-cept-ed hour, as on the day of Pen-te-cost des-cend with all thy power.

2 We meet with one accord
in our appointed place,
and wait the promise of our Lord,
the Spirit of all grace.

3 Like mighty rushing wind
upon the waves beneath,
move with one impulse every mind,
one soul, one feeling breathe.

4 The young, the old inspire
with wisdom from above,
and give us hearts and tongues of fire
to pray, and praise, and love.

5 Spirit of light, explore
and chase our gloom away,
with lustre shining more and more
unto the perfect day.

James Montgomery 1771-1854

483

WHEN GOD OF OLD CAME DOWN

PRIMROSE 8 6 8 6

from Kentucky Harmony 1821
harmonized by Frederick R C Clarke 1931-

1 When God of old came down from heaven, in power and wrath he came;
be - fore his feet the clouds were riven, half dark-ness and half flame.

2 But when he came the second time,
he came in power and love;
softer than gale at morning prime
hovered his holy dove.

3 The fires, that rushed on Sinai down
in sudden torrents dread,
now gently light, a glorious crown,
on every sainted head.

4 And as on Israel's awe-struck ear
the voice exceeding loud,
the trump, that angels quake to hear,
thrilled from the deep, dark cloud;

5 so, when the Spirit of our God
came down his flock to find,
a voice from heaven was heard abroad,
a rushing, mighty wind.

6 It fills the church of God; it fills
the sinful world around;
only in stubborn hearts and wills
no place for it is found.

7 Come Lord, come wisdom, love and power:
open our ears to hear;
let us not miss the accepted hour;
save, Lord, by love or fear.

John Keble 1792-1866

484

IN THY PENTECOSTAL SPLENDOUR

EBENEZER 8 7 8 7 8 7

Thomas John Williams 1869–1944

1 In thy pen-te-cos-tal splen-dour rise, O liv-ing God, a-rise;
smoke of bat-tle blurs and blinds us, blow thy wind and clear our eyes:
Al-le - lu-ia, al - le - lu - ia! Thou art God of vic - to-ries!

2 Thou of old didst lead thy people,
through the desert as they went;
thou upon the mount to Moses
didst thy tenfold rule present:
Alleluia!
Thou art law and covenant!

3 Him who stooped to die for sinners
thou hast glorified again;
he, captivity led captive,
now obtaineth gifts for men:
Alleluia!
Thou art giver, now as then!

4 Thou at Pentecost didst shower
gracious rain from heaven above;
on all flesh didst pour thy Spirit,
silver-winged, descending dove:
Alleluia!
Thou art liberty and love!

5 Let the fire of thy near presence
melt our fears, like wax, away;
touch our lips with songs of courage,
teach us with thy saints to say,
Alleluia!
Thou, God, lead'st us all the way!

John Edward Speers 1916–
This may be sung to Rhuddlan 223

485

SPIRIT OF MERCY

JENA 8 8 8 8

melody from Melchior Vulpius c1560-1616
harmonized by Stanley L Osborne 1907-

1 Spir - it of mer - cy, truth, and love,
O shed thine in - fluence from a - bove;
and still from age to age con - vey
the won - ders of this sa - cred day.

2 In every clime, by every tongue,
   be God's eternal praises sung;
   let all the listening earth be taught
   the acts our great redeemer wrought.

3 Unfailing comfort, heavenly guide,
   still o'er thy holy church preside;
   still let mankind thy blessings prove,
   spirit of mercy, truth, and love.

Author unknown

486

REJOICE! THE YEAR UPON ITS WAY

BEATA NOBIS GAUDIA 8 8 8 8   FIRST TUNE

plainsong melody
arranged by Healey Willan 1880-1968

1 Re - joice! the year up - on its way
has brought a - gain that bless - ed day,
when on the cho - sen of the Lord
the Ho - ly Spir - it was out - poured. A - men.

2   On each the fire, descending, stood
in quivering tongues' similitude –
tongues, that their words might ready prove,
and fire, to make them flame with love.

3   To all in every tongue they spoke;
amazement in the crowd awoke,
who mocked, as overcome with wine,
those who were filled with power divine.

4 And now, O holy God, this day
  regard us as we humbly pray,
  and send us from thy heavenly seat
  the blessings of the Paraclete.

5 To God the Father, God the Son,
  and God the Spirit, praise be done;
  may Christ the Lord upon us pour
  the Spirit's gift for evermore.

from the Latin c4th century
tr. Richard Ellis Roberts 1878-1953

ST GREGORY 8 8 8 8   SECOND TUNE   from Knorr's 'Neuer Helicon,' Nürnberg 1684

1 Re-joice! the year up-on its way has brought a-gain that bless-ed day, when on the cho-sen of the Lord the Ho-ly Spir-it was out-poured.

AND THE FOLLOWING

487

Ravenscroft's Psalter 1621

1 Have mer-cy on us, God most high, who lift our hearts to thee;
have mer-cy now, most mer-ci-ful, most ho-ly tri-ni-ty.

2 Thou wert not born; there was no fount
  from which thy being flowed;
  there is no end which thou canst reach;
  but thou art simply God.

3 When heaven and earth were yet unmade,
  when time was yet unknown,
  thou in thy bliss and majesty
  didst live and love alone.

4 How wonderful creation is,
  the work that thou didst bless;
  and O what then must thou be like,
  eternal loveliness!

5 Most ancient of all mysteries!
  low at thy throne we lie;
  have mercy now, most merciful,
  most holy trinity.

Frederick William Faber 1814-1863

488

HOLY, HOLY, HOLY, LORD

PSALM 135 777777

Genevan Psalter 1562

1 Ho-ly, ho-ly, ho-ly, Lord God of hosts, e-ter-nal King, by the heavens and earth a-dored, an-gels and arch-an-gels sing, chant-ing ev-er-last-ing-ly to the bless-ed tri-ni-ty.

2 Since by thee were all things made,
and in thee do all things live,
be to thee all honour paid;
praise to thee let all things give,
singing everlastingly
to the blessed trinity.

3 Thousands, tens of thousands stand,
spirits blest before thy throne,
speeding thence at thy command;
and when thy command is done,
singing everlastingly
to the blessed trinity.

4 Cherubim and seraphim
veil their faces with their wings;
eyes of angels are too dim
to behold the King of kings,
while they sing eternally
to the blessed trinity.

5 Thee, apostles, prophets, thee,
thee, the noble martyr band
praise with solemn jubilee,
thee, the church in every land,
singing everlastingly
to the blessed trinity.

6 Alleluia! Lord, to thee,
Father, Son, and Holy Ghost,
three in one, and one in three,
join we with the heavenly host,
singing everlastingly
to the blessed trinity.

Christopher Wordsworth 1807-1885
This may be sung to Dix 435

489

FATHER MOST HOLY

CHRISTE SANCTORUM 11 11 11 5

melody from Cluny Antiphoner 1686
harmonized by Derek Holman 1931–

1 Father most holy, merciful and loving,
Jesus, redeemer, ever to be worshipped,
life-giving Spirit, comforter most gracious,
God everlasting;

for a lower setting see 506

2 three in a wondrous unity unbroken,
  one perfect Godhead, love that never faileth,
  light of the angels, succour of the needy,
  hope of all living:

3 all thy creation serveth its creator;
  thee every creature praiseth without ceasing;
  we too would sing thee psalms of true devotion;
  hear, we beseech thee.

4 Lord God almighty! unto thee be glory,
  one in three persons, over all exalted;
  thine, as is meet, be honour, praise and blessing
  now and for ever.

from the Latin c10th century
tr. Alfred Edward Alston 1862-1927

490

GOD IS UNIQUE AND ONE

LITTLE CORNARD 666688

Martin Fallas Shaw 1875-1958

1 God is u-nique and one: fa-ther, sus-tain-er, Lord!

Pat-terns of life were spun by his cre-a-tive word.

Of his in-ten-tion, love and care we are with grow-ing trust a-ware.

2 Love came to earth in Christ,
man's common life to share,
choosing to be the least,
willing a cross to bear.
He died, he rose, that we might live
and all our love, responding, give.

3 The Holy Spirit moves
man to discover man;
his inspiration proves
more than the mind can span.
Each listening heart is led to find
the will of God for all mankind.

4 He shall forever reign,
ruler of time and space,
God in the midst of men,
seen in the human face.
We give expression to our creed
by love in thought, in word and deed.

Frederik Herman Kaan 1929-

AND THE FOLLOWING

50 Holy, holy, holy, Lord God almighty
62 Come, thou almighty King
68 I bind unto myself today
92 The Lord almighty spoke the word
235 Thou whose almighty word

491

JESUS, NAME OF WONDROUS LOVE

DA CHRISTUS GEBOREN WAR 7777

composed or adapted by
Johann Friedrick Doles 1715-1797

1 Je - sus, name of won-drous love, name all o - ther names a - bove,
un - to which must ev-ery knee bow in deep hu - mi - li - ty.

2 Jesus, name of priceless worth
to the fallen sons of earth,
for the promise that it gave –
'Jesus shall his people save.'

3 Jesus, only name that's given
under all the mighty heaven,
whereby man, to sin enslaved,
bursts his fetters and is saved.

4 Jesus, name of wondrous love,
human name of God above!
Pleading only this we flee,
helpless, O our God, to thee.

William Walsham How 1823-1897

492

'TIS GOOD, LORD, TO BE HERE

CARLISLE 6686 FIRST TUNE

Charles Lockhart 1745-1815

1 'Tis good, Lord, to be here! Thy glo-ry fills the night;
thy face and gar-ments, like the sun, shine with un-bor-rowed light.

2 'Tis good, Lord, to be here,
   thy beauty to behold,
   where Moses and Elijah stand,
   thy messengers of old.

3 Fulfiller of the past,
   promise of things to be,
   we hail thy body glorified,
   and our redemption see!

4 Before we taste of death,
   we see thy kingdom come:
   O might we hold the vision bright
   and make this hill our home!

5 'Tis good, Lord, to be here!
   Yet we may not remain;
   but, since thou bidst us leave the mount,
   come with us to the plain.

Joseph Armitage Robinson 1858-1933
based on Luke 9:28-36

GARELOCHSIDE 6686 SECOND TUNE

Kenneth George Finlay 1882-

1 'Tis good, Lord, to be here! Thy glo-ry fills the night;
thy face and gar-ments, like the sun, shine with un-bor-rowed light.

493

NOT ALWAYS ON THE MOUNT

FINNART 8 8 8 8

Kenneth George Finlay 1882–

1 Not al - ways on the mount may we
rapt in the heaven - ly vi - sion be;
the shores of thought and feel - ing know
the Spir - it's ti - dal ebb and flow.

2 'Lord, it is good abiding here'
    we cry, the heavenly presence near:
    the vision vanishes, our eyes
    are lifted into vacant skies.

3 Yet has one such exalted hour
    upon the soul redeeming power,
    and in its strength through after days
    we travel our appointed ways,

4 till all the lowly vale grows bright,
    transfigured in remembered light,
    and in untiring souls we bear
    the freshness of the upper air.

5 The mount for vision; but below
    the paths of daily duty go,
    and nobler life therein shall own
    the pattern on the mountain shown.

Frederick Lucian Hosmer 1840-1929
based on Luke 9:28-36

AND THE FOLLOWING

494

SING OF MARY
IN BABILONE 8 7 8 7 D

Dutch traditional melody
arranged by Julius Röntgen 1855-1932

1 Sing of Ma-ry, pure and low-ly, maid-en mo-ther, wise and mild.
Sing of God's own Son most ho-ly, who be-came her lit-tle child.
Fair-est child of fair-est mo-ther, God the Lord who came to earth,
word made flesh, our ve-ry bro-ther, takes our na-ture by his birth.

2 Sing of Jesus, son of Mary,
   in the home at Nazareth.
   Toil and labour cannot weary
   love enduring unto death.
   Constant was the love he gave her,
   though it drove him from her side,
   forth to preach, and heal, and suffer,
   till on Calvary he died.

3 Joyful mother, full of gladness,
   in thine arms thy Lord was borne.
   Mournful mother, full of sadness,
   all thy heart with pain was torn.
   Glorious mother, now rewarded
   with a crown at Jesus' hand,
   age to age thy name recorded
   shall be blest in every land.

4 Glory be to God the Father;
   glory be to God the Son;
   glory be to God the Spirit;
   glory to the three in one.
   From the heart of blessed Mary,
   from all saints, the song ascends,
   and the church the strain re-echoes
   unto earth's remotest ends.

Roland Ford Palmer 1891-

495

TELL OUT, MY SOUL, THE GREATNESS OF THE LORD

ELING 10 10 10 10   Godfrey Ridout 1918-

1 Tell out, my soul, the great-ness of the Lord!
Un - num-bered bless-ings, give my spir - it voice;
ten - der to me the pro - mise of his word;
to God my Sav - iour shall my heart re - joice.

2 Tell out, my soul, the greatness of his name!
Make known his might, the deeds his arm has done;
his mercy sure, from age to age the same;
his holy name – the Lord, the mighty one.

3 Tell out, my soul, the greatness of his might!
Powers and dominions lay their glory by;
proud hearts and stubborn wills are put to flight,
the hungry fed, the humble lifted high.

4 Tell out, my soul, the glories of his word!
Firm is his promise, and his mercy sure.
Tell out, my soul, the greatness of the Lord
to children's children and for evermore!

Timothy Dudley-Smith 1926-
based on Luke 1:46-56

496

PRAISE WE THE LORD THIS DAY

SANDYS 6686 melody from Sandys' 'Christmas Carols' 1833

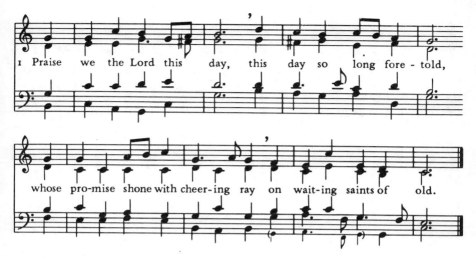

1 Praise we the Lord this day, this day so long fore-told,
whose pro-mise shone with cheer-ing ray on wait-ing saints of old.

2 The prophet gave the sign
for faithful men to read:
a virgin, born of David's line,
shall bear the promised seed.

3 Ask not how this should be,
but worship and adore,
like her, whom heaven's own majesty
came down to shadow o'er.

4 Meekly she bowed her head
to hear the gracious word,
Mary, the pure and lowly maid,
the favoured of the Lord.

5 Blessed shall be her name
in all the church on earth,
through whom that wondrous mercy came,
the incarnate Saviour's birth.

6 Jesus, the virgin's Son,
we praise thee and adore,
who art with God the Father one
and Spirit evermore.

Author unknown c1846

AND THE FOLLOWING

403 From east to west, from shore to shore

497

THE ETERNAL GIFTS OF CHRIST THE KING

CHURCH TRIUMPHANT 8 8 8 8   FIRST TUNE   James William Elliott 1833-1915

1 The e-ter-nal gifts of Christ the King, the a-pos-tles' glo-ry, let us sing; and all, with hearts of glad-ness, raise due hymns of thank-ful love and praise.

2 For they the church's leaders are,
triumphant in her peaceful war,
in heavenly courts a princely band,
true lights to lighten every land.

3 Theirs is the steadfast faith of saints,
unconquered hope that never faints,
and perfect love of Christ their Lord
to smite the evils of this world.

4 In them the Father's glory shone,
in them the will of God the Son,
in them exults the Holy Ghost,
through them rejoice the heavenly host.

5 To thee, Redeemer, now we cry,
that thou wilt join to them on high
thy servants, who this grace implore,
for ever and for evermore.

Aurelius Ambrose 340-397
tr. John Mason Neale 1818-1866
and the compilers

AETERNA CHRISTI MUNERA 8 8 8 8 SECOND TUNE   late form of plainsong melody
from Guidetti's 'Directorium Chori' 1582, arranged by Robert H Bell 1932-

Unison

1 The e-ter - nal gifts of Christ the King,
the a-pos - tles' glo - ry, let us sing;
and all, with hearts of glad - ness, raise
due hymns of thank - ful love and praise.

2 For they the church's leaders are,
  triumphant in her peaceful war,
  in heavenly courts a princely band,
  true lights to lighten every land.

3 Theirs is the steadfast faith of saints,
  unconquered hope that never faints,
  and perfect love of Christ their Lord
  to smite the evils of this world.

4 In them the Father's glory shone,
  in them the will of God the Son,
  in them exults the Holy Ghost,
  through them rejoice the heavenly host.

5 To thee, Redeemer, now we cry,
  that thou wilt join to them on high
  thy servants, who this grace implore,
  for ever and for evermore.

Aurelius Ambrose 340-397
tr. John Mason Neale 1818-1866
and the compilers

498

WE BLESS THE GOD AND FATHER

LLANFYLLIN 7 6 7 6 D

adapted from a Welsh air

1 We bless the God and Fa - ther of Je - sus Christ our Lord,
for saints of old who suf - fered by fire or cross or sword,
passed through the fi - ery fur - nace as gold with-out al - loy,
tri - um-phant o - ver tri - als, ac - count-ing it all joy.

2 He heard thy word eternal
  by whom the worlds were made,
  St Peter at his labour,
  a fisherman by trade;
  beside the shining water
  he heard the 'Follow me,'
  laid down his nets, and followed;
  and so, dear Lord, may we.

3 God bless all seamen, braving
  the peril of the deep;
  all fishermen and mariners
  in thy protection keep;
  as thou didst save St Peter,
  as thou didst save St Paul,
  from reef and shoal and tempest,
  O Lord, defend them all.

4 We bless the God and Father
  of Jesus Christ our Lord,
  for saints of old who suffered
  by fire or cross or sword.
  O may we join our voices
  with those whose strife is o'er,
  who wear the crown of glory,
  and praise thee evermore.

Philip Carrington 1892–

499

HOW BRIGHT THESE GLORIOUS SPIRITS SHINE

SENNEN COVE 8 6 8 6   FIRST TUNE   William Henry Harris 1883–

1 How bright these glo - rious spir - its shine!
Whence all their white ar - ray?
How came they to the bliss - ful seats
of ev - er - last - ing day?

2　Lo! these are they from sufferings great
　who came to realms of light,
　and in the blood of Christ have washed
　those robes which shine so bright.

3　Now, with triumphal palms, they stand
　before the throne on high,
　and serve the God they love, amidst
　the glories of the sky.

4　His presence fills each heart with joy,
　tunes every mouth to sing;
　by day, by night, the sacred courts
　with glad hosannas ring.

BALLERMA 8 6 8 6   SECOND TUNE

from a melody by
François Hippolyte Barthélémon 1741-1808
harmonized by Stanley L Osborne 1907-

1 How bright these glo - rious spir - its shine!
Whence all their white ar - ray?
How came they to the bliss - ful seats
of ev - er - last - ing day?

5 Hunger and thirst are felt no more,
   nor suns with scorching ray:
   God is their sun, whose cheering beams
   diffuse eternal day.

6 The Lamb which dwells amidst the throne
   shall o'er them still preside,
   feed them with nourishment divine,
   and all their footsteps guide.

7 To pastures green he'll lead his flock
   where living streams appear;
   and God the Lord from every eye
   shall wipe off every tear.

adapted from Isaac Watts 1674-1748

500

KING OF THE MARTYRS' NOBLE BAND

plainsong melody

REX GLORIOSE MARTYRUM 8 8 8 8 FIRST TUNE arranged by Healey Willan 1880–1968

1 King of the mar - tyrs' no - ble band,
crown of the true of ev - ery land,
strength of the pil - grim on his way,
bea - con by night and cloud by day: A - men.

2 hear us now as we celebrate
faith undeterred by cruel hate;
hear and forgive us, for we too
know all too well the wrong we do.

3 Dying, through thee they overcame;
living, were faithful to thy name.
Turn our rebellious hearts, and thus
win a like victory in us.

4 Glory to God the Father be;
glory to Christ, who set us free;
and to the Spirit, living flame,
glory unceasing we proclaim.

from the Latin 6th century
tr. John Webster Grant 1919–

REX GLORIOSE 8 8 8 8   SECOND TUNE

Andernach Gesangbuch 1608
harmonized by Charles Peaker 1900-

1 King of the mar-tyrs' no-ble band,
crown of the true of ev-ery land,
strength of the pil-grim on his way,
bea-con by night and cloud by day:

2 hear us now as we celebrate
   faith undeterred by cruel hate;
   hear and forgive us, for we too
   know all too well the wrong we do.

3 Dying, through thee they overcame;
   living, were faithful to thy name.
   Turn our rebellious hearts, and thus
   win a like victory in us.

4 Glory to God the Father be;
   glory to Christ, who set us free;
   and to the Spirit, living flame,
   glory unceasing we proclaim.

from the Latin 6th century
tr. John Webster Grant 1919-

501

FOR ALL THE SAINTS

SINE NOMINE 10 10 10 4

Ralph Vaughan Williams 1872-1958

Unison vv. 1, 2, 3, 7, 8

For all the saints who from their la-bours rest,

who thee by faith be - fore the world con - fessed,

thy name, O Je - sus, be for ev - er blest.

Al - le - lu - ia, al - le - lu - ia!

Harmony vv. 4, 5, 6

4 O blest com - mu - nion, fel - low-ship di - vine!

We fee - bly strug - gle, they in glo - ry shine;

Yet all are one in thee, for all are thine. Al - le - lu - ia, al - le - lu - ia!

2 Thou wast their rock, their fortress, and their might;
thou, Lord, their captain in the well-fought fight;
thou in the darkness drear their one true light. Alleluia!

3 O may thy soldiers, faithful, true, and bold,
fight as the saints who nobly fought of old,
and win with them the victor's crown of gold. Alleluia!

4 O blest communion, fellowship divine!
We feebly struggle, they in glory shine;
yet all are one in thee, for all are thine. Alleluia!

5 And when the strife is fierce, the warfare long,
steals on the ear the distant triumph-song,
and hearts are brave again, and arms are strong. Alleluia!

6 The golden evening brightens in the west;
soon, soon to faithful warriors comes their rest;
sweet is the calm of Paradise the blest. Alleluia!

7 But lo, there breaks a yet more glorious day –
the saints triumphant rise in bright array:
the King of glory passes on his way. Alleluia!

8 From earth's wide bounds, from ocean's farthest coast,
through gates of pearl streams in the countless host,
singing to Father, Son, and Holy Ghost. Alleluia!

William Walsham How 1823-1897   for a lower setting see 107

502

FOR ALL THY SAINTS, O LORD   composer unknown
BOWDEN 6686   harmonized by Samuel Sebastian Wesley 1810-1876

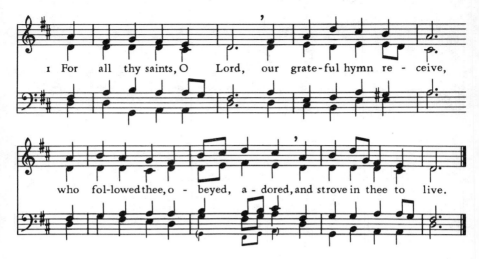

1 For all thy saints, O Lord, our grate-ful hymn re - ceive,
who fol-lowed thee, o - beyed, a - dored, and strove in thee to live.

2 For all thy saints, O Lord,
   accept our thankful cry,
   who counted thee their great reward,
   and strove in thee to die.

3 Thine earthly members fit
   in all their paths to move,
   in one communion ever knit,
   one fellowship of love.

4 Jesus, thy name we bless,
   and humbly pray that we
   may follow them in holiness,
   and live and die in thee.

5 All might, all praise, be thine,
   Father, co-equal Son,
   and Spirit, bond of love divine,
   while endless ages run.   Richard Mant 1776-1848

503

GIVE ME THE WINGS OF FAITH

WESTMINSTER 8686

James Turle 1802–1882

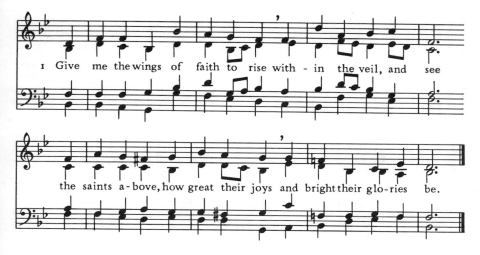

1 Give me the wings of faith to rise with-in the veil, and see the saints a-bove, how great their joys and bright their glo-ries be.

2 Once they were mourning here below,
and wet their couch with tears:
they wrestled hard, as we do now,
with sins, and doubts, and fears.

3 I ask them, whence their victory came:
they with united breath
ascribe their conquest to the Lamb,
their triumph to his death.

4 They marked the footsteps that he trod –
his zeal inspired their breast –
and, following their incarnate God,
possess the promised rest.

5 Our glorious leader claims our praise
for his own pattern given,
while the long cloud of witnesses
show the same path to heaven.

Isaac Watts 1674–1748

504

WHO ARE THESE LIKE STARS APPEARING

ALL SAINTS 8 7 8 7 7 7   from Geistreiches Gesangbuch, Darmstadt 1698

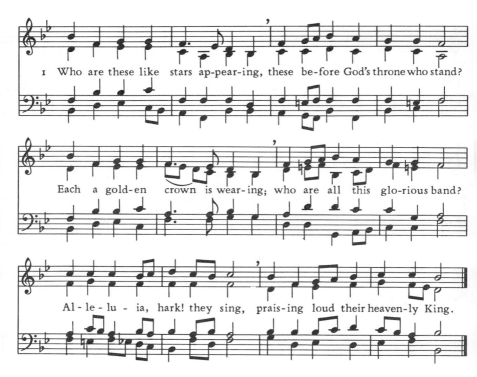

1 Who are these like stars ap-pear-ing, these be-fore God's throne who stand?

Each a gold-en crown is wear-ing; who are all this glo-rious band?

Al - le - lu - ia, hark! they sing, prais-ing loud their heaven-ly King.

2 Who are these in dazzling brightness,
clothed in God's own righteousness?
These whose robes of purest whiteness
shall their lustre still possess,
still untouched by time's rude hand –
whence come all this glorious band?

3 These are they who have contended
for the Saviour's honour long,
wrestling on till life was ended,
following not the sinful throng;
these who well the fight sustained,
triumph through the Lamb have gained.

4 These are they whose hearts were riven,
sore with woe and anguish tried,
who in prayer full oft have striven
with the God they glorified;
now, their painful conflict o'er,
God has bid them weep no more.

5 These, the Almighty contemplating,
did as priests before him stand,
soul and body always waiting
day and night at his command:
now in God's most holy place
blest they stand before his face.

Heinrich Theobald Schenck 1656-1727
tr. Frances Elizabeth Cox 1812-1897

505

LO! ROUND THE THRONE

ERSCHIENEN IST DER HERRLICH TAG 8 8 8 8 and alleluia

N Herman 1480-1561
harmonized by Stanley L Osborne 1907-

1 Lo! round the throne, a glorious band, the saints in countless myriads stand, of every tongue redeemed to God, arrayed in garments washed in blood. Alleluia!

2 Through tribulation great they came,
they bore the cross, despised the shame;
from all their labours now they rest,
in God's eternal glory blest.

3 They see their Saviour face to face,
and sing the triumphs of his grace;
him day and night they ceaseless praise,
to him the loud thanksgiving raise:

4 'Worthy the Lamb, for sinners slain,
through endless years to live and reign;
thou hast redeemed us by thy blood
and made us kings and priests to God.'

5 O may we tread the sacred road
that saints and holy martyrs trod,
wage to the end the glorious strife,
and win like them a crown of life.

Rowland Hill 1744-1833

The following hymns are also suitable: 147, 152, 184

CHRIST, THE FAIR GLORY

CHRISTE SANCTORUM II II II 5

Cluny Antiphoner 1686
harmonized by Derek Holman 1931-

1 Christ, the fair glory of the ho - ly an - gels, ru - ler of all men, au - thor of cre - a - tion, grant us in mer - cy grace to win by pa - tience joys ev - er - last - ing.

for a higher setting see 489

2 Send thine archangel Michael from thy presence:
peacemaker blessèd, may he hover o'er us,
hallow our dwellings, that for us thy children
all things may prosper.

3 Send thine archangel, Gabriel the mighty:
on strong wings flying, may he come from heaven,
drive from thy temple Satan the old foeman,
succour our weakness.

4 Send thine archangel, Raphael the healer:
through him with wholesome medicines of salvation
heal our backsliding, and in paths of goodness
guide our steps daily.

5 Father almighty, Son, and Holy Spirit,
Godhead eternal, grant us our petition;
thine be the glory through the whole creation
now and for ever.

ascribed to Rabanus Maurus 9th century
tr. compilers of Hymns Ancient and Modern 1950
This may be sung to Coelites Plaudant 359

AND THE FOLLOWING

The following hymns are suitable for the days indicated

Liturgical appendix

The rules for chanting are the rules for good speaking. Every word must be pronounced clearly, with the natural emphasis of deliberate reading. The notes of the chant have no fixed time-value, but must be shortened or lengthened to suit the rhythm of the words. The pace of the recitation should be that of good choral speech; the size of the building and of the congregation must be taken into consideration. Care must be taken that there is no change of pace at the bar-line, nor any hesitation in the flow of the phrase. The signs have been kept to a minimum in the interests of uninterrupted reading. The bar-line of the chant is indicated by a small vertical stroke (|): it does not imply an accent. A point between words of syllables shows their grouping within the measure. The syllables before the point are sung to the first note, and those after the point to the second note of the measure. A point under a word is a reminder that only a short reciting note is required, and that the syllable is to be sung lightly and quickly. The final syllable 'ed' should be pronounced separately only when indicated by a hyphen.

GLORY TO THE FATHER

1   Glory be to the Father, and|to the|Son,
and|to the|Holy|Ghost;
as it was in the beginning, is now, and|ever|shall be,
world without|end.|A|men.

2   Glory|be·to the|Father,
and to the Son,|and·to the|Holy|Spirit;
as it|was in·the be|ginning,
is now, and ever shall be,|world with·out|end. A|men.

3   Glory to the Father, and to the Son,
and to the|Holy|Spirit;
as in the beginning, so now, and for|ever.|A|men.

HOLY COMMUNION I

John Merbecke ?-c1585

organ accompaniment arranged by Healey Willan 1880-1968

RESPONSES TO THE COMMANDMENTS

Lord, have mer - cy up - on us, and in - cline our hearts to keep this law.

After the last commandment

Lord, have mer-cy up-on us, and write all these thy laws in our hearts, we be-seech thee.
(both)

LORD, HAVE MERCY

Lord, have mer-cy up-on us. Christ, have mer-cy up-on us. Lord, have mer-cy up-on us.

re-ceive our prayer. Thou that sit-test at the right hand of God the Fa-ther,

have mer - cy up-on us. For thou on-ly art ho-ly; thou on-ly art the Lord;

thou on-ly, O Christ, with the Ho-ly Ghost, art most high in the glo-ry of God the Fa-ther. A-men.

BEFORE THE COLLECT OF THE DAY AND THE GOSPEL

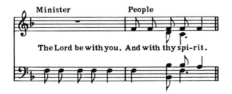

Minister   People

The Lord be with you. And with thy spi-rit.

AFTER THE COLLECT

A - men

Glo-ry be to thee, O Lord.

Praise be to thee, O Christ.

THE CREED

I
We be-lieve in one God the Fa-ther al-migh-ty, ma-ker of hea-ven and earth,

and of all things vi-si-ble, and in-vi-si-ble: and in one Lord Je-sus Christ,

the on-ly be-got-ten Son of God, be-got-ten of the Fa-ther be-fore all worlds,

God of God, light of light, ve-ry God of ve-ry God,

who spake by the pro-phets. And {I be-lieve one, ho-ly, ca-tho-lic, and a-pos-to-lic church. {we

{I ac-know-ledge one bap-tism for the re-mis-sion of sins. {We

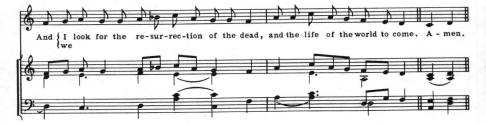

And {I look for the re-sur-rec-tion of the dead, and the life of the world to come. A-men. {we

SURSUM CORDA

Minister: The Lord be with you;
People: and with thy spi-rit.
Minister: Lift up your hearts;
Org.

People: we lift them up un-to the Lord.
Minister: Let us give thanks un-to our Lord God;

People ... Minister

it is meet and right so to do.

...prais-ing thee, and say-ing,

SANCTUS

People

Ho - ly, ho - ly, ho - ly Lord God of hosts.

Org.

Hea-ven and earth are full of thy glo-ry. Glo-ry be to thee, O Lord Most High.

BENEDICTUS QUI VENIT

Bless-ed is he that com-eth in the name of the Lord: Ho-san-na in the high-est.

PAX

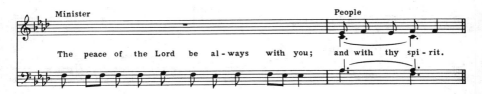

AGNUS DEI

508

HOLY COMMUNION II
RESPONSE TO THE COMMANDMENTS

Healey Willan 1880-1968

Unison

Lord, have mer-cy up-on us, and in-cline our hearts to keep this law.

After the tenth

Lord, have mer-cy up-on us, and write all these thy laws in our hearts, we be-seech thee.

SANCTUS

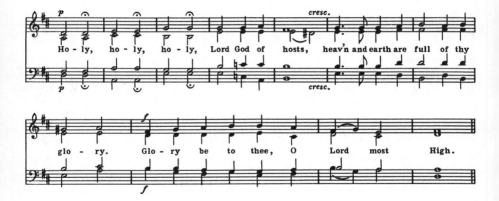

Ho-ly, ho-ly, ho-ly, Lord God of hosts, heav'n and earth are full of thy glo-ry. Glo-ry be to thee, O Lord most High.

BENEDICTUS QUI VENIT

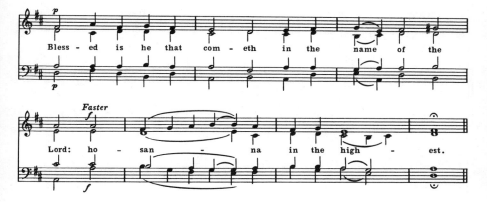

Bless - ed is he that com - eth in the name of the Lord: ho - san - na in the high - est.

AGNUS DEI

Unison (1st time men's voices; 2nd time, trebles)   Harmony

O Lamb of God, that tak-est a-way the sin of the world, have mer- cy up - on us.

Unison (full)   Harmony

O Lamb of God, that tak-est a-way the sin of the world, grant us thy peace.

HOLY COMMUNION III
LORD, HAVE MERCY

Godfrey Ridout 1918-

GLORY TO GOD

SANCTUS AND BENEDICTUS

Ho - ly, ho - ly, ho - ly Lord, God of power and might, heaven and

earth are full of your glo - ry. Ho - san - na in the high - est.

Blessed is he who comes in the name of the Lord. Ho - san - na in the high - est.

AGNUS DEI

Je - sus, Lamb of God: have mer - cy on us. Je - sus, Lamb of God: have

mer - cy on us. Je - sus, bear-er of our sin: have mer - cy on us.

Je - sus, bear-er of our sin: have mer-cy on us. Je - sus, re - deem-er of the world:

give us your peace. Je - sus, re - deem-er of the world: give us your peace.

I believe in God the Father almighty,
  maker of heaven and earth;

and in Jesus Christ his only Son our Lord,
  who was conceived by the Holy Ghost,
  born of the Virgin Mary,
  suffered under Pontius Pilate,
  was crucified, dead, and buried:
  he descended into hell;
  the third day he rose again from the dead;
  he ascended into heaven,
  and sitteth on the right hand of God the Father almighty;
  from thence he shall come to judge the quick and the dead.

I believe in the Holy Ghost;
  the holy Catholic Church;
  the communion of saints;
  the forgiveness of sins;
  the resurrection of the body;
  and the life everlasting. Amen.

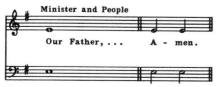

Minister O Lord, show thy mercy up - on us; **People** and grant us thy sal - va - tion.

Minister O Lord, save the Queen; **People** and mercifully hear us when we call up - on thee.

Minister Endue thy ministers with right - eous - ness; **People** and make thy chosen people joy - ful.

Minister O Lord, save thy peo - ple; **People** and bless thine in - her - i - tance.

Minister Give peace in our time, O Lord; **People** and evermore mightily de - fend us.

Minister O God, make clean our hearts with-in us; **People** and take not thy Holy Spirit from us.

THE LITANY   harmonized by John Cozens 1906–

Each of the four Invocations is sung first by the Minister, and then by the People.

O God the Father, Creator of heaven | and earth: have mer-cy up-on us.
O God the Son, Redeemer of | the world:
O God the Holy Ghost, Sanctifier of | the faithful:
O holy, blessed, and glorious trinity, three persons and one | God:

Minister

Remember not, Lord, ... most pre - cious blood.

People

Spare us, good Lord.

Minister

From all evil ... everlasting con - dem - nation,

People

good Lord, de - liver us.

Minister

We sinners ... in the right way,

People

we be - seech thee, good Lord.

Minister

Son of God, we be-seech thee to hear us.

People

Son of God, we be-seech thee to hear us.

Minister

O Lamb of God, that takest away the sin of the world; have mer - cy up-on us.

People

512

A SUPPLICATION

Minister and People

O Lord, arise, help us, and deliver us for thy name's sake.

Minister

O God,... be-fore them.

People

O Lord, arise, help us, and deliver us for thine hon-our.

Minister

Glory be to the Father... Holy Ghost;

People

as it was... world without end. A - men.

Minister and People

O Lord, arise, help us, and deliver us for thy name's sake.

Minister

From our enemies... O Christ;
Pitifully behold ... our hearts;

People

graciously look upon our af - flic -tions.
mercifully forgive the sins of thy peo - ple.

Minister

Favourably with mercy... our prayers;
Both now and ever... O Christ;

People

O Son of David, have mercy up - on us.
graciously hear us ... O Lord Christ.

Minister

O Lord, let thy mercy be shown up - on us;

People

as we do put our trust in thee.

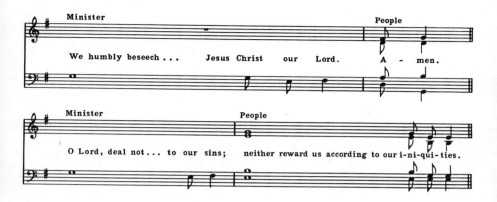

We humbly beseech ... Jesus Christ our Lord. A - men.

O Lord, deal not ... to our sins; neither reward us according to our i-ni-qui-ties.

513

A BLESSING

Numbers 6:24

Frederick R C Clarke 1931-

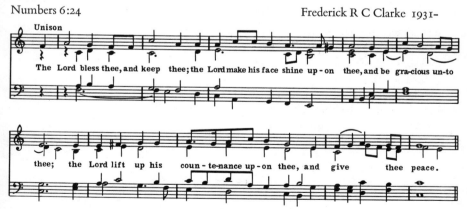

The Lord bless thee, and keep thee; the Lord make his face shine up-on thee, and be gra-cious un-to thee; the Lord lift up his coun-te-nance up-on thee, and give thee peace.

THE BEATITUDES

Frederick Chubb 1885–

Edward John Hopkins 1818–1901

1 Blessed are the┃poor in┃spirit:
   for┃theirs·is the┃kingdom·of┃heaven.
2 Blessed are┃they that┃mourn:
   for┃they┃shall be┃comforted.
3 Blessed┃are the┃meek:
   for┃they·shall in┃herit·the┃earth.
4 Blessed are they that do hunger and thirst┃after┃righteousness:
   for┃they┃shall be┃filled.
5 Blessed┃are the┃merciful:
   for┃they·shall ob┃tain┃mercy.
6 Blessed are the┃pure in┃heart:
   for┃they shall┃see┃God.
7 Blessed┃are the┃peacemakers:
   for they shall be┃called the┃children·of┃God.
8 Blessed are they which are persecuted for┃righteous·ness┃sake:
   for┃theirs·is the┃kingdom·of┃heaven.

515

O SAVIOUR OF THE WORLD

arranged from Allison's 'Psalmes', 1599
by L Flintoft   ?–1727

1   O Saviour of the world, who by thy cross and precious blood|hast re|deemed us:
    save us and help us we|humbly·be|seech thee,·O|Lord.

2   Thou didst save thy disciples when|ready to|perish:
    hear us and|save us,·we|humbly·be|seech thee.

3   Let the pitifulness of|thy great|mercy:
    loose us from our|sins, we|humbly·be|seech thee.

4   Make it appear that thou art our Saviour and|mighty·de|liverer:
    O save us that we may|praise thee,·we|humbly·be|seech thee.

5   Draw near according to thy promise from the|throne of·thy|glory:
    look down and hear our|crying,·we|humbly·be|seech thee.

6   Come again and dwell with us, O|Lord Christ|Jesus:
    abide with us for|ever,·we|humbly·be|seech thee.

7   And when thou shalt appear with|power and·great|glory:
    may we be made like unto thee,|in thy|glorious|kingdom.

8   Thanks be to|thee, O|Lord:
    Alle|luia.|A|men.

William Byrd 1543-1623

Thomas Tallis c1505-1585

William Smith ?-1645

Johann G Naumann 1741-1801

Robert Ramsay c1635

Orlando Gibbons 1583-1625

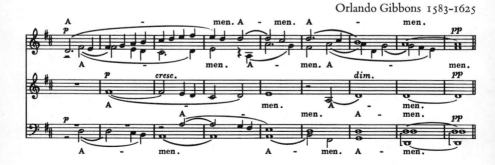

Orlando Gibbons 1583–1625

Alfred Whitehead 1887–

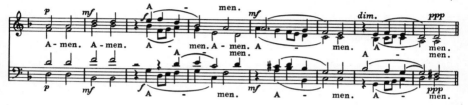

ADVENT	Our King and Saviour'draweth'nigh: O'come,'let us'worship.
CHRISTMASTIDE	Unto us a'child is'born: O'come,'let us'worship.
EPIPHANY AND TRANSFIGURATION	The Lord hath manifested'forth his'glory: O'come,'let us'worship.
LENT	The goodness of God'leadeth·to re'pentance: O'come,'let us'worship.
PASSIONTIDE	Christ our Lord became obedient'unto'death: O'come,'let us'worship.
EASTERTIDE	Alleluia.'Christ is'risen: O come, let us worship.'Alle'lu'ia.
ASCENSIONTIDE	Alleluia. Christ hath ascended'into'heaven: O come, let us worship.'Alle'lu'ia.
WHITSUNTIDE	Alleluia. God hath sent forth the'Spirit·of his'Son: O come, let us worship.'Alle'lu'ia.
TRINITY SUNDAY	Holy and reverend'is his'name: O'come,'let us'worship.
FESTIVALS OF THE VIRGIN MARY	The word was'made'flesh: O'come,'let us'worship.
SAINTS' DAYS	The Lord is glorious'in his'saints: O'come,'let us'worship.
DEDICATION FESTIVAL	The Lord is in his'holy'temple: O'come,'let us'worship.
OTHER SUNDAYS	The Lord God om'nipo·tent'reigneth: O'come,'let us'worship.
OTHER WEEKDAYS	The Lord is'gracious and'merciful: O'come,'let us'worship.

518

PSALM OF APPROACH

1 O come, let us|sing unto·the|Lord:
    let us heartily rejoice in the|strength of|our sal|vation.
2 Let us come before his|presence with|thanksgiving,
    and show ourselves|glad in|him with|psalms.
3 For the Lord is a|great|God,
    and a great|King a-bove|all|gods.
4 In his hand are all the|corners·of the|earth:
    and the|strength of·the|hills is·his|also.
5 The sea is|his and·he|made it:
    and his|hands prepared the·dry|land.
6 O come, let us worship and|fall|down:
    and|kneel be·fore the|Lord, our|maker.
7 For he is the|Lord our|God;
    and we are the people of his pasture, |and the|sheep of·his|hand.
8 Today, O that ye would|hear his|voice:
    Harden not your hearts as in the provocation, and as in the day of temp|tation|
        in the|wilderness;
9 when your fathers|tempted|me,
    proved|me and|saw my|works.
10 Forty years long was I grieved with that gene|ration and|said,
    It is a people that do err in their hearts, for they|have not|known my|ways;
11 unto whom I|sware·in my|wrath:
    that they should not|enter|into my|rest.

F A G Ouseley 1825-1889

R Goodson

W Byrd 1538-1623

G A MacFarren 1813-1887

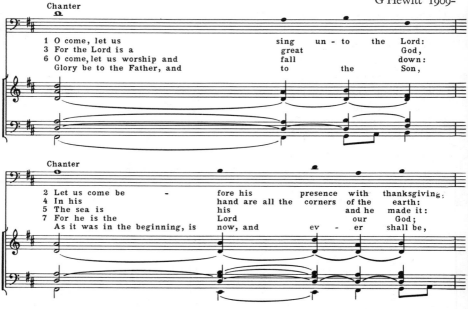

Chanter

1 O come, let us   sing   un - to   the   Lord:
3 For the Lord is a   great   God,
6 O come, let us worship and   fall   down:
  Glory be to the Father, and   to   the   Son,

G Hewitt 1909-

Chanter

2 Let us come be   -   fore his   presence   with   thanksgiving;
4 In his   hand are all the   corners   of the   earth:
5 The sea is   his   and he   made it:
7 For he is the   Lord   our   God;
  As it was in the beginning, is   now, and   ev - er   shall be,

1 O come, let us'sing unto·the'Lord:
   let us heartily rejoice in the'strength of'our sal'vation.

2 Let us come before his'presence with'thanksgiving,
   and show ourselves'glad in'him with'psalms.

3 For the Lord is a'great'God,
   and a great'King a–bove'all'gods.

4 In his hand are all the'corners·of the'earth:
   and the'strength of·the'hills is·his'also.

5 The sea is'his and·he'made it:
   and his'hands prepared the·dry'land.

6 O come, let us worship and'fall'down:
   and'kneel be·fore the'Lord, our'maker.

7 For he is the'Lord our'God;
   and we are the people of his pasture,'and the'sheep of·his'hand.

8 Today, O that ye would'hear his'voice:
   Harden not your hearts as in the provocation, and as in the day of temp'tation'
   in the'wilderness;

9 when your fathers'tempted'me,
   proved'me and'saw my'works.

10 Forty years long was I grieved with that gene'ration and'said,
   It is a people that do err in their hearts, for they'have not'known my'ways;

11 unto whom I'sware·in my'wrath:
   that they should not'enter'into my'rest.

Choir and People

let us heartily rejoice in the	strength	of	our	sal	-	va	-	tion.
and a great		King a-bove	all	gods.
and			kneel be-fore the Lord,	our		mak	-	er.
and			to the	the	Ho	-	ly	Ghost:

Choir and People

and show ourselves glad in		him	with	psalms.
and the strength of the hills is		his		also.
and his hands prepared the		dry		land.
and we are the people of his pasture, and the		sheep	of his	hand.
world without		end.	A	-	men.

CANTICLE OF PRAISE

I

W H Havergal 1793-1870

W Croft 1678-1727

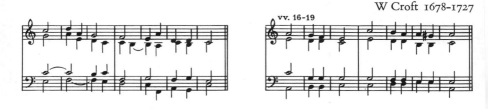

II

O H Peasgood 1902-c1965

Tonus Peregrinus c9th century

III

J Goss 1800-1880

W Hawes 1785-1846

W Russell 1777-1813

vv. 16-19

1　We praise|thee, O|God;
　　we acknowledge|thee to|be the|Lord.

2　All the|earth doth|worship thee,
　　the|Father|ever|lasting.

3　To thee all angels|cry a|loud,
　　the heavens and|all the|powers there|in.

4　To thee|cherubim and|seraphim
　　con|tinual|ly do|cry,

5　Holy,|holy,|holy,
　　Lord|God|of|hosts;

6　heaven and|earth are|full
　　of the|majes-ty|of thy|glory.

7　The glorious company of the a|postles|praise thee;
　　the goodly fellowship|of the|prophets|praise thee;

8　the noble army of|martyrs|praise thee;
　　the holy church throughout all the world|doth ac|knowledge|thee,

9　the Father, of an|infi·nite|majesty;
　　thine honourable, true and only Son; also the|Holy|Ghost, the|Comforter.

10　Thou art the King of|glory, O|Christ.
　　Thou art the ever|lasting|Son of·the|Father.

11　When thou tookest upon thee to de|liver|man,
　　thou didst not ab|hor the|Virgin's|womb.

12　When thou hadst overcome the|sharpness of|death,
　　thou didst open the kingdom of|heaven to|all be|lievers.

13　Thou sittest at the right hand of God, in the|glory·of the|Father.
　　We believe that thou shalt|come to|be our|judge.

14　We therefore pray thee,|help thy|servants,
　　whom thou has redeemed|with thy|precious|blood.

15　Make them to be numbered|with thy|saints,
　　in|glory|ever|lasting.

16　O Lord, save thy people, and|bless thine|heritage;
　　govern them and|lift them|up for|ever.

17　Day by day we|magni·fy|thee;
　　and we worship thy name,|ever|world with·out|end.

18　Vouchsafe, O Lord, to keep us this|day with·out|sin.
　　O Lord, have mercy up|on us, have|mercy up|on us.

19　O Lord, let thy mercy lighten upon us, as our|trust is·in|thee.
　　O Lord, in thee have I trusted: let me|never|be con|founded.

SONG OF THE THREE CHILDREN

D Holman 1931-

D Holman 1931-

1   O all ye works of the Lord, |bless · ye the|Lord;
     O ye angels of the Lord, |bless · ye the|Lord;
     O ye heavens, |bless · ye the|Lord;
     praise him and|magnify|him for|ever.

2   O ye waters that be above the firmament, |bless · ye the|Lord;
     O all ye powers of the Lord, |bless · ye the|Lord;
     O ye sun and moon, |bless · ye the|Lord;
     praise him and|magnify|him for|ever.

3   O ye stars of heaven, |bless · ye the|Lord;
     O ye showers and dew, |bless · ye the|Lord;
     O ye winds of God, |bless · ye the|Lord;
     praise him and|magnify|him for|ever.

4   O ye fire and heat, |bless · ye the|Lord;
     O ye winter and summer, ye dews and frosts, |bless · ye the|Lord;
     O ye frosts and cold, ye ice and snow, |bless · ye the|Lord;
     praise him and|magnify|him for|ever.

5   O ye nights and days, |bless · ye the|Lord;
     O ye light and darkness, |bless · ye the|Lord;
     O ye lightnings and cloud, |bless · ye the|Lord;
     praise him and|magnify|him for|ever.

6   O let the earth|bless ye the|Lord;
     O ye mountains and hills, all ye green things upon the earth, |bless · ye the|Lord;
     O ye wells, ye seas and floods, |bless · ye the|Lord;
     praise him and|magnify|him for|ever.

7   O all ye that move in the waters, |bless · ye the|Lord;
     O all ye fowls of the air, |bless · ye the|Lord;
     O all ye beasts and cattle, |bless · ye the|Lord;
     praise him and|magnify|him for|ever.

8   O ye children of men, |bless · ye the|Lord;
     O let Israel|bless ye the|Lord;
     O ye priests of the Lord, |bless · ye the|Lord;
     praise him and|magnify|him for|ever.

9   O ye servants of the Lord, |bless · ye the|Lord;
     O ye spirits and souls of the righteous, |bless · ye the|Lord;
     O ye holy and humble men of heart, |bless · ye the|Lord;
     praise him and|magnify|him for|ever.

521

CANTICLE OF BLESSING

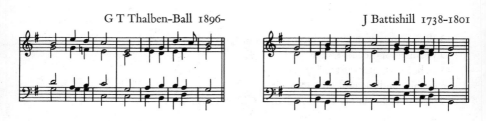

G T Thalben-Ball 1896-   J Battishill 1738-1801

1 Blessed be thou, Lord God of|Israel·our|father
  for|e|ver and|ever.
2 Thine, O Lord, is the greatness and the|power·and the|glory
  and the|victory|and the|majesty:
3 for all that|is·in the|heaven
  and|in the|earth is|thine;
4 thine is the|kingdom,·O|Lord,
  and thou art ex|alted·as|head a·bove|all.
5 Both riches and|honour·come of|thee,
  and thou|reignest|over|all.
6 And in thine hand is|power·and|might,
  and in thine hand it is to make great and to give|strength|unto|all.
7 Now therefore, our|God, we|thank thee
  and|praise thy|glorious|name.

PSALM OF JOY

G J Elvey 1816-1893

J Nares 1715-1783

J Battishill 1738-1801

1 O be joyful in the Lord, |all ye|lands:
serve the Lord with gladness, and come before his|presence|with a|song.

2 Be ye sure that the|Lord·he is|God;
it is he that hath made us, and not we ourselves; we are his people, |and the|sheep of·
his|pasture.

3 O go your way into his gates with thanksgiving, and into his|courts with|praise;
be thankful unto him, |and speak|good of·his|name.

4 For the Lord is gracious, his mercy is|ever|lasting;
and his truth endureth from gene|ration to|gene|ration.

SONG OF ZECHARIAH

G H Knight 1908–

J Goss 1800–1880

W Bayley c1850

1 Blessed be the Lord⸍God of⸍Israel;
   for he hath visited⸍and re⸍deemed his⸍people;

2 and hath raised up a mighty sal⸍vation⸍for us,
   in the⸍house of·his⸍servant⸍David;

3 as he spake by the mouth of his⸍holy⸍prophets,
   which have been⸍since the⸍world be⸍gan;

4 that we should be⸍saved from·our⸍enemies,
   and from the⸍hands of⸍all that⸍hate us;

5 to perform the mercy promised⸍to our⸍forefathers.
   and to re⸍member his⸍holy⸍covenant;

6 to perform the oath which he sare to our⸍fore·father⸍Abraham,
   that⸍he would⸍grant⸍us

7 that we, being delivered out of the⸍hands of·our⸍enemies,
   might⸍serve him·with⸍out⸍fear,

8 in holiness and⸍righteousness be⸍fore him,
   all the⸍days of⸍our⸍life.

9 And thou, child, shalt be called the⸍prophet·of the⸍Highest:
   for thou shalt go before the face of the⸍Lord·to pre⸍pare his⸍ways;

10 to give knowledge of salvation⸍unto his⸍people
   for the re⸍mission⸍of their⸍sins;

11 through the tender mercy⸍of our⸍God;
   whereby the dayspring⸍from on⸍high hath⸍visited us;

12 to give light to them that sit in darkness, and in the⸍shadow of⸍death,
   and to guide our feet⸍into the⸍way of⸍peace.

plainsong, tone 5
arranged by Robert H Bell 1932-

1 Bless - ed   be the Lord God of   Is - rael;   for he hath visited and re - deemed his peo - ple;

2 and|hath|raised up a mighty salvation for| us ___,
   in the house of his|ser|vant|Da|vid;

3 as|he|spake by the mouth of his holy|pro|phets,
   which have been|since|the|world|began;

4 that|we|should be saved from our|en|emies,
   and from the hands of |all|that|hate|us;

5 to|per|form the mercy promised to our fore|fa|thers,
   and to remember his|ho|ly|co|venant,

6 to|per|form the oath which he sare to our forefather|A|braham,
   that|he|would|grant|us

7 that|we,|being delivered out of the hands of our|en|emies,
   might serve|him|with|out|fear,

8 in|ho|liness and righteousness be|fore|him,
   all the|days|of|our|life.

9 And|thou,|child, shalt be called the prophet of the|High|est:
   for thou shalt go before the face of the Lord|to|pre|pare|his ways;

10 to|give|knowledge of salvation unto his|peo|ple
   for the remis|sion|of|their|sins;

11 through|the|tender mercy of our|God ___;
   whereby the dayspring from on high hath|vi|sit|ed|us;

12 to|give|light to them that sit in darkness and in the shadow of| death ___,
   and to guide our feet in|to|the|way|of peace.
   Glo|ry|be to the Father, and to the| Son ___,
   and|to|the|Ho|ly Ghost;
   as|it|was in the beginning, is now, and ever|shall|be,
   world with|out|end.|A|men.

*This note is not sung in verses 2, 11, 12, and 'Glory be to the Father ...'

optional accompaniments

524

ARISE, SHINE

H Nicholson 1875–1947

1 Arise, shine, for thy'light is'come,
and the glory of the Lord is'risen up'on thee.

2 For behold, the darkness shall'cover the'earth,
and gross'darkness the'people.

3 But the Lord shall a'rise up'on thee,
and his glory shall be'seen up'on thee.

4 And the Gentiles shall'come to·thy'light,
and kings to the'brightness·of thy'rising.

5 Thy gates shall be'open con'tinually;
they shall not be shut'day nor'night.

6 The sons also of'them that·af'flicted thee
shall come bending'unto'thee;

7 and all'they that·des'pised thee
shall bow themselves down at the'soles of·thy'feet.

8 And they shall call thee the'‘City·of the'Lord,’
the Zion of the'Holy One·of'Israel.

9 Violence shall no more be'heard in thy'land,
wasting nor destruction with'in thy'borders.

10 But thou shalt call thy'walls Sal'vation,
and thy'gates'Praise.

11 The sun shall be no more thy'light by'day,
neither for brightness shall the moon give'light un-to'thee.

12 But the Lord shall be unto thee an ever'lasting'light,
and thy'God thy'glory.

SONG OF MARY

R Cooke 1768-1814

W Crotch 1775-1847

J Turle 1802-1882

1 My soul doth|magnify the|Lord,
and my spirit hath re|joiced in|God my|Saviour.

2 For|he hath·re|garded
the|lowli·ness|of his|handmaiden.

3 For be|hold from|henceforth
all gene|rations shall|call me|blessed.

4 For he that is mighty hath|magni·fied|me;
and|holy|is his|name.

5 And his mercy is on|them that|fear him
throughout|all|gene|rations.

6 He hath showed|strength·with his|arm;
he hath scattered the proud in the imagin|ation|of their|hearts.

7 He hath put down the mighty|from their|seat,
and hath ex|alted the|humble and|meek.

8 He hath filled the|hungry with|good things;
and the rich he|hath sent|empty a|way.

9 He, re|membering his|mercy,
hath|holpen his|servant|Israel;

10 as he promised|to our|forefathers,
Abraham|and his|seed for|ever.

SONG OF SIMEON

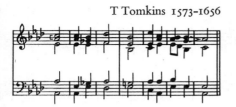   

1 Lord, now lettest thou thy servant de|part in|peace,
ac|cording|to thy|word.
2 For mine eyes have|seen thy·sal|vation,
which thou has prepared be|fore the|face of·all|people;
3 to be a light to|lighten the|Gentiles,
and to be the|glory of·thy|people|Israel.

plainsong, tone 6
arranged by Robert H Bell 1932-

2 For|mine|eyes have seen thy sal|va|tion,
which thou hast prepared before the face|of|all|peo|ple;
3 to|be|a light to lighten the|Gen|tiles,
and to be the glory of thy|peo|ple|Is|rael.

optional accompaniment

527

PSALM OF BLESSING

G M Garrett 1834–1897

J Turle 1802–1882

E J Hopkins 1818–1901

1 God be merciful unto⸍us and⸍bless us,
   and show us the light of his countenance, and be⸍merci·ful⸍unto⸍us;

2 that thy way may be⸍known up·on⸍earth,
   thy saving⸍health a⸍mong all⸍nations.

3 Let the people⸍praise thee·O⸍God;
   yea, let⸍all the⸍people⸍praise thee.

4 O let the nations re⸍joice and·be⸍glad;
   for thou shalt judge the folk righteously, and govern the⸍nations up⸍on⸍earth.

5 Let the people⸍praise thee·O⸍God;
   yea, let⸍all the⸍people⸍praise thee.

6 The earth hath brought⸍forth her⸍increase;
   and God, even our own⸍God shall⸍give us·his⸍blessing.

7 God⸍shall⸍bless us;
   and all the⸍ends of·the⸍world shall⸍fear him.

528

CHRISTMAS CANTICLE

E F Rimbault 1816-1876 P Hayes 1738-1797

1 Behold a virgin shall conceive and |bear a |son,
   and shall |call his |name Im |manuel.
2 Unto us a |child is |born,
   unto |us a |son is |given.
3 In this was manifested the love of |God toward |us,
   because that God sent his only-begotten Son into the world that |we might |live
      through |him.
4 Blessed be the God and Father of our Lord |Jesus |Christ,
   who hath blessed us with all spiritual blessings in |heaven·ly |places in |Christ.

529

GOOD FRIDAY CANTICLE

E G Monk 1819-1900 G T Thalben-Ball 1896-

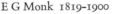

1 Behold the |Lamb of |God,
   which taketh a |way the |sin of·the |world.
2 He was wounded for |our trans |gressions,
   he was |bruised for |our in |iquities:
3 the chastisement of our |peace·was up |on him;
   and |with his |stripes·we are |healed.
4 Herein is love, not that we loved God, but that |he loved |us,
   and sent his Son to be the propitia |tion |for our |sins.
5 Worthy is the Lamb that was slain to receive power and riches and |wisdom
      and |strength,
   and |honour and |glory and |blessing.

530

EASTER CANTICLE

Pelham Humphrey 1647-1674

G A MacFarren 1813-1887

1   Christ, our passover, is ˡsacri-ficed ˡfor us:
      therefore, ˡlet us ˡkeep the ˡfeast,

2   not with the old leaven, nor with the leaven of ˡmalice and ˡwickedness,
      but with the unleavened bread of sin ˡceri ˡty and ˡtruth.

3   Christ being raised from the dead ˡdieth no ˡmore;
      death hath no more do ˡminion ˡover ˡhim.

4   For in that he died, he died unto ˡsin ˡonce:
      but in that he liveth, he ˡliveth ˡunto ˡGod.

5   Likewise reckon ye also yourselves to be dead in ˡdeed unto ˡsin,
      but alive unto God, through ˡJesus ˡChrist our ˡLord.

6   Christ is ˡrisen-from the ˡdead,
      and became the ˡfirst-fruits-of ˡthem that ˡslept.

7   For since by ˡman came ˡdeath,
      by man came also the resur ˡrection ˡof the ˡdead.

8   For as in ˡAdam all ˡdie,
      even so in Christ shall ˡall be ˡmade a ˡlive.

531

WHITSUNDAY CANTICLE

G A MacFarren 1813-1887

J Battishill 1738-1801

1 O sing unto the Lord a|new|song;
for|he hath·done|marvell·ous|things.

2 Christ, being by the right hand of God exalted, and having received of the Father
the promise of the|Holy|Ghost,
hath shed forth this, which|ye now|see and|hear.

3 And because|ye are|sons,
God hath sent forth the Spirit of his Son into our hearts,|crying,|Abba,|Father.

4 We all, with|open|face
behold as in a glass the|glory|of the|Lord,

5 are changed into the same image from|glory to|glory,
even as by the|Spirit|of the|Lord.

SOULS OF THE RIGHTEOUS

W Morley 1680–1731

J Turle, from Henry Purcell 1658–1695

1 The souls of the righteous are in the|hand of|God,
and|there shall·no|torment|touch them.

2 In the sight of the unwise they|seemed to|die,
and their de|parture is|taken·for|misery,

3 and their going from us to be|utter de|struction:
but|they|are in|peace.

4 For though they be punished in the|sight of|men,
yet is their hope|full of|immor|tality.

5 And having been a little chastened, they shall be|greatly re|warded,
for God proved them and found them|worthy|for him|self.

6 As gold in the furnace|hath he|tried them
and re|ceived them|as a·burnt|offering.

7 And in the time of their visitation|they shall|shine
and run to and fro like|sparks a|mong the|stubble.

8 They shall judge the nations and have dominion|over the|people,
and the Lord shall|reign for|ever and|ever.

533

LET US NOW PRAISE FAMOUS MEN

Ralph Vaughan Williams
1872-1958

Let us now praise fa-mous men, and our fa-thers that be-
gat us. Such as did bear rule in their king - doms, men re-nown-ed
for their power. Lead - ers of the peo-ple by their
coun-sels, and by their know - ledge. Such as found out mu - si-cal tunes
and re - ci - ted ver-ses in wri - ting: All these were hon-oured in their

gen - er-a-tions, and were the glo - ry of their times.

And some there be which have no me-mo - ri - al; who are per-ished as though

they had ne - ver been. Their bo - dies are bu - ried in

peace; but their name liv-eth for ev - er -

more.

Indices

Index of first lines

Alphabetical index of tunes

Metrical index of tunes

Index of chants

Subject index

INTROIT

INVOCATION
See Introit

INVITATION

JESUS, HIS BIRTH
See Christmas   400-429

JESUS, HIS CROSS

Index of authors and sources

Index of translators and arrangers

Composers, arrangers, and sources

Acknowledgements

The Publishers acknowledge their obligations to many authors, composers, and owners or holders of copyright for permission to use the texts and tunes listed below. Items not listed are assumed to be in the public domain. Every effort has been made to trace the owner or holder of each copyright. If any rights have been inadvertently overlooked, the Publishers ask that the omission be excused and agree to make the necessary corrections in subsequent editions. If for any entry the second column is left blank, it is to be understood that the Publishers have been unable to trace the owner or holder of the copyright. An asterisk indicates that permission has been granted without payment.

TEXTS

AUTHOR OR TRANSLATOR	OWNER OR HOLDER OF COPYRIGHT	HYMN NUMBER
Adams J	*Trustees of the Fellowship Hymn Book	282
Alington C A	The Proprietors of *Hymns Ancient and Modern*	469
Alston A E	Mr Christopher Alston	489
Ambrose G	House of the Sacred Mission	300
Arlott J	author	381
Arnott C B	*author	158 251
Baring-Gould S	J Curwen and Sons Ltd	178
Bax C	A D Peters and Co	73
Bayly A F	*author	83 208 212 247 295
Bell M F	Oxford University Press, from *The English Hymnal*	461
Bentley D K	*author	335
Bidgrain S	World Student Christian Federation	332
Bonhöffer D	SCM Press Ltd	105
Bourne G H	Oxford University Press	324
Bovet J-J	World Student Christian Federation	1
Brandon G	*The Hymn Society of America, from *Ten New Hymns on the Bible* copyright 1953	264
Bridge B E	Free Church Choir Union	323
Bridges R S	Oxford University Press, from *The Yattendon Hymnal*	134 365 368 443
Brooks R T	*author	94
Byrne M	Chatto and Windus Ltd	253
Caird G B	*author	96 291
Carrington P	*author	498
Carter S	Galliard Ltd	106 428
Chao T C	Cooperative Recreation Service Inc	61
Chapieu H	World Student Christian Federation	326
Chesterton G K	Oxford University Press	214
Cook J S	Miss A L Cook	420
Cropper M B	*author	450

Struther J	Oxford University Press, from *Enlarged Songs of Praise*	262
Thiem J	F E L Publications Ltd	336
T'ien Ching-Fu		413
Tucker F B	Church Pension Fund	107 219 225 454
van Dyke H	Charles Scribner's Sons	19
Waters M A J	*author	103
Watson C E	*Rodborough Tabernacle Congregational Church	92
Weir R S	*Secretary of State for Canada	217
Whiteley F J	*author	318
Wiant B	*translator	61 413
Wilbur R	'The Christmas Hymn' copyright 1961 by the author; from his volume *Advice to the Prophet and Other Poems* by permission of Harcourt Brace Jovanovich Inc	424
Woodward G R	A R Mowbray and Co Ltd, from *The Cowley Carol Book*	409
Wren B A	author	328
Yardley H F	*author	318

Permission has also been given by A R Mowbray and Co Ltd for the use of text 471, reprinted from *The Cowley Carol Book*.

The Compilers have made alterations in the text of several older hymns, but do not wish to claim any copyright for these versions.

MUSIC

COMPOSER OR ARRANGER	OWNER OF HOLDER OF COPYRIGHT	HYMN NUMBER
Allen H P	*Barclay's Bank Trust Company Ltd	94
Bancrott H H	*composer	153
Baring-Gould S	J Curwen & Sons Ltd	122
Bell R H	*composer	255 396 446 497 523 526
Bissell K W	*composer	215
Blake L J	Novello and Co Ltd	328
Boyd W	Novello and Co Ltd	175
Brown A H	Oxford University Press	284
Buck P C	Mr A Buck	63
—	Oxford University Press	445
—	Stainer and Bell Ltd	5
Burleigh H T		149
Cabena H B	*composer	312 412
Carter S	Galliard Ltd	106 428
Chadwyck-Healey H P	Royal School of Church Music	378
Chubb F		514
Clarke F R C	*composer	4 15 51 90 91 92 99 129 148 205 209 223 240 289 325 346 373 400 413 425 467 483 513
Cocker N	Oxford University Press	187
Cozens J	*composer	511
Davies H W	Novello and Co Ltd	243
—	Oxford University Press	69
Day G H	Church Pension Fund	125
Douglas C W	Church Pension Fund	160 450
Drynan M	*composer	144 329 341
Dykes Bower J	composer	244
Evans D	*Oxford University Press	237
Fan T'ien-hsiang	*Cooperative Recreation Service Inc	413
Ferguson W H	Oxford University Press	304
—	Royal School of Church Music	42
Finlay K G	composer	200 297 492 493
Fleming R J B	composer	274 426
Foster M B	Proprietors of *Hymns Ancient and Modern*	231
France W	*composer	97 168 349
Gardner G	S P C K	300
George G	composer	2 120
—	Abingdon Press	175
—	H W Gray Co Inc	449
Gibbs C A	Boosey and Hawkes (Canada) Ltd	213 399
Greenwood E N	*Mrs E N Greenwood	208
Harris W H	Oxford University Press	270 499
Harwood B	Public Trustee Office	2 152

Willan H	Sons and Daughter of the composer	25 245 272 324
	343 356 371 390 403 429 432 434 437 445 472 486 500 508	
—	*Concordia Publishing House, from the anthem	
	Sing to the Lord of Harvest copyright 1954	382
—	Oxford University Press, from the Unison	
	Service in D, Response to the commandments	508
Williams T J	*Gwenlyn Evans Ltd	167 484
Wood C	A R Mowbray and Co Ltd, from The Cowley	
	Carol Book, altered	409
Wood T	Oxford University Press, from Enlarged Songs	
	of Praise	354 375
Woodward G R	A R Mowbray and Co Ltd, from The Cowley	
	Carol Book	100

Permission has also been given
by the Proprietors of Hymns Ancient and Modern for the harmonization of tune 469
by Oxford University Press for tune 198, simplified, from The BBC Hymn Book
by Stainer and Bell Ltd for the harmonization of tune 132
by the Compilers of Hymns for Church and School 1964 for tune 198

The Music Editors have made alterations in the harmony and part writing of many older
tunes, but do not wish to claim any copyright for these versions.

This book

was designed by

ALLAN FLEMING

with the assistance of

LAURIE LEWIS

and was printed by

SOUTHAM·MURRAY

a division of the Southam Printing Company Limited

on paper developed and produced by

THE E. B. EDDY COMPANY

The music engravings were made by

UNIVERSITÄTSDRUCKEREI H STÜRTZ AG

Würzburg, Germany

and the type was set by

COOPER & BEATTY, LIMITED

Toronto, Canada

1971